Victor Mollo's
Winning Double

by the same author

*

BRIDGE IN THE MENAGERIE
BRIDGE: MODERN BIDDING
THE BRIDGE IMMORTALS
(*Faber & Faber*)
STREAMLINED BRIDGE
(*Newnes*)
SUCCESS AT BRIDGE
(*Newnes*)
BRIDGE PSYCHOLOGY
(*Duckworth*)
WILL YOU BE MY PARTNER
(*Duckworth*)
In collaboration with Nico Gardiner
CARD PLAY TECHNIQUE
(*Newnes*)
BRIDGE FOR BEGINNERS
(*Duckworth*)

Victor Mollo's Winning Double

The Shortest Cut to Expert Play

VICTOR MOLLO

FABER AND FABER
24 Russell Square
London

First published in 1968
by Faber and Faber Limited
24 Russell Square London WC1
Printed in Great Britain by
Latimer Trend & Co Ltd Plymouth
All rights reserved

SBN 571 08761 2

Contents

Author's Preface

The dictum that you cannot have your cake and eat it, too, has always struck me as sheer defeatism. Of course you can and I invite the reader to do it with me in the pages which follow. For this is a textbook and a quiz-book in one, and sets out to exploit the advantages of both without incurring the disabilities of either —in short, to gain on the swings as well as on the roundabouts.

A textbook is admittedly the best medium for passing on to the reader the keys to correct card play. But who will tell him how, and above all when, each key should be turned in the appropriate lock? This is where the quiz comes into its own, quickening the reader's powers of perception and alerting him against the dangers of doing the right thing—at the wrong time.

As in medicine, so in bridge, the diagnosis should precede the cure. Not so in textbooks, where, by the nature of things, the logical sequence is often reversed. At the card table the player must identify each problem as it arises. Then only can he set out to solve it. The textbook tells him what it is before he even sees his hand. A glance at the chapter heading and he knows whether he is expected to execute a safety-play or an end-play, a savant squeeze or a subtle piece of deception. He is taught the correct treatment and is expected to develop the appropriate complaint all on his own.

Here the quiz method scores every time. With the spotlight fixed on RECOGNITION, the diagnosis comes first, where it belongs. No chapter headings guide the reader. No rules of continuity hamper the author. He is free to plan confusion scientifically, so as to put before the reader a series of seemingly unrelated situations, just as they are apt to come up at the card table.

The quiz has many advantages, but, of course, the correct

9

diagnosis will not save the patient unless he pursues the right treatment afterwards. The one must come before the other, but both are indispensible. The question arises: can the secrets of recognition and the mechanics of card play be communicated simultaneously?

The reader will judge for himself. I invite him to join me in seeking the answers to a hundred and fifty questions and I predict that by the time he reaches the last one he will have proof-positive that his card play has improved appreciably. What's more, he will know exactly by *how much* it has improved. For built into these pages is a yardstick to measure his progress, and this brings us to the design behind these quizzes.

A PREVIEW

The hundred and fifty quizzes are divided into three equal parts. The first fifty are easier than the others; but all range over the entire field of card play and, though every stratagem finds a place, the focus is always on the everyday situations, which call for more horse-sense than science.

Quizzes 51 to 150 are divided into two parts with marks awarded for the correct answers. Most of the quizzes earn 5 points each, but some are more difficult than others and then the bonus rises to 8 points or to 10. The total for each of the last two parts is 295, but I hope that no reader will be so selfish as to reach the summit. After all, if he knows the right answers already, I must have put the wrong questions and what author could admit a thing like that? But no matter how well or badly the reader fares, I defy him not to do much better as he reads on.

A CHALLENGE

Whatever he scores for his first fifty quizzes, he will return a higher score for his next fifty. This is both a prophesy and a challenge, for the reader will not be able to help himself. And since the result is a foregone conclusion, I am willing, like every true sportsman, to bet on it heavily.

Will some suspicious reader refuse to bet on the pretext that it's too easy for me to fix the race before the start? Why, he may say, all the author need to do to win his bet is to make the hands in Part III easier than those in Part II. He cannot lose.

If this distrustful reader will double the stakes I will undertake to show him at once how unworthy are his suspicions. Done? Very well. Let him tackle Part III *before* Part II. He will now return a better score for quizzes 51 to 100 than for the next fifty, and apart from the trifling inconvenience of turning over the pages in an unusual sequence, it will make no difference.

The quizzes are set out in groups, usually three, four or five on each page. Then, overleaf, come the answers. This arrangement lacks uniformity, but spares the reader from having to refer, hand after hand, to the back of the book. Alternatively, it preserves him from the temptation of peeping surreptitiously at the answers across the page. If his willpower is equal to it, he will do best to complete his own answers for each group before turning the page to study the analysis and mark his score.

So much for the procedure. One thing more remains to be said about the substance. The sophisticated reader may dismiss one or two of the first fifty quizzes as too easy. The less advanced may find some in the next hundred too difficult. That is as it should be for at the card table the same hand, posing two or more problems, may be both easy and difficult. The winning player does not always solve the latter, but he is rarely careless over the former. He wins not because he is brilliant, but because he avoids mistakes, especially childish mistakes. For winning is a technique on its own and its prime exponents are not the players who execute clever and complex coups, but those who bring home, hand after hand, the everyday contracts that are easy to make—and sometimes easier still to lose. And since more contracts are lost in the first thirty seconds that at any other time, most of the questions bear on the first two or three tricks. In short, the quizzes have been selected and arranged to reproduce as nearly as possible the conditions which prevail at the card table. Now the reader knows nearly everything. Quiz 1 awaits him.

Part One

At times, opponents selfishly enter the bidding, making it harder for us to reach the right contract. In return, they raise a little the veil which hides their holdings. For every bid carries a message and the skilful declarer makes use of all the information which comes his way.

The reader can assume that every bid and every sequence in these pages is simple and straightforward. He need pay no heed to systems or conventions and he can expect every opening no trump to be of the weak variety, 12 to 14 points.

In defence, as in bidding, opponents follow strictly standard methods. They play the king from A K, and though they do not promise to lead invariably the fourth highest of their longest suits or not to false card, the defence is always honest. No fiendish traps await the declarer, either in the first fifty hands or in the more sophisticated ones which follow.

(1)

♠ A 10 9 8 5 4 ♠ K 7 6
♡ K Q 5 ♡ A 7 4 3 2
◇ A K ◇ Q J
♣ A Q ♣ K 9 8

North leads the ◇ 10 against West's 6 ♠.
(a) How should declarer play trumps?
(b) Should declarer play trumps the same way if the opening lead
is the ♡ 6?

(2)

♠ K 10 8 7 5 ♠ A 9 6 4
♡ K 4 ♡ A 7 3 2
◇ A K 3 ◇ 10 4
♣ Q J 9 ♣ A 3 2

North leads the ◇ 7 against West's 6 ♠.
How should declarer play the trumps?

(3)

♠ A 9 8 7 5 4 ♠ K 10 6
♡ K 4 ♡ A 7 3 2
◇ A J 3 ◇ K Q 2
♣ Q J ♣ A 10 9

North leads the ◇ 7 against West's 6 ♠.
What card should declarer lead at trick two?

(4)

♠ A 9 6 5
♡♣ Q J 3
◇ J 3 2
♣ A K Q

♠ K J 4 2
♡ A K 2
◇ Q 5 4
♣ 4 3 2

N
W E
S

(a) Seeing the two hands, what contract would you like to be in?
(b) Assuming the best defence and the worst distribution, can you
     guarantee to make game?
(c) How will you play the spades?

(5)

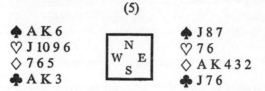

♠ A K 6
♡ J 10 9 6
◇ 7 6 5
♣ A K 3

♠ J 8 7
♡ 7 6
◇ A K 4 3 2
♣ J 7 6

N
W E
S

North leads the ace, king, queen and a fourth heart. South
follows three times. On winning the fourth heart, declarer leads
a diamond and ducks in dummy. He wins the spade return, leads
a diamond (trick seven) and again ducks in dummy.
(a) What is the contract?
(b) The play to the first six tricks is the same as in (a). At trick
     seven declarer again plays a diamond (the second round of
     diamonds), but this time he goes up with dummy's ace.
     What is the contract?

ANSWERS

(1)

(*a*) A low trump from the closed hand and a low one from dummy
—unless North plays the ♠ Q or ♠ J.

If North has all four trumps (Q J 3 2), dummy's ♠ 6 will
hold the trick. If South wins, the trumps cannot be worse than
3–1, so there will be no other loser. Should North show out on
the first round, dummy's king is played and again the defence
is confined to one trick. This is a standard SAFETY PLAY—
compulsory on a diamond opening, but—

(*b*) things are different when North opens the ♡ 6. This could well
be a singleton, and if so, declarer cannot afford the SAFETY
PLAY, because the risk of a heart ruff is greater than the risk of
a 4–0 trump break.

(2)

A low trump to dummy's ace and another to the king in the
closed hand.

Since declarer expects to lose a club, he cannot afford to think
of safety plays. If he had the ♣ K instead of the ♣ 9 (♣ K Q J),
he would lead a low trump at trick two and play dummy's ♠ 4—
if North followed with the deuce or three.

It is true that if North has ♣ K x or if South has ♣ 10 x, declarer can avoid the loss of a club trick by good guessing. This is
far too much to expect. A 2–2 trump break, which is almost an
even money bet, is a far better proposition. One should know all
the routine safety plays—and when to avoid them.

(3)

The ♣ Q.

If the finesse succeeds, declarer will make a SAFETY PLAY in
trumps. Should the club finesse fail, declarer will not be able to
afford the luxury of a SAFETY PLAY. He will lead the ♠ A, then
the ♠ K, hoping for a 2–2 split. It's a very good slam to be in, and
should it fail, there will be no need to complain of bad luck—for it
will really be unlucky.

16

ANSWERS

(4)

(*a*) 3 NT.

(*b*) Yes.

(*c*) ♠ K, then a low spade to the nine—unless South plays an honour.

Declarer has eight tricks on top. A spade or diamond opening will present him with his ninth trick, so assume that the lead is a heart or a club. Declarer needs three spade tricks and ensures them by making the standard SAFETY PLAY—the king, then a low one to the nine. If North wins with the ♠ 10, the suit will have broken 3–2 and all will be well. If South shows out on the second round, declarer will go up with the ♠ A and lead another up to dummy's ♠ J.

(5)

(*a*) 2 NT.

Since declarer can afford to lose two diamonds, his objective must be eight tricks. By ducking twice he maintains communications with dummy and makes certain of three diamond tricks —and his contract—even if the suit breaks 4–1.

(*b*) 3 NT.

Declarer's play shows that he needs four tricks in diamonds. Therefore he must be trying to make nine tricks.

Note that if the contract were 1 NT declarer would not need to duck at all. If, however, he were seeking to make the maximum —his contract being safe—he would duck once only.

(6)

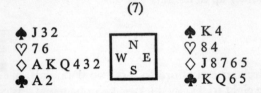

♠ J 3 2   ♠ K 4
♡ 7 6   ♡ A 8 4
◇ A K Q 4 3 2   ◇ J 7 6 5
♣ A 2   ♣ K 6 5 3

North, who bid 1 ♠ as dealer, leads the ♠ 6 against West's 3 NT.

(a) What card should declarer play from dummy?

(b) What card should declarer play from dummy had South (not North) dealt and bid 1 ♠?

(7)

♠ J 3 2   ♠ K 4
♡ 7 6   ♡ 8 4
◇ A K Q 4 3 2   ◇ J 8 7 6 5
♣ A 2   ♣ K Q 6 5

North, who bid 1 ♠ as dealer, leads the ♠ 6 against West's 3 NT.

What card should dealer play from dummy?

QUESTIONS

(8)

♠ A J 3   ♠ K 10 2
♡ K J 9   ♡ A Q 10
♢ J 10   ♢ Q 4
♣ A 5 4 3 2 ♣ K J 8 7 6

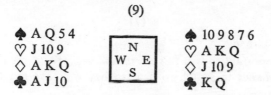

North leads the ♡8 against West's 5 ♣. Declarer draws trumps.
(a) Which club should he play from his own hand?
(b) If there are no trump losers, can declarer make certain of his contract?
(c) Which suit should declarer play after drawing trumps?

(9)

♠ A Q 5 4   ♠ 10 9 8 7 6
♡ J 10 9   ♡ A K Q
♢ A K Q   ♢ J 10 9
♣ A J 10   ♣ K Q

North leads a diamond. Spades are trumps.
(a) At trick two declarer leads the ace of spades. What is the contract?
(b) At trick two declarer leads a heart to dummy, then a spade. South plays the deuce and West the queen.
What is the contract?

ANSWERS

(6)

(*a*) and (*b*) The ♠ 4.

It makes no difference who bid 1 ♠ or who has the ace or queen. By playing low from dummy declarer makes certain of losing no more than one trick. Should he go up with the king and find South with the ace, he can lose six tricks—unlucky, perhaps, but no more than he deserves.

Is this hand too easy? If so, it is a measure of the advance made by the masses in recent years. In 1935, a player of repute (who took part in the Master Pairs) misplayed this hand—and complained of bad luck afterwards!

(7)

The king.

It is important to win this *particular trick*, for if the defenders get the chance to switch to hearts, they will take five tricks, at least.

On the previous hand, declarer's prime purpose was to prevent defenders from running off the spades. This time he has a different objective. He must seize the initiative *quickly*. Time is no longer on his side,

The low spade from dummy is the correct play—if declarer can afford it. Last time he could and this time he can't.

(8)

(*a*) The ace.

If trumps break 2–1 it will make no difference. If South has all three, a trump trick must be lost anyway. But if North has Q 10 9, declarer can finesse against him successfully—but only if he leads the ace first.

(*b*) Yes.

(*c*) Hearts.

Having ELIMINATED (played off) the hearts, declarer leads a diamond. Defenders can take two diamonds only. If they lead a third diamond, declarer will be presented with a ruff and discard. A spade will find the queen for him. Either way he will make his contract.

(9)

(*a*) 6 ♠.

Declarer is making a SAFETY PLAY in trumps. If the spades split 2–2 nothing matters and if North has K J x, nothing helps. But North may have a singleton honour. If so, it will drop on the ace and declarer will have no further problems. Note that if South holds K J x (x), nothing is lost by laying down the ace.

(*b*) 7 ♠.

This time declarer cannot afford to lose even one trump trick and must find South with K x—or with K x x and North with the singleton jack.

QUESTIONS

(10)

```
♠ — —                    ♠ J 9 6 5 4
♡ Q J 10 9 8     N       ♡ A K
◇ Q J 10 9    W     E    ◇ A K
♣ 8 4 3 2        S       ♣ A 7 6 5
```

North leads a spade against West's 4 ♡. West ruffs. What cards should declarer play at:

(a) Trick two?
(b) Trick three?
(c) Trick four?

(11)

```
♠ A J                    ♠ 7 6 5 4
♡ A K Q J 10 9   N       ♡ 8 7
◇ 9 8          W     E   ◇ A Q 10
♣ Q J 10         S       ♣ 6 5 4 3
```
N/S vulnerable.

South	West	North	East
3 ♠	4 ♡	— —	— —

A hand is thrown in. The cards are not shuffled and are then dealt three at a time with four cards on the last round. This is known as a GOULASH and usually leads to freak distributions.

North leads the king, ace and another club. South follows once, throws a spade on the second club and ruffs the third. He continues with the king of spades. North discards a diamond on West's ace and another on the ace of trumps.

Declarer tables his hand, specifying the ten tricks which he will make.

(a) Which tricks does he claim?
(b) What will he discard from dummy on his long trumps?

QUESTIONS

(12)

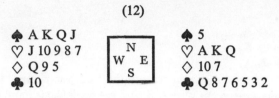

♠ A K Q J   ♠ 5
♡ J 10 9 8 7   ♡ A K Q
◇ Q 9 5   ◇ 10 7
♣ 10   ♣ Q 8 7 6 5 3 2

North leads a spade. Declarer plays a second spade and:
(a) discards dummy's ace of hearts.
(b) discards dummy's ◇ 7.
What is the contract in each case?

(13)

♠ A 3 2   ♠ 6 5
♡ A J 4   ♡ 10 6 5
◇ A K 4 2   ◇ 6 5
♣ 10 8 2   ♣ A Q J 9 7 3

North leads the king of spades against West's 3 NT. Declarer plays low and North continues with the queen. South follows. Should declarer win or play low again?

(14)

♠ A 3 2   ♠ 6 5
♡ A 3   ♡ 6 5
◇ A K J 4 2   ◇ 6 5 3
♣ 10 8 2   ♣ A Q J 9 7 3

North leads the king of spades against West's 3 NT.
(a) Should declarer win the trick or hold up his ace?
(b) If he holds it up and North leads another spade, should he hold up his ace a second time?

(10)

(*a*) The $\diamondsuit$ A.

(*b*) The $\diamondsuit$ K.

(*c*) The $\clubsuit$ A.

Declarer must resist the temptation to draw trumps. To do that he would have to cash the A K and get back to his hand by ruffing a second spade. This would leave him with one trump only and one of the defenders would probably have two (the odds are nearly 2–1 against a 3–3 break).

A far better plan is to cross-ruff the hand. After cashing the ace and king of diamonds, declarer returns to his hand twice by ruffing spades and ruffs two diamonds with dummy's top trumps.

There is just one danger. While declarer is ruffing diamonds, a defender may discard two clubs. Then the ace may be ruffed. Cash it quickly—before anyone can discard anything.

(11)

(*a*) Six trumps, the $\clubsuit$ A and three diamonds.

> Since South showed out on the second round, North must have five clubs. He failed to follow to both majors, so his remaining cards must be all diamonds. The double finesse cannot, therefore, go wrong.

(*b*) Two spades.

> Four rounds of trumps must be drawn (South, who had five, ruffed once) and that calls for two discards from dummy. One slip and all is lost. After finessing the $\diamondsuit$ 10, declarer will have to get back to his hand to finesse again and the only available re-entry will be a club ruff. Declarer must be careful to discard two spades and to retain dummy's fourth, vital club.

It's an easy contract, so long as declarer counts the suits in the opposing hands. North has shown five clubs (South had one only) and he couldn't follow to spades or hearts. He must, therefore, have eight diamonds.

ANSWERS

(12)

(*a*) 3 NT.

Declarer will take four spades and five hearts—but only if he UNBLOCKS by throwing dummy's three top hearts on his spades.

(*b*) 4 ♡.

Declarer cannot make ten tricks without ruffing a diamond. He intends to lead a third spade and to throw on it dummy's second diamond.

(13)

Play low.

Declarer should hold up his ace once more. Then he can take the club finesse in safety, for if it loses and South produces a fourth spade the suit is split 4–4 and cannot hurt him. The danger is that North has five spades and South three. To guard against it declarer should hold up his ace till South's third spade has gone.

The HOLD-UP disrupts communications between defenders.

(14)

(*a*) Declarer should win the trick with alacrity.

The spades may break 4–4, but given the chance, the defence may switch to hearts and if the club finesse fails, that would be fatal.

(*b*) No.

Seize the trick before it is too late. If you held up the ace the first time, you have tempted Providence enough.

QUESTIONS

(15)

♠ A 2   ♠ Q 4 3
♡ A K Q 2   ♡ 5 4
◇ A 7 3 2   W   E   ◇ 6 5 4
♣ 10 9 2   ♣ A K J 8 7

North leads the ♣ 6 against West's 3 NT.
What card should declarer play from dummy?

(16)

♠ A 2   ♠ Q 4 3
♡ A K 3 2   N   ♡ 6 5 4
◇ A 3 2   W   E   ◇ 5 4
♣ 10 9 7 2   S   ♣ A Q J 8 5

North leads the ♠ 5 against West's 3 NT.
What card should declarer play from dummy?

(17)

♠ A 7   ♠ 10 6
♡ 9 8   N   ♡ A 10 3
◇ Q J 6   W   E   ◇ K 10 2
♣ A K 9 8 7 6   S   ♣ 10 5 4 3 2

West	*East*
1 ♣	2 ♣
2 NT	3 NT

North leads the ♠ 2 against West's 3 NT. South covers dummy's
ten with the queen.
(*a*) Should declarer win or hold up his ace?
(*b*) What card should declarer lead when he comes in with the ♠ A?

(18)

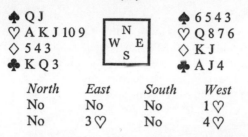

♠ Q J
♡ A K J 10 9
◇ 5 4 3
♣ K Q 3

♠ 6 5 4 3
♡ Q 8 7 6
◇ K J
♣ A J 4

North	East	South	West
No	No	No	1 ♡
No	3 ♡	No	4 ♡

After three passes West opens 1 ♡ and becomes declarer in
4 ♡. North leads his singleton ♠ 2 to his partner's king. He throws
the deuce of clubs on the ace and the deuce of diamonds on the third
spade, which declarer ruffs. After drawing trumps in two rounds,
declarer leads a diamond. North plays the six.

Which card should declarer play from dummy? Is it an even
money chance or do the odds favour playing one honour in pre-
ference to the other?

(19)

♠ Q 5 4
♡ A K 3 2
◇ Q 10 3 2
♣ K Q

♠ A 3 2
♡ 8
◇ J 8 4
♣ A 10 9 8 3 2

South	West	North	East
1 ♠	Dble	No	3 ♣
No	3 NT		

North opened the ♠ K, his partner's suit. West cannot remember
how he played the hand, but he knows that he went down and he
wonders what went wrong. Tell him. Within reason (or rather un-
reason) only two mistakes were possible.
(a) What was the first mistake?
(b) What was the second?

27

ANSWERS

(15)

A low spade.

If the club finesse fails and South returns a spade, dummy's queen will remain as an effective stopper and the contract will be safe. If declarer goes up with the queen, he may find the king with South. The ace will be driven out, and if the club finesse loses, the defence may take four spades to beat the contract.

(16)

The queen.

If the club finesse succeeds the play to the first trick will not matter. If it fails declarer will have eight tricks only. His best, if not his only hope of a ninth, is to find the queen of spades on the right side of the king.

In the previous example declarer could afford to play safe. This time he must take a risk. If he plays low to the first trick and loses the club finesse, opponents may switch to diamonds. He could then go down even if the ♠ K were well placed for him.

(17)

(*a*) Declarer should win the first trick.

The purpose of a HOLD-UP is to sever communications between defenders. This cannot apply here unless North (or South) has seven spades, which is unlikely. The lead of the deuce suggests that North has four spades, and if so, South has five—though his partner doesn't know it. Should declarer hold up his ace, South's return will give an indication of his length.

(*b*) The ◇ J.

Declarer has eight tricks only and his best chance of a ninth is to 'steal' a diamond. If North has the ace, he may play low to the jack, hoping that his partner has the queen. Should the clubs be played first, defenders will be better able to count the tricks against them and to exchange information by their discards. There will then be little hope of stealing anything.

ANSWERS

(18)

The King.

The odds in favour of playing the king are overwhelming.

Since North could not follow to the second round of spades, South must have started with six spades headed by the ace and king. Yet he could not open the bidding. He is hardly likely, therefore, to have the ace of diamonds.

(19)

(*a*) Playing ♠ A at trick one.

(*b*) Not overtaking his second top club.

The more glaring error of the two would be to win the first trick, killing dummy's vital entry to the clubs. Surely West wasn't as bad as that. He probably played low and North continued with a second spade to the queen.

West led the ♣ K, then the ♣ Q, playing low from dummy. South showed out and declarer, cursing his luck, was confined to three club tricks, not enough to ensure his contract. All West had to do was to overtake the ♣ Q with the ♣ A and to concede a trick to the ♣ J.

QUESTIONS

(20)

♠ 10 9 8			♠ A K J
♡ A 4 3	N		♡ Q 2
◇ A 9 8	W E		◇ K J 10
♣ A 8 7 6	S		♣ K Q J 10 9

North leads a diamond against West's 6 ♣. South plays the queen on dummy's jack and declarer wins with the ace.

What card should declarer play at trick two?

(21)

♠ A K Q 2			♠ 4 3
♡ Q 10 8	N		♡ 7 5
◇ 3 2	W E		◇ A K Q J 10
♣ A K 7 6	S		♣ 5 4 3 2

(*a*) North leads the ♣ Q. Declarer wins and leads the ♠ 2.
What is the contract?

(*b*) North leads the ◇ 9. Declarer leads out his four spades, throwing a heart and a club from dummy.
What is the contract?

QUESTIONS

(22)

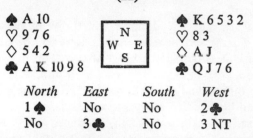

♠ A 10   ♠ K 6 5 3 2
♡ 9 7 6   ♡ 8 3
◇ 5 4 2   ◇ A J
♣ A K 10 9 8   ♣ Q J 7 6

North	*East*	*South*	*West*
1 ♠	No	No	2 ♣
No	3 ♣	No	3 NT

North leads the ♡ K, finds partner with ♡ A J 4 2 and takes four heart tricks before continuing with the ◇ K. South has a train to catch, so to oblige him, declarer spreads his cards and claims nine tricks.

Which will be his ninth trick?

(20)

A low heart.

If North has the ♡ K declarer will throw dummy's ♠ J on the ♡ A. To succeed declarer must, however, be careful with his entries. Unless he plays a heart at trick two he will lose the ♡ A!! Should he thoughtlessly lead a trump, for instance, it won't help him to find the ♡ K well placed for he will have no way back to his hand to enjoy the ace.

Of course, if South, not North, produces the ♡ K, declarer will have to take the spade finesse. But that is only an even money bet and declarer doubles his chances by trying two equal possibilites instead of restricting himself to one.

(21)

(a) 4 ♠.

By playing low at trick two, declarer ensures trump control. The defence can take two hearts only, before declarer regains the lead, draws trumps and enjoys the diamonds.

(b) 4 ♠.

This time declarer cannot afford to play a low spade for a second diamond would cut him off from dummy. If he is to enjoy the diamonds, he must draw trumps and hope that defenders will be unable to take more than two hearts before he regains the lead.

ANSWERS

(22)

The ◊ J or a small spade.

On the bidding North is marked with four (or more) spades and with the ◊ Q. This is consistent with the play. When declarer leads his last club (the tenth trick), the position will be:

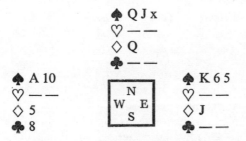

♠ Q J x
♡ — —
◊ Q
♣ — —

♠ A 10
♡ — —
◊ 5
♣ 8

N
W   E
S

♠ K 6 5
♡ — —
◊ J
♣ — —

and North will have to discard on the club *before* dummy. This is a POSITIONAL SQUEEZE. Reverse the North and South hands and there would be no squeeze, because South would not discard until AFTER he had seen dummy's discard.

(23)

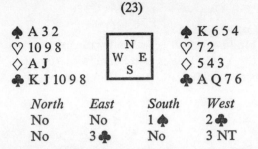

♠ A 3 2			♠ K 6 5 4
♡ 10 9 8			♡ 7 2
◇ A J			◇ 5 4 3
♣ K J 10 9 8			♣ A Q 7 6

North	East	South	West
No	No	1♠	2♣
No	3♣	No	3 NT

North leads a heart from ♡ A J 4 3 against West's 3 NT, finds partner with K Q 6 5 and the first four tricks are won by the defence. At the fifth trick South switches to the ◇ K. This time it is North who has a train to catch, but West is just as obliging. He spreads his hand and claims nine tricks.

Which will be his ninth trick?

QUESTIONS

(24)

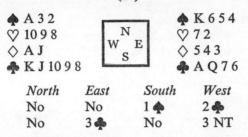

♠ A 3 2
♡ 10 9 8
◇ A J
♣ K J 10 9 8

♠ K 6 5 4
♡ 7 2
◇ 5 4 3
♣ A Q 7 6

North	East	South	West
No	No	1 ♠	2 ♣
No	3 ♣	No	3 NT

Yes, they are the same hands as in the previous example and the bidding, too, is the same. The play is *almost* the same, but not quite. This time the hearts are blocked. South wins the first three tricks with the ♡ A K Q and switches to the ◇ K.

(a) Can West claim nine tricks on a squeeze as before?

(b) Suppose that after taking three hearts, South switches not to the ◇ K, but to the ♠ Q. Would that make a difference?

(23)

The ◇ J or a small spade.

This time South discards *after* dummy, but declarer's menaces are *divided* and the result is the same. Having to fight on two fronts South is outnumbered, and West knows it.

On the bidding, North cannot have more than two spades, so South must keep three spades and the ◇ Q (with which he is marked both on the bidding and the play) to the bitter end, which will be:

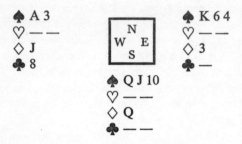

On declarer's last club a diamond is thrown from dummy and South is squeezed.

(24)

(*a*) No squeeze this time.

Until declarer loses a fourth trick he cannot turn on the heat. There is an 'idle' card about and opponents can breathe. When West leads his last club there will be five (not four) cards left:

♠ A 3 2
♡ — —
◇ J
♣ 8

N
W   E
S

♠ K 6 5 4
♡ — —
◇ 3
♣ — —

♠ Q J 10 9
♡ — —
◇ Q
♣ — —

and South will throw an 'idle' spade. For a squeeze to take effect no losers must be left unlost—except ONE. That loser can be turned into a winner, but only if all the slack has been taken up.

(*b*) Yes, the squeeze is on again.

West *ducks* the ♠ Q. It is his fourth loser and it disposes of the 'idle' card. In technical language the COUNT HAS BEEN RECTIFIED.

QUESTIONS

(25)

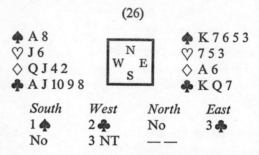

♠ 5 4 3
♡ A Q 8
◇ A K Q
♣ A 6 5 2

♠ A K Q 6
♡ K 7 3
◇ J 10 9
♣ K 4 3

North leads a spade against West's 6 NT. Declarer wins with the ace.

(a) What cards from dummy and from the closed hand should declarer play at trick two?

(b) Will it be possible to make the contract if neither spades nor clubs break evenly? If so, on what will the contract depend?

(26)

♠ A 8
♡ J 6
◇ Q J 4 2
♣ A J 10 9 8

♠ K 7 6 5 3
♡ 7 5 3
◇ A 6
♣ K Q 7

South	West	North	East
1 ♠	2 ♣	No	3 ♣
No	3 NT	— —	

North opens a heart from ♡ K 10 8 2, finds South with ♡ A Q 9 4 and takes four hearts before switching to the ♠ 9, partner's suit.

Turn to the three-card ending. Which should be declarer's last three cards and which should be the last three cards in dummy?

QUESTIONS

(27)

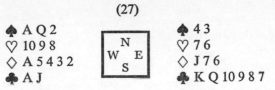

♠ A Q 2
♡ 10 9 8
◇ A 5 4 3 2
♣ A J

♠ 4 3
♡ 7 6
◇ J 7 6
♣ K Q 10 9 8 7

North opens the bidding with 1 ♠. After two passes, West doubles and ends up as declarer in 3 NT. North opens a heart, finds South with ♡ K Q and the defence take four heart tricks before North switches to the ◇ K.

If neither the ♠ K nor the ◇ Q is thrown on the clubs, can declarer make his contract?

If so, which will be his ninth trick?

(28)

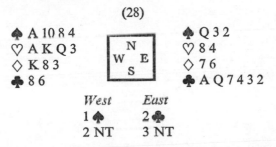

♠ A 10 8 4
♡ A K Q 3
◇ K 8 3
♣ 8 6

♠ Q 3 2
♡ 8 4
◇ 7 6
♣ A Q 7 4 3 2

West	East
1 ♠	2 ♣
2 NT	3 NT

North leads the ♡ J against West's 3 NT. South follows with ♡ 6.

(*a*) Which card should declarer play from his hand?

(*b*) Which cards should declarer play from his hand and from dummy at trick two?

(29)

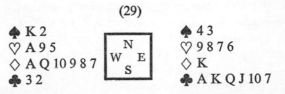

♠ K 2
♡ A 9 5
◇ A Q 10 9 8 7
♣ 3 2

♠ 4 3
♡ 9 8 7 6
◇ K
♣ A K Q J 10 7

North leads the ♠ A and the ♠ 10 against West's 5 ◇. What cards should declarer play from his own hand and from dummy to trick three?

(25)

(*a*) A low club from both hands.

(*b*) Yes.

The contract can still be made if the same defender holds both the long spades *and* the long clubs—four or more in each suit. After eight cards have been played (one spade, one club and six red cards) that defender will be down to five cards and he will need six. The last (sixth) red card will, therefore, squeeze him, forcing him to let go his long spade or his long club. Two points should be noted:

1. There will be no squeeze unless declarer first concedes his inevitable loser. That club, given away at trick two, is an 'idle' card. Unless it is removed, North will throw it on the sixth red card and still retain six black ones. The COUNT must be RECTIFIED.

2. This is a typical situation for a squeeze. Declarer has eleven tricks and needs one more, and he can afford to lose a trick without giving up any alternative line of play.

(26)

```
♠ 8           ┌───────┐      ♠ K 7 6
♡ — —         │   N   │      ♡ — —
♢ Q           │ W   E │      ♢ — —
♣ 8           │   S   │      ♣ — —
              └───────┘
```

The key to the hand is to play off the ♢ A before settling down to the clubs. Had South passed, West would have taken the diamond finesse. But South's 1 ♠ bid marks him with the ♢ K (he could otherwise have no more than nine points) as well as four or five spades. In the three-card ending he will be squeezed in spades and diamonds—but only if declarer UNBLOCKED the diamonds by playing off the ace. The technical term is: VIENNA COUP.

Note the SQUEEZE MOTIF. South is outnumbered, having to keep three spades against East and the ♢ K against West. And the COUNT has been RECTIFIED. *All* declarer's losers have been lost.

(27)

♠ Q.

When the last club is played two other cards will remain. Dummy will have one spade and the ◇ J. Declarer will retain ♠ A Q. Unless North throws his ◇ Q, he will be obliged to bare his ♠ K and it will drop tamely on the ♠ A. Observe that declarer will not be called upon to guess anything. Once South shows up with the ♡ K Q, he cannot have either the ◇ Q or the ♠ K. With 7–8 points he would not have passed his partner's opening bid.

(28)

(*a*) The ♡ K.

To win with the ♡ Q would give away the position. South would go up with the ♡ A or ♡ K if he had it. So if declarer wins with the queen, he must have the king and ace as well. That's how it will look to North. How about winning the first trick with the ♡ A? That would be a little disingenuous. Both defenders will realise that without the king behind it, declarer would hold up the ace. The best card for declarer to play, therefore, is the king. It conceals the ace from South and the queen from North.

(*b*) Low clubs from both hands.

By losing the first trick, declarer retains a second club to take the finesse and to enjoy five club tricks—if the finesse succeeds and the suit breaks 3–2.

(29)

The ◇ A and the ◇ K.

He will continue with the ◇ Q and ◇ 10, driving out the jack, and whatever defenders do, he can get back to his hand with the ♡ A to draw the last trump—if a trump is still out. The rest of the tricks will be his. If declarer tries to draw trumps by taking the king, getting back to his hand with the ♡ A and continuing with the ◇ A and ◇ Q, he will probably go down. The odds favour a 4–2 trump break and there is a serious risk that defenders will come in with the ◇ J and take a heart—or two hearts—before West can bring in dummy's clubs.

(30)

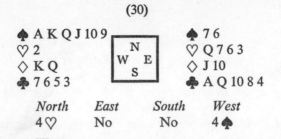

♠ A K Q J 10 9		♠ 7 6
♡ 2		♡ Q 7 6 3
◇ K Q		◇ J 10
♣ 7 6 5 3		♣ A Q 10 8 4

North	East	South	West
4♡	No	No	4♠
—			

North leads the ♡ K, then the ◇ 9. South wins with the ace and returns the deuce of diamonds. North ruffs and continues with the ♡ 10. Dummy's queen is ruffed by South and over-ruffed by West. Declarer draws trumps finding that North started with a singleton and South with four. How should declarer play the clubs?

(31)

♠ A K 3		♠ J 6 5
♡ A Q		♡ J 6 5 4 2
◇ A J 10 5 4 3		◇ 2
♣ 8 2		♣ A 10 4 3

West is declarer in 3 ◇.

(*a*) How should he play the trumps?
(*b*) If North leads the ♣ K and declarer goes up with the ace, what cards should he play from dummy and from his own hand at trick two?

(32)

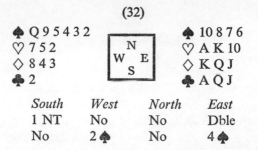

♠ Q 9 5 4 3 2   ♠ 10 8 7 6
♡ 7 5 2   ♡ A K 10
◇ 8 4 3   ◇ K Q J
♣ 2   ♣ A Q J

South	West	North	East
1 NT	No	No	Dble
No	2 ♠	No	4 ♠

North leads the ♠ J against West's 4 ♠. South wins with the ♠ A, cashes the ♠ K (North throws a club) and continues with ♡ Q to dummy's ace.

(a) Can West make certain of his contract?

(b) What card should declarer play at trick four?

(33)

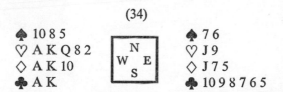

♠ Q 6 2   ♠ K 10 7
♡ J 4 3   ♡ A 10
◇ A Q 10 2   ◇ K 3
♣ 7 4 2   ♣ K Q J 10 9 8

East	South	West	North
1 ♣	1 ♠	1 NT	No
3 NT			

North leads ♠ 9.

What card should declarer play from dummy?

(34)

♠ 10 8 5   ♠ 7 6
♡ A K Q 8 2   ♡ J 9
◇ A K 10   ◇ J 7 5
♣ A K   ♣ 10 9 8 7 6 5

North leads the ♠ K and ♠ A against West's 4 ♡. South follows with the three, then the deuce. North continues with a low spade.

Which card should declarer play from dummy?

ANSWERS

(30)

Declarer should lead lead the ♣ 5 (or 6 or 7) and *run* it unless North covers.

The key to the play lies in counting North's cards. He has produced seven hearts—South had a singleton—one spade and one diamond. Therefore he must have all four clubs, the K J 9 2. If North covers the ♣ 5, declarer finesses deeply, returns to his hand twice by ruffing hearts and each time repeats the finesse.

In the post mortem South will point out that his ◇ 2 was an unmistakable suit signal, demanding a club. Meanwhile, East-West will add up the score.

(31)

(*a*) The ◇ A, then a low one.

If the suit breaks 3–3, two tricks must be lost no matter how West plays. But the diamonds may be divided 4–2, and if so, one of the defenders may have a doubleton honour. Then playing ace-small will pay a dividend. The king (or queen) will fall on the three and declarer will have the J 10 intact to deal with the Q 9.

(*b*) A heart.

The finesse will succeed half the time, and will then be worth a certain trick. To use dummy's sole entry for a trump lead will not help unless South has ◇ K Q x, and then only if declarer knows the position.

ANSWERS

(32)

(*a*) Yes.

He can throw his losing heart on a club—after finding out who has the king. To do that he . . .

(*b*) leads a diamond.

If North has the ace, South must have the ♣ K for his 1 NT opening and declarer takes a ruffing finesse, playing the ♣ A first, then the queen. If South has the ♢ A, he cannot have the ♣ K, too, for that would give him 17 points. West takes, therefore, a simple finesse against North.

(33)

♠ K.

North's lead, together with the bidding, leaves no doubt that South's spades are headed by the A J. If he wins the first trick with the ace and returns the suit, West will let it run up to dummy's ten. If he returns anything else, declarer will have time to drive out the ♣ A.

Should declarer play, mistakenly, dummy's ♠ 10, South will put up the ♠ J. What will declarer do then? If he wins with the ♠ Q, North may come in with the ♣ A and lead another spade through dummy's K 7. If declarer allows the ♠ J to hold the trick, South may clear the suit and come in again with the ♣ A.

The ♠ K at trick one disposes of both risks.

(34)

♢ 5.

Why did South play high-low, the three before the deuce? It isn't clear. Maybe he has ♠ Q. Maybe he has four trumps to the ten and wants declarer to ruff high. Maybe he has a doubleton spade and also the ♡ 10, Declarer has no need to speculate. Having a losing diamond, he gets rid of it at trick three instead of later. Subsequently, he will ruff a diamond.

This is a variant on the LOSER-ON-LOSER theme.

QUESTIONS

(35)

```
♠ Q 10 8 4                    ♠ A 9 3
♡ A 10 9         N            ♡ 8 7
◇ Q 10 8      W     E         ◇ K J 9 6 4 2
♣ A J 4          S            ♣ K 3
```

North leads the ♠ 5 against West's 3 NT.
How many tricks should declarer make?

(36)

```
♠ 5 4 3 2                     ♠ K Q 10
♡ 2              N            ♡ A 7 6 5
◇ 5 4 3 2     W     E         ◇ A Q 6
♣ 5 4 3 2        S            ♣ 8 7 6
```

North	East	South	West
1 ♡	No	2 ♡	No
No	Dble	No	2 ♠

Had East been given a preview of his partner's mini-Yarborough, he would have passed 2 ♡ quickly instead of coming in to balance with a double. But it's no use crying over spilt milk and West must gird his loins.

North leads ♡ K.

Assuming a reasonably favourable distribution, consistent with the bidding, how can West make 2 ♠?

Which eight tricks can he hope to win?

(37)

```
♠ K Q J                       ♠ — —
♡ A K 7 6 5      N            ♡ 4 3 2
◇ A K         W     E         ◇ J 10 9 8 7
♣ A 3 2          S            ♣ K Q J 10 9
```

North leads a spade against West's 6 ♡. Declarer ruffs in dummy.

What cards should declarer play from dummy and from his own hand at trick two?

(38)

```
♠ — —            ♠ J 10 4
♡ A K 10 9       ♡ Q J 8
◇ A K 8          ◇ 7 6 5 2
♣ A J 10 7 4 2   ♣ K Q 9
```

Hearts are trumps. North leads ♠ K.
(a) Declarer ruffs and leads a trump. What is the contract?
(b) Declarer throws a diamond. What is the contract?

(39)

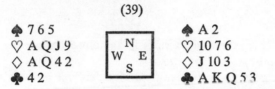

```
♠ 7 6 5          ♠ A 2
♡ A Q J 9        ♡ 10 7 6
◇ A Q 4 2        ◇ J 10 3
♣ 4 2            ♣ A K Q 5 3
```

North led the ♣ J against West's 3 NT. Declarer won with the ace and continued with the ♡ 10 which held the trick. Surprisingly, the contract was defeated.

What card did declarer play at trick three?

ANSWERS

(35)

Nine—only.

With every card right, declarer can make twelve tricks, but he must not jeopardise his contract. Opponents will attack hearts at the first opportunity and if the first trick is lost to the ♠ K, they may come to five tricks—a spade (the K), a diamond (the A), and at least three hearts. By going up with the ♠ A declarer makes certain of his contract—but he no longer expects to come to more than nine tricks.

(36)

The ♡ A; three heart ruffs in the closed hand; the ◇ A and ◇ Q, and two trump tricks.

West goes up with dummy's ♡ A, ruffs a heart in the closed hand, crosses to dummy with a diamond, finessing against the king, and ruffs a second heart. Returning to the table with the ◇ A, he leads dummy's fourth heart, ruffs again and exits with his last trump. Unless South has both the ♠ A and the ♠ J, declarer expects to make two of dummy's trumps.

Ruffing losers in dummy comes naturally. When there is a void or singleton in the closed hand, the same technique may be used in reverse.

(37)

♡ 2 and ♡ 5.

Declarer must draw trumps, but in so doing he is bound to lose a trick and if, at that point, there is no trump in dummy, the defence will take the ♠ A. By losing the *first* trump trick—while a trump remains in dummy—this danger is averted.

ANSWERS

(38)

(*a*) 6 ♡ (conceivably 7 ♡).

Having ruffed, declarer depends on a 3–3 heart break and the odds are roughly 2–1 against it. There is, however, no alternative for if declarer discarded a diamond, North would only lead another spade. Of course, the right contract is 6 ♣, but that's another story. Minor suit contracts are always difficult to reach.

(*b*) 4 ♡.

Declarer can afford to lose the first three spade tricks and avoids the risk of shortening his trumps.

(39)

Another heart.

What doubtless happened, was that declarer repeated, without thinking, the heart finesse. North came up unexpectedly with the king, switched to a spade and found South with a lusty five-card suit. The clubs broke 4–2.

As soon as he could count on two heart tricks, declarer should have made certain of his contract by developing three tricks in diamonds. North ought to have won the first heart, but since he didn't, declarer shouldn't have given him a second chance.

It is a simple hand, but it carries a message: card by card, declarer should always keep his mind focussed on the number of tricks he needs, and as the situation changes, so should his plan of campaign change with it.

QUESTIONS

(40)

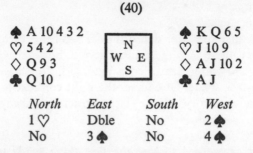

♠ A 10 4 3 2		♠ K Q 6 5
♡ 5 4 2	N	♡ J 10 9
◇ Q 9 3	W E	◇ A J 10 2
♣ Q 10	S	♣ A J

North	East	South	West
1 ♡	Dble	No	2 ♠
No	3 ♠	No	4 ♠

North leads the three top hearts. On the last round South throws the ◇ 8. North continues with a club.

(a) Which card should declarer play from dummy?
(b) How should he play the trumps? King or ace first?
(c) How should he play the diamonds? Which card first?

(41)

♠ A 10		♠ 9 6
♡ A K Q	N	♡ J 10 9
◇ K Q 4 3	W E	◇ J 7 5 2
♣ A K 7 4	S	♣ Q J 10 3

West	East
2 ♣	2 ◇
3 NT	—

North leads the ♠ 5 to the queen and ace.
What cards should declarer play to the next three tricks?

QUESTIONS

(42)

♠ A Q 10 9 7 6 2   ♠ 8 5 4
♡ 9 8 7   ♡ K J
♢ 9 8   ♢ K J
♣ 2   ♣ A 9 8 7 5 4

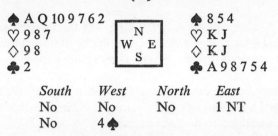

South	West	North	East
No	No	No	1 NT
No	4♠		

North leads the ♣ K against West's sporting contract of 4 ♠. South follows with the ♣ J on dummy's ace. Declarer is lucky with trumps, finding South with the ♠ K J and North with the ♠ 3 Anxious to show his skill, declarer tables his hand, states his line of play and claims ten tricks.

(a) What cards from his own hand and from dummy did declarer say that he would play at trick four?

(b) Which ten tricks did he claim?

(43)

♠ Q 6 5 3 2   ♠ A 10 8 4
♡ K Q 10   ♡ J 9 8
♢ A Q 3   ♢ K J 10
♣ A J   ♣ K Q 7

North leads a diamond against West's horrible contract of 6♠.

In which hand should declarer win the trick and what card should he play next?

(40)

(*a*) ♣ A.

Yes, North probably has the king, but the finesse can't help.
To make his contract declarer needs the diamond finesse and
if that succeeds he can get rid of his losing club.

(*b*) ♠ K.

Declarer is only concerned with a 4–0 trump break. If South
has ♠ J x x x, the jack is finessible. If North has that holding,
there's nothing to be done anyway.

(*c*) ◇ 9.

If the ◇ Q is played first, North, who might have ◇ K 8 7 6,
will play low. The ◇ 9 will have to be overtaken in dummy
and declarer will find himself in the wrong hand. North could
have:

♠ — — ♡ A K Q 8 7 ◇ K 8 7 6 ♣ 9 8 6 5.

(41)

The ace and king of clubs, then the ◇ K.

With eight tricks on top, declarer must try to steal a ninth before
an avalanche of spades descends upon him. He seeks to foster the
illusion that he has no more clubs and looks to dummy's ◇ J as
an entry. Maybe the defender with the ◇ A will hold it up.

Note that declarer should go up at once with the ♠ A. The
sight of the ♠ 10 on the first trick would only alert opponents to
the true position without severing communications between them
—unless North had a seven-card suit.

Of course, accurate signalling by the defence will foil declarer.
But defenders do not always signal accurately—or read each
other's signals correctly.

ANSWERS

(42)

(*a*) Any red card from his hand and the king from dummy.

If the king wins, there's no further problem. If it loses to South's ace, North must have the other ace and dummy's second king will win.

Since South's ♣ J is surely a singleton, he has only three black cards. With so much shape, two red aces, and the ♠ K J, he wouldn't have passed as dealer. It follows that by going up each time with one of dummy's kings, declarer cannot fail to make the right play once.

(*b*) His ten tricks will be: eight black cards, one heart ruff in dummy and *one red king*.

(43)

Declarer should win in the closed hand and lead the ♠ Q.

Since, come what may, a heart trick must be lost, declarer cannot afford to lose a trump trick as well. The only hope is to find North with ♠ K 9 7 and South with the singleton jack.

Note that a singleton king with either defender wouldn't help. The J 9 7 with the other defender would make a trick anyway.

QUESTIONS

(44)

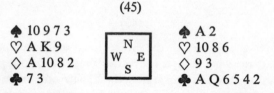

♠ K Q J 3 2   ♠ 10 8 7 6 5 4
♡ A Q J   ♡ 3 2
◇ K 4   ◇ A J
♣ 4 3 2   ♣ 7 6 5

North leads the ◇ 6 against West's 4 ♠.

(a) Which card should declarer play from dummy?

(b) If the first trick is won in dummy, which East-West cards should make up trick two?

(c) Which East-West cards should make up trick two if the first trick is won in the closed hand?

(45)

♠ 10 9 7 3   ♠ A 2
♡ A K 9   ♡ 10 8 6
◇ A 10 8 2   ◇ 9 3
♣ 7 3   ♣ A Q 6 5 4 2

North leads the ♠ K to dummy's ♠ A against West's 3 NT. Which East-West cards should make up trick two?

54

QUESTIONS

(46)

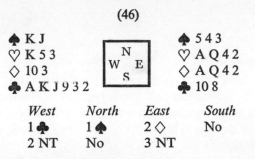

♠ K J
♡ K 5 3
◇ 10 3
♣ A K J 9 3 2

♠ 5 4 3
♡ A Q 4 2
◇ A Q 4 2
♣ 10 8

West	North	East	South
1♣	1♠	2◇	No
2 NT	No	3 NT	

North leads ◇ 6 against West's 3 NT.

(a) Which card should declarer play from dummy at trick one?

(b) Which East-West cards should be played on the first round of clubs?

(47)

♠ K J
♡ A K Q J 10 9
◇ A Q 2
♣ 8 2

♠ Q 9 6 4
♡ 8 7 6
◇ 5 4 3
♣ A 7 6

North leads the ♣ K against West's 4 ♡. Declarer wins. What card should declare lead at trick two?

(48)

♠ A K 7 6 5
♡ A 7 6 5
◇ — —
♣ A K 3 2

♠ Q 4 3 2
♡ K 3 2
◇ Q J 10 9
♣ 5 4

North leads the ♡ Q against West's 6 ♠. Declarer wins in his hand. Trumps break 3–1.

(a) In which hand should declarer win the third round of trumps?

(b) Which twelve tricks should he try to realise?

(c) How good are declarer's chances—fifty-fifty, eight in ten or better still?

ANSWERS

(*a*) ◇ J.

(*b*) The ♡ 2 and ♡ Q.

(*c*) ♠ 2 and ♠ 10.

Declarer has four top losers and can only make his contract if he is lucky. A successful heart finesse will enable him to throw one of dummy's clubs on a heart, but for this to work two entries will be needed in dummy. Hence the ◇ J at trick one. If South has the ◇ Q, declarer's only hope will lie in finding North with the ♠ A 9. Should North fail to go up with the ace, the ♠ 10 will provide a quick entry.

Just as declarer takes safety plays to guard against the worst—and least likely—distributions, when his contract appears unbeatable, so he does the opposite and assumes the luckiest breaks —or slips by the defence—when nothing else can bring success.

(45)

The ♣ 2 and the ♣ 3.

The contract cannot be made without bringing in the club suit and the correct play, since dummy has no side entry, is to duck a club, then to finesse. If the suit breaks 3–2 and North has the king, all is well. If he hasn't, it isn't. Declarer can do nothing against K x x with South and he will probably go down if South has a doubleton king—since declarer won't know the position. He can, however, improve his chances by leading the first club (trick two) from dummy. South may not have the nerve to play low from K x and if he goes up with the ♣ K, it will be all over.

The same two East-West cards will make up the first club trick, anyway, but there is a psychological advantage in starting from dummy. (Compare with 28.)

(46)

(a) ◇ A.

(b) ♣ 10 and ♣ 2.

The contract is unmakeable without bringing in the clubs and unbreakable if the club finesse succeeds. Should South, however, come in at the first trick with the ◇ K (or worse still with the ◇ J) and lead a spade, the defence may take six or seven tricks before clubs are even touched.

Declarer should go up with the ◇ A and run the ♣ 10. To lay down the ♣ A—so as to cater for a singleton queen with North—is to play against the odds. If the clubs split 4–1, the queen is four times as likely to be with the player holding four clubs as with his partner who has a singleton. To catch the queen, however, the finesse must be repeated and that will require both dummy's clubs.

(47)

A diamond.

The club was an unlucky lead. On any other opening declarer could spread his hand. Now dummy's only entry has been killed and he must make the most of his one chance to lead up to his hand. The diamond finesse must, therefore, be taken immediately for there will be no other opportunity.

This is a very easy hand to play correctly—but only at trick one. As on so many hands, the first few seconds are decisive.

(48)

(a) Dummy.

(b) Five trumps, two hearts, two clubs, one club ruff in dummy and *two diamonds*.

(c) The contract is almost a certainty as soon as both defenders follow to the first round of trumps.

If North had ◇ A K he would have opened a diamond and not the ♡ Q. Therefore, it may be assumed that the diamond tops are divided or that South has both. Declarer draws trumps, ending in dummy, and leads the ◇ Q. If it isn't covered he throws a loser. He wins the next trick, enters dummy and leads the ◇ J. The second top diamond, which must be with South, is under the hammer and two winning diamonds remain in dummy.

QUESTIONS

(49)

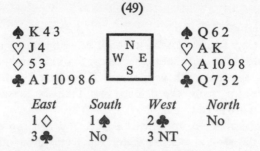

♠ K 4 3
♡ J 4
◇ 5 3
♣ A J 10 9 8 6

♠ Q 6 2
♡ A K
◇ A 10 9 8
♣ Q 7 3 2

East	South	West	North
1 ◇	1 ♠	2 ♣	No
3 ♣	No	3 NT	

North leads the ♠ 9 against West's 3 NT.

(*a*) What card should declarer play from dummy at trick one?

(*b*) Assuming the best defence and the worst distribution, consistent with the bidding, can declarer make certain of his contract?

(50)

♠ A
♡ 7 6 5 4
◇ 10 7 6 5 4
♣ A 5 4

♠ J 10 8
♡ A K 2
◇ A K
♣ K J 10 9 2

North leads the ♠ 5 against West's 3 NT.

(*a*) What card should declarer play from dummy?

(*b*) What card should he play at trick two?

ANSWERS

(49)

(*a*) ♠ Q.

(*b*) Yes.

Unless North has the ♣ K, declarer can count ten top tricks. Assuming, therefore, that the club finesse will fail, his main concern should be to cut communications between the defenders. Going up with the ♠ Q at trick one has the same effect as a hold-up play. If South wins and continues spades, declarer plays his king, crosses to dummy and finesses against the ♣ K. Should North produce a third spade, the suit will not be dangerous, and if he has no more spades he will be unable to put his partner in.

Unless declarer goes up with the ♠ K at trick two (having lost the first trick to the ♠ A), the defence may switch to diamonds and break the contract with: two spades, two diamonds and the ♣ K.

(50)

(*a*) ♠ J.

(*b*) ♣ 4.

If South has an honour and can be induced to put it up, dummy's ♠ 10 8 may well provide a second stopper in spades—a certain stopper if North can be kept out of the lead. To coax the king or queen, play ♠ J at trick one. On the ♠ 8 South will obviously play the nine, if he has it.

Declarer needs four club tricks. If he leads the ♣ A first and then finesses, he may find that North started with ♣ Q x x x. To catch the ♣ Q will require a second finesse and therefore an entry —no longer available—to the closed hand. A low club first (trick two) will allow declarer to return to his hand with the ♣ A. Note that laying down the ♣ A first gains only when South has the bare ♣ Q (one chance in five) and loses when South's singleton is any other club (four chances in five). If South has more than one club the question doesn't arise.

Yes, the same principle applies as in 46.

Part Two

The reader is reminded that marks—shown in the right-hand column—are awarded for each one of the next hundred quizzes. By comparing his scores for PART TWO and PART THREE, he will be able to measure his progress. And should he suspect a trap, he can leave PART TWO until he has completed the answers to PART THREE (page 105). Whichever he does first, he will win.

(51)

```
♠ — —              ♠ Q 10
♡ A Q 10 8 7 6 3   ♡ K J 9 4
◇ K 4 2            ◇ 10 7
♣ 9 8 7            ♣ A 6 5 4 2
```

North leads the ♠ K against West's 4 ♡.
(a) What card should declarer play to trick one?
(b) If the clubs break 3–2, can declarer make certain of his contract? If so, which three tricks will the defence make?

(52)

```
♠ Q J 10 9 8 7     ♠ A K
♡ 4 3 2            ♡ A Q 10 9 8
◇ 2                ◇ A 4 3
♣ J 10 2           ♣ 9 8 7
```

North leads the three top clubs against West's 4 ♠, then he switches to a nondescript diamond. On the second round of trumps South throws a diamond. Declarer crosses to his hand by ruffing a diamond (the ace was played at trick four) and draws trumps.
Which two cards should he throw from dummy?

(53)

♠ 4 3	♠ A K 2
♡ A Q 9 8 7 6	♡ 5 4 3
◇ K 10 4	◇ A J 6 5
♣ A 4	♣ 3 2

North leads the ♣ Q against West's 4 ♡. Declarer wins.
(a) What card should declarer play at trick two?
(b) How should declarer continue?

(54)

♠ A 9 6 5	♠ K J 4 2
♡ Q J 10	♡ A K 2
◇ Q 3 2	◇ J 5 4
♣ 4 3 2	♣ A K J

West is declarer in 4 ♠. North leads the ◇ A, the ◇ K and a low diamond. All follow.
Which card should declarer lead at trick four?

(55)

♠ A K Q 10 3 2	♠ J 8
♡ A J 10	♡ 4 3 2
◇ Q J	◇ 9 4 3 2
♣ A K	♣ 5 4 3 2

North leads the two top diamonds, then a club to declarer's ace. At trick four declarer leads the deuce of spades and plays dummy's eight on North's six.
(a) What is the contract?
(b) If dummy's eight wins, which card will declarer play next?

ANSWERS

(51)   *Marks*

(*a*) A club.   2

(*b*) Yes. Two spades and one diamond.   3

Whatever action North takes at trick two, declarer crosses to dummy with a trump, leads the ♠ Q and discards another club. North wins, but he cannot touch diamonds without giving away a trick and he cannot prevent declarer from ruffing out the clubs.

It looks at first as if declarer can lose four tricks—two clubs and two diamonds. By exchanging two spade losers for the two losing clubs, declarer protects his vulnerable position in diamonds.

If clubs break 4–1, nothing is lost. Declarer can still lead a diamond up to his king.

(52)

Two hearts.   5

Things are not promising, but declarer can still make his contract if he is lucky—if North has both the king and jack of hearts. After drawing trumps declarer will take a double finesse in hearts. If it succeeds, he is home—but only if he can get back to his hand to finesse again. Should he carelessly throw a diamond from the table when he draws trumps, he will find himself locked in dummy. And what could be more mortifying than to bring off a double finesse and to be unable, through thoughtlessness, to take advantage of it?

ANSWERS

(*a*) ♡ A.   3

(*b*) The ace and king of spades, a spade ruff, then EXIT with
a club.   5

This is a combination of a SAFETY PLAY and an ELIMINA-
TION PLAY. Either defender, winning the second club (trick
six), will have to concede a ruff and discard or lead into a
diamond tenace. The only alternative is a trump, a play
which will allow declarer to lose one trump only.

Note that declarer makes his contract even if ♡ K J x
are over him—without having to make the right guess in
diamonds.

(54)

A club.   5

If the club finesse succeeds, declarer can afford to take a
SAFETY PLAY in trumps—the king, then a low one to the
nine. If South has the ♣ Q, declarer must try to make all
the trumps. To give himself the best chance, he will lead the
♠ A and a low one towards dummy, intending to finesse
against North's queen.

(55)

(*a*) 4 ♠.   4

In 3 NT (or 3 ♠) declarer would have nine tricks on top.
He would not need—and could not afford—to finesse
against the nine of spades.

(*b*) A heart.   4

Declarer needs two entries in dummy so as to finesse
twice in hearts. He hopes for split honours (or for South
to have both).

(56)

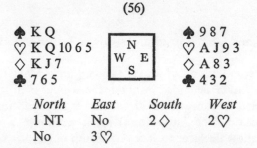

♠ K Q	
♡ K Q 10 6 5	♠ 9 8 7
◇ K J 7	♡ A J 9 3
♣ 7 6 5	◇ A 8 3
	♣ 4 3 2

North	East	South	West
1 NT	No	2 ◇	2 ♡
No	3 ♡		

North leads the king, queen and jack of clubs. South overtakes the jack with the ace and plays a spade to North's ace. The trumps split 3–1, South having the singleton.

A kibitzer offers to lay declarer 2–1 against his contract. Another says that he will accept a bet if declarer lays *him* 2–1 that he will make it.

(*a*) Should declarer accept either bet—or neither or both?

(*b*) How should he play the diamonds?

(57)

♠ A K 9 7 6	♠ Q J 10 8
♡ A Q 10	♡ 4 3 2
◇ A K 3	◇ 6 5
♣ A K	♣ 6 5 4 3

North leads a diamond against West's 6 ♠.

(*a*) What card should declarer lead at trick two?

(*b*) Can declarer make certain of his contract if the trumps break:
    (1) 2–2.
    (2) 3–1.

QUESTIONS

(58)

♠ A 10 7 5 4		♠ K 9 3 2
♡ K Q 4	N	♡ A 9 7 3 2
◇ A 3	W E	◇ K Q
♣ A Q J	S	♣ K 9

North leads the ♡ 10 against West's 6 ♠.
(a) Which card should declarer play from dummy?
(b) How should declarer play the trumps?

(59)

♠ K 8 7 6 5 4 2		♠ A J 3
♡ A 4	N	♡ 3 2
◇ K J 3	W E	◇ A 10 9 8 7
♣ J	S	♣ A 4 3

North leads a heart against West's 6 ♠. West wins with the
ace and leads the king of trumps.

If all follow, can declarer make certain of his contract, and if so,
what card should he lead at trick three?

(56)   *Marks*

(*a*) Declarer should accept both bets with alacrity. He can
hardly lose.   2

(*b*) The ♢ K, then ♢ A (or vice versa).   3

The finesse is the natural play and offers, on the face of it,
and even money chance. In fact, it cannot possibly succeed.
North has shown 6 points in clubs and 4 in spades (he could
have 5 if he has the ♠ J). All the high cards in hearts are on
view, so he must have the ♢ Q to justify his opening 1 NT.
Perhaps that is why the first kibitzer offered to lay the odds
against declarer. He was very rash for the ♢ Q must drop.
South's take-out of 1 NT into 2 ♢ indicates a five-card suit.
North, therefore, has a doubleton (since he bid 1 NT, it
cannot be a singleton). Declarer must win both bets—so
long as he doesn't finesse.

(57)

(*a*) ♣ K.   4

(*b*) Yes, if the trumps are 2–2, but not if they are 3–1.   1

Thinking ahead is all-important. Declarer should play off
both the ♣ K and ♣ A before touching trumps. At trick
four he crosses to dummy with a trump and ruffs a club
high. Returning to the table with a second trump, he ruffs
high dummy's last club. Now the ♢ K is played (the ♢ A
won the first trick) and the ♢ 3 is ruffed. Four cards remain
and the lead is in dummy.

♠ 9
♡ A Q 10   N W E S   ♠ Q
♡ 4 3 2

A heart is led and the ten is inserted from the closed hand.
North may win with the jack, but unless he has another
trump he must present declarer with a ruff and discard or
lead into his heart tenace.

If North has a third trump—the odds still favour declarer
since he can take a second finesses in hearts.

ANSWERS

(58) *Marks*

(*a*) ♡ A. 4

(*b*) ♠ 2—covering in the closed hand any card played by South. 1

Declarer can make a SAFETY PLAY to ensure against a 4–0 trump break by leading low from *either* hand and covering in the other any card played by the first defender (e.g., the ♠ 8 with the nine or ten, as the case may be). But from which hand, dummy or his own, should he play first? In itself it doesn't matter, but the opening lead introduces a new factor. North would hardly have opened the ♡ 10 from ♡ 10 8 6 5, and if he didn't, South cannot have a singleton. The first trump should, therefore, be ducked into North's hand since he can't give his partner a ruff. The ♡ 10, however, could be a singleton, so the first trump trick must not be lost to South.

(59)

Yes. The ♣ J. 5

If all follow to the ♠ K, declarer mustn't lead trumps again just yet or he will be short of an entry to dummy. At trick three the ♣ J is led, overtaken with the ace and a club is ruffed in the closed hand. Now the ♠ A provides a vital entry to dummy and another club is ruffed. Clubs and trumps having been eliminated, declarer leads a heart. Defenders must either concede a ruff and discard or find the ◇ Q for declarer.

QUESTIONS

(60)

```
♠ 9 6 4 3          ┌─────┐          ♠ A K 2
♡ A K Q 10         │  N  │          ♡ 9 4 3 2
◇ 8                │W   E│          ◇ A 7 6 4 3 2
♣ 10 9 8 7         │  S  │          ♣ ─ ─
                   └─────┘
```

North leads the ◇ 9 against West's 4 ♡. Declarer wins with the ace.

(a) What card should he play next?

(b) Which ten tricks does he expect to make for his contract?

(61)

```
♠ A K Q 10 7 2     ┌─────┐          ♠ J 9 8
♡ A K              │  N  │          ♡ J 4 3 2
◇ A Q 2            │W   E│          ◇ 5 4 3
♣ Q J              │  S  │          ♣ 8 7 2
                   └─────┘
```

GAME ALL

North	East	South	West
1 ♣	No	No	2 ♣
No	2 ♡	No	3 ♠
No	4 ♠		

North leads the king, ace and ten of clubs.

(a) What card should declarer play from his hand to the third (club) trick?

(b) What card should declarer play from his hand to the fourth trick?

QUESTIONS

(62)

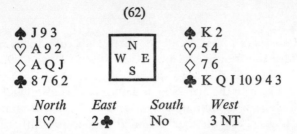

♠ J 9 3		♠ K 2
♡ A 9 2		♡ 5 4
◇ A Q J		◇ 7 6
♣ 8 7 6 2		♣ K Q J 10 9 4 3

North	East	South	West
1 ♡	2 ♣	No	3 NT

North opens the ♠ 4.

(a) What card should declarer play from dummy?

(b) What card should declarer play from dummy had North bid 1 ♠ instead of 1 ♡?

(63)

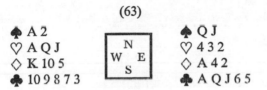

♠ A 2		♠ Q J
♡ A Q J		♡ 4 3 2
◇ K 10 5		◇ A 4 2
♣ 10 9 8 7 3		♣ A Q J 6 5

North leads the ◇ Q against West's 3 NT.

(a) In which hand should declarer win the first trick?

(b) Which card should he lead to the second trick?

(c) Can the contract be made against any distribution of the cards?

(64)

♠ A K J 10 9		♠ Q 8 7
♡ A Q 2		♡ 7 6 4 3
◇ K Q		◇ 4 3 2
♣ 4 3 2		♣ J 6 5

LOVE ALL—E/W 60.

North bids 1 NT (12–14 points), East and South pass, and West becomes declarer in 2 ♠. North leads out the three top clubs and continues with a trump. All follow to this and to the next round of trumps.

What card should declarer play next (trick six)?

71

ANSWERS

(60)

(*a*) ♠ K. 2

(*b*) Two spades, one diamond, three club ruffs in dummy, 3
three top trumps and one other—the ♡ 10 or ♡ 9.

After cashing the two top spades, declarer will ruff three
diamonds, with the ace, king and queen in his own hand and
three clubs with dummy's 4, 3 and 2. That will come to
nine tricks. Now another diamond (dummy's fifth) will be
ruffed with the ten in the closed hand. If it is over-ruffed,
dummy's ♡ 9 will win the tenth trick.

Note that if the top spades are not cashed first, North might
throw spades on diamonds and later ruff the ace or king of
spades. His hand could be:

♠ Q 8   ♡ J 8 7 6   ◇ 9   ♣ K J 5 4 3 2

An unlucky distribution? Possibly. But why be unlucky?

(61)

(*a*) One of the three *top* trumps. 2

(*b*) ♡ A. 3

Declarer needs entries to dummy and only by overtaking
his trumps can he cross to the table. He must, therefore, keep
three trumps lower than the J 9 8.

Declarer must try to avoid the diamond finesse, which he
expects to lose. After playing off his two hearts, he enters
dummy and ruffs a heart. Unless the ♡ Q drops, he goes
back to dummy with another trump and leads the ♡ J, intending to discard a diamond. If North has the ♡ Q he may
have to concede a ruff and discard or to lead a diamond into
declarer's A Q. Note that if North has a third trump—or
if South turns up with the ♡ Q—nothing is lost. Declarer
can still take the diamond finesse—or better still, he can play
North for the doubleton king.

ANSWERS

(62)

(a) ♠ K.   3
(b) ♠ K.   2

If North has both the ace and queen of spades declarer's play to the first trick is immaterial. If, however, North has one of the honours only, it is more likely on the bidding to be the ace than the queen. The danger is that should South win the trick, he will switch to hearts. Declarer must, therefore, win the first trick, if possible, and clear his clubs before opponents attack hearts. If the ♠ 4 is a true card—the fourth highest—North has four spades only. It follows that even had his opening bid been 1 ♠ (instead of 1 ♡), the spade suit by itself would not break the contract. A heart switch would still be the main danger (see hands 6 and 7).

(63)

(a) Dummy.   1
(b) A heart.   3
(c) Yes.   1

The contract is in no danger so long as declarer sets up his ninth trick before attending to the other eight. If he does 'what comes naturally' and takes the club finesse first, a spade from South could be disastrous. But he can afford to lose a trick to North—if he has the king of hearts—because North can do no harm. It comes to this: the club can wait. The hearts can't.

(64)

◇ K.   5

It is essential to find out who has the ◇ A. If North has it, he cannot have the king of hearts as well for it would give him a 16 count, too much for his 1 NT. Declarer will, therefore, enter dummy with the ♠ Q, retained for that purpose, and take the heart finesse with confidence. If South shows up with the ◇ A, North must have the ♡ K for his bid. Declarer's only chance will then be to lead out the ♡ A, followed by the deuce, hoping to find North with a doubleton king. His hand could be:

    ♠ 6 5 3   ♡ K 10   ◇ J 8 7 6   ♣ A K Q 8

If it isn't, it's just too bad.

QUESTIONS

(65)

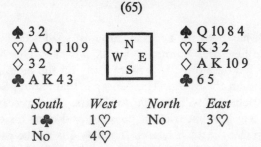

♠ 3 2
♡ A Q J 10 9
◇ 3 2
♣ A K 4 3

♠ Q 10 8 4
♡ K 3 2
◇ A K 10 9
♣ 6 5

South	West	North	East
1 ♣	1 ♡	No	3 ♡
No	4 ♡		

North leads the eight of clubs. South's nine is taken by the ace.

What card should declarer play at trick two?

(66)

♠ Q 8 7 2
♡ A 6
◇ A K 8 3 2
♣ K 7

♠ A 6
♡ K 10 4
◇ Q 7 6 5 4
♣ Q 8 2

North bids 1 ♣ and after a bold bidding sequence, in which North-South take no further part, West becomes declarer in 6 ◇. North leads the ◇ 9. Declarer draws trumps, which split 2–1.

How should he continue to give himself the best chance?

QUESTIONS

(67)

♠ Q 8
♡ A 9
◇ A J 7 6 5 4
♣ K J 7

♠ A 6
♡ K 10 4
◇ K Q 8 3 2
♣ Q 10 2

South opens 1 ♡, but his side bids no more and West ends up as declarer in 6 ◇. North leads the ♡ 8 to the jack and ace. After drawing trumps, declarer leads a club. South goes up with the ace and returns another club.

When declarer leads his last trump, what cards should he have left and which should be the last three cards in dummy?

(68)

♠ K Q J 10 9
♡ A K
◇ 7 6 4 2
♣ 6 2

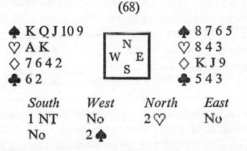

♠ 8 7 6 5
♡ 8 4 3
◇ K J 9
♣ 5 4 3

South	West	North	East
1 NT	No	2 ♡	No
No	2 ♠		

North responds 2 ♡ to South's opening 1 NT (12–14) and West 'balances' with 2 ♠

North leads the ♣ 10 to South's ace, king and queen. Declarer ruffs and draws trumps, finding South with the ♠ A 4 2. A kibitzer wants to make a bet with you:

(a) Will you lay 2–1 on declarer?

(b) Where are the ◇ A and ◇ Q?

(65)   *Marks*

The ♣ 3.   5

North's eight may be a singleton and if declarer tries to
cash his king of clubs before drawing trumps, North may
ruff. There is no need to run the risk. Declarer loses nothing
by conceding a club at trick two. He will ruff his other low
club later with dummy's king of trumps, draw trumps and
then take the king of clubs.

(66)

♠ Q.   5

Declarer's prospects are bleak for in addition to an inescapable club loser, he has a painful cavity in spades. His
best hope lies in bamboozling North, who is marked on the
bidding with the ♠ K, but may not have the J or 10 behind
it. Expecting declarer to have the ♠ J, North may not
cover the queen. His hand could be:

    ♠ K 9 5 4   ♡ Q J 8 7   ◇ 9   ♣ A J 10 9

It is advisable to execute a pseudo-finesse as early as possible, before defenders learn too much about the hand.
Declarer cannot expect to make his wretched contract, but
he tries to give himself the best chance and this lies in hocus
pocus.

ANSWERS

(67)

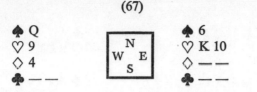

♠ Q
♡ 9
◇ 4
♣ — —

♠ 6
♡ K 10
◇ — —
♣ — —

8

The useless spade will be thrown from dummy on the ◇ 4 and South will be between the devil and the deep blue sea. He is marked on the bidding with both the ♡ Q and the ♠ K, and he will be hopelessly squeezed by the last trump. Compelled to come down to two cards he will be unable to part with any one of three—the ♠ K, the ♡ Q or the small heart protecting the queen.

The key to the hand—a Vienna Coup—is to play off the ♠ A, so as to UNBLOCK, to open the way for the ♠ Q which can then menace South's ♠ K. Try not playing off the ♠ A. In the three-card ending South could throw his king with impunity.

(68)

(a) Yes (quickly).

1

(b) North has both honours in diamonds.

4

South has shown up already with ♣ A K Q and the ♠ A. By inference, he should have the ♣ J, too, since North led the ♣ 10. That is all South can have for his 1 NT (12–14). Therefore, his partner must have both the ◇ A and the ◇ Q. So long as declarer does not play the ◇ 9 on the first round— if North plays low—he must make two diamond tricks and his contract.

77

QUESTIONS

(69)

```
♠ K Q J 10 9 8        ┌───────┐        ♠ A J
♡ K                   │   N   │        ♡ 9 3 2
◇ Q 10 9              │ W   E │        ◇ J 8 7
♣ Q 5 4 2             │   S   │        ♣ A J 9 6 3
                      └───────┘
```

North	East	South	West
No	No	No	1 ♠
No	2 ♣	No	3 ♣
No	3 ♠		

West bids 1 ♠ after three passes and becomes declarer in 3 ♠. North leads the ◇ K, the ◇ A and the ◇ 10, which South ruffs. He returns the ♡ Q and West's lone king falls to North's ace. Another heart is ruffed in the closed hand and trumps are drawn in three rounds (South had four originally).

How should declarer play the clubs?

(70)

```
♠ 5 4 3               ┌───────┐        ♠ A K 2
♡ K Q 9               │   N   │        ♡ A J 10
◇ A Q 3 2             │ W   E │        ◇ K 5 4
♣ K 3 2               │   S   │        ♣ A Q 5 4
                      └───────┘
```

North leads a heart. West wins in dummy and plays the deuce of spades.

What is the contract?

QUESTIONS

(71)

♠ 6 5
♡ A K Q J 10 9 3
◇ 3 2
♣ K 2

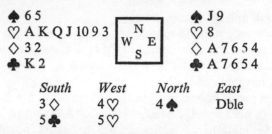

♠ J 9
♡ 8
◇ A 7 6 5 4
♣ A 7 6 5 4

South	West	North	East
3 ◇	4 ♡	4 ♠	Dble
5 ♣	5 ♡		

North leads the ♠ K and the ♠ Q, South following with the three, then the deuce. North continues with the ♣ 3 to the 4, 8 and king. On the ♡ A, South discards a high diamond.
(a) Which card or cards can yield declarer his eleventh trick?
(b) Which will be the last four cards in the East-West hands?

(72)

♠ 10 8
♡ A K Q
◇ Q J
♣ A K Q 7 4 3

♠ 5 4 3 2
♡ J 10 9
◇ K 10 5 3
♣ 6 2

North	East	South	West
No	No	No	2 NT
No	3 NT		

North leads the ♣ J against West's 3 NT. South plays ♣ 8.
(a) What card should West play?
(b) What card should declarer play after winning his first trick?

ANSWERS

A low club and ♣A from dummy.   5

Declarer's only hope is that South has a singleton ♣ K.
North has shown five diamonds headed by the ace and king,
and also the ♡ A. Had he been dealt the ♣ K, as well, he
would not have passed in the first place.

Yes, it's a pretty poor hope, but there is no other. Declarer
can throw in his hand, if he feels like it, but he shouldn't go
through the motions of a finesse which cannot possibly
succeed.

(70)

6 NT.   5

Declarer's play makes sense only if he is RECTIFYING
THE COUNT, removing an idle card, before executing a
squeeze. He has eleven tricks in top cards and looks to a long
club or a long diamond for the twelfth. Maybe neither minor
will break evenly, but even so the contract can be made,
providing the same defender is long in both suits. His partner
will then be of no help and he will have to retain eight cards
(four in each minor) when he is reduced to seven, which is
manifestly impossible. But first the inevitable loser must be
lost.

(71)

(*a*) ◇ 2 or the ♣ 6.   2

(*b*)   8

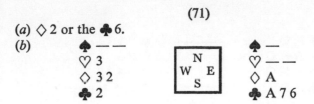

♠ — —	♠ —
♡ 3	♡ — —
◇ 3 2	◇ A
♣ 2	♣ A 7 6

What has South kept? If he has two diamonds, he can only have two clubs. The ♣ A, followed by a ruff, will set up dummy's third club. If South has retained three clubs, he can have one diamond only. Declarer will cash the ◇ A, come back with a club ruff and score the eleventh trick with ◇ 2.

Note that declarer can place every card at trick four. South's high-low play in spades, intended to give his partner a count (he couldn't ruff anyway) places North with a seven card suit. Since South has no trumps, North must have five and he has also played a club. The thirteen cards which remain for South are:

♣ 3 2   ♡ — —   ◇ K Q J 10 9 8   ♣ Q J 10 9 8

This fits in with South's bidding.

Should he have passed 4 ♠ doubled? No doubt, but that's not West's problem which is to make his eleventh trick on a TRUMP SQUEEZE.

(72)

(*a*) The ♣ 7.   2

(*b*) ◇ J.   3

It is obvious to West that South's ♣ 8 is a singleton, but North doesn't know it and by concealing the four and the three declarer creates the impression that South is signalling for the suit to be continued—which is what West wants.

Even if North is taken in and leads another club, West will have eight tricks only—five clubs and three hearts. His best chance of a ninth trick will be a second piece of deception. The ◇ J at trick three will suggest that he is missing the queen and if North has the ◇ A, he may play low. If declarer first cashes his clubs, defenders will exchange information by their discards. It will then be more difficult to steal a trick.

(73)

♠ K Q		♠ 7 6 4 2
♡ A K Q J 10	N	♡ 3 2
◇ A K Q	W E	◇ 5 4 3 2
♣ A 3 2	S	♣ K 5 4

North leads ♠ A and another spade against West's 6 NT. South follows the first time but throws a club on the second spade. North discards a spade on the third round of diamonds. Declarer puts down his hand and claims the rest.

(a) If North clings on to a spade and South keeps his fourth diamond, which will be declarer's twelfth trick?

(b) Would a switch at trick two have broken the contract?

(74)

♠ 7 6 5		♠ A J 10
♡ A K J 9	N	♡ 8 3 2
◇ 5 4	W E	◇ K Q 7 6 3 2
♣ K J 10 2	S	♣ A

North leads a club against West's 3 NT.

What cards should be played from the East and West hands at trick two?

(75)

♠ Q 10 8 5 2		♠ K J 9
♡ 9 7 6	N	♡ A 4 2
◇ J 3 2	W E	◇ K Q 4
♣ J 3	S	♣ A Q 10 2

South	West	North	East
1 NT	No	No	Dble
(12–14)			
No	2 ♣	No	3 ♠

North opens the ♠ A, followed by the ♡ 10 to dummy's ♡ A.

What East-West cards should make up the third trick?

QUESTIONS

(76)

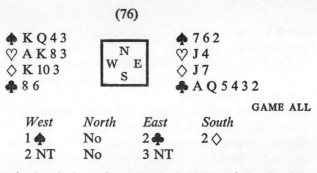

♠ K Q 4 3
♡ A K 8 3
◇ K 10 3
♣ 8 6

♠ 7 6 2
♡ J 4
◇ J 7
♣ A Q 5 4 3 2

GAME ALL

West	North	East	South
1 ♠	No	2 ♣	2 ◇
2 NT	No	3 NT	

North leads the ◇ A against West's 3 NT, and South plays the deuce. North switches to the ♠ J, South following with the ♠ 8, and West wins.

How should declarer play the clubs?

(77)

♠ 5 4 3 2
♡ A Q 10 9 8
◇ J 10
♣ K 3

♠ A
♡ K 2
◇ A K Q 9 8 7
♣ 7 6 5 4

North, whose side bid up to 4 ♠, leads the ♠ K against West's 5 ♡.

What cards should declarer play from dummy and from his own hand at trick two?

(78)

♠ A Q
♡ A 5 4 3 2
◇ A 5 4 3 2
♣ K

♠ J 10 3
♡ Q J
◇ Q J
♣ A J 10 9 8 7

North leads ♠ 7 against West's 3 NT. South follows and the ♠ Q wins.

(a) What cards should he play from his own hand and from dummy to the second trick?

(b) What East-West cards should make up trick three?

ANSWERS

Marks

(*a*) ♣ 2.   3

(*b*) Yes, a club switch.   5

The defence is subjected to a double squeeze. When declarer leads his last heart dummy remains with a spade, a diamond and ♣ K 4. North, who must come down to three cards before dummy, keeps his spade and is left, therefore, with two clubs only. The spade is now thrown from dummy and it is South's turn to squirm. To retain his diamond he, too, is reduced to two clubs. Declarer remains with ♣ A 3 2 and all three are now winners.

A club lead or switch breaks up the squeeze. If declarer wins on the table, dummy is dead. If he takes the trick in his hand, he cannot get back in the three-card end-play to make his deuce.

(74)

◇ 2 and ◇ 4.   10

Declarer has no weak spots, but he needs four diamond tricks and dummy has only one certain entry. If West leads the ◇ K or crosses to his hand and leads a diamond towards dummy, he may find South with ◇ A 9 8. The ace will be held up. The defence will win the second diamond, but to clear the suit declarer will have to play it a third time and he will not be able to do that without using the ♠ A prematurely. By making certain that he loses the *first* trick, while he has another diamond himself, declarer keeps open his communications.

(75)

The ♣ A and the ♣ 3.   5

Declarer can see four more losers—two hearts, a diamond and a club, for South must have the ♣ K for his bid. South, however, doesn't know that declarer has the ♣ J and if he plays the ace from dummy, then the deuce, South may play low. After all, West could have a singleton.

Declarer should leave the trumps till later, creating the impression that he needs entries in dummy to set up a club.

ANSWERS

(76)

Declarer should first duck a club and go up with the ♣ A
on the second round.   5

Normally he would finesse the second time, but after
North has shown up with the ◇ A (and the ♠ J), South
seems likely to have all the outstanding honour cards. Without the ♣ K he has, at best, 9 points. Don't finesse. It is a
better proposition to play for the doubleton king.

(77)

The ♡ 2 and the ♡ 8.   5

Declarer's main concern must be to guard against the
likely 4–2 trump break. If North wins trick two with the jack,
he can do no harm. The king of trumps remains in dummy
to ward off the spades, and if any other suit is led, declarer
draws trumps and spreads his hand. Declarer cannot risk
drawing trumps in the ordinary way—king, queen and ace—
for unless the jack comes down, he will find himself in dire
trouble.

(78)

(*a*) ♣ K and ♣ A.   3
(*b*) ♣ J and ♠ A.   7

The danger is that defenders will clear their spades before
declarer can bring in the clubs. To forestall them, declarer
clears the clubs and transfers the spade stopper from his own
hand to dummy in one happy swoop. Throwing the ♠ A is
spectacular, but costs nothing for in any case the spades can
be stopped once only.

If defenders keep off spades, a red queen will ensure
access to the clubs.

(79)

♠ A Q 5　　　　　　　　　　♠ 9 7 3
♡ 10 9 8　　　　　♡ Q
◇ Q J　　　　　　　　　　　◇ A K 10 9
♣ A 10 8 4 3　　　　　　　　♣ Q J 9 7 6

North leads the ♠ 6. South plays ♠ J.

(*a*) Declarer wins with the ♠ Q and leads the ♣ A.

(*b*) Declarer wins with the ♠ Q, leads a diamond to dummy's king and plays the ♣ Q.

(*c*) Declarer wins the first trick with ♠ A, crosses to dummy and leads the ♣ Q.

In each case, what is the contract?

(80)

♠ 10 9　　　　　　　　　　♠ K 8
♡ A 9 7 6 5　　　♡ K J 10 8
◇ Q J　　　　　　　　　　　♣ 9 3 2
♣ A Q J 7　　　　　　　　　♣ K 10 9 8

North	East	South	West
No	No	No	1 ♡
No	3 ♡	No	4 ♡

After opening 1 ♡ fourth in hand West becomes declarer in 4 ♡. North leads the ◇ K, the ◇ A and the ◇ 10. South follows.

How should declarer play trumps?

QUESTIONS

(81)

♠ 4 3 2
♡ A K 4 3 2
◇ — —
♣ A Q J 10 3

♠ A K 5
♡ Q J 10
◇ 6 5 4 3 2
♣ K 2

Hearts are trumps. North leads the ◇ K.

(a) Having seen dummy, what contract would declarer wish to be in?

(b) To make the optimum contract what cards should he play to tricks two and three?

(c) Which tricks will make up declarer's total?

(82)

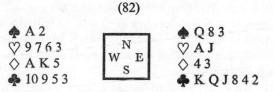

♣ A 2
♡ 9 7 6 3
◇ A K 5
♣ 10 9 5 3

♠ Q 8 3
♡ A J
◇ 4 3
♣ K Q J 8 4 2

North leads the ♡ 5 against West's 3 NT.

(a) If North has five hearts and also the ♣ A, will declarer make his contract or merely complain about his bad luck?

(b) Which is the vital trick and which is the vital card to play to it?

(79)

Marks

(a) 5 ♣. 3
(b) 6 ♣. 3
(c) 3 NT. 4

Declarer's play in (a) shows that he can afford to lose two tricks. By laying down the ♣ A he avoids the risk of a spade ruff. This could happen if North had the ♣ K and six spades—an unnecessary risk to take if the contract is 5 ♣. If the contract is 6 ♣, declarer must give himself the best chance of not losing a trump. Hence the finesse in (b).

The play of the ♠ A at trick one in (c) makes sense only if the contract is 3 NT. Declarer fears that if he wins the first trick with the ♠ Q and the club finesse fails, North will switch to hearts. Winning South's ♠ J with the ace will make North think that South has the ♠ Q and he will, no doubt, persist with spades. This deception play—winning with an unnecessarily high card to conceal another—lends itself to numerous variations.

(80)

Declarer should lead a low heart to the king, then play the jack and run it. 5

The contract is unmakable unless North has the ♠ A. Declarer must assume, therefore, that he has it. Together with the ◇ A K, this gives North 11 points. If he had another queen he would have surely opened the bidding. Since he passed, West should place South with the ♡ Q.

ANSWERS

Marks

(*a*) 7 ♡.   1
(*b*) After ruffing the first diamond in his hand, he will cross   2
to dummy with a low trump and ruff a second diamond.
Going back to the table with a spade, he will ruff a third
diamond high. Then he will draw trumps, making in all
(*c*) two spades, five clubs, three diamond ruffs and three   2
trumps, dummy's Q J 10.

This play is known as DUMMY REVERSAL. Played the
ordinary way, the trumps yield five tricks. By ruffing three
times in his own hand and drawing trumps from dummy,
declarer makes one trump trick more—six instead of five.

(82)

(*a*) Declarer should make his contract.   1
(*b*) Dummy's ♡ A at trick one.   4

The first trick is the vital one. Before playing to it, declarer
should visualise the distribution of the heart suit. From
K Q 10 x x North would have led the king, not the five.
Therefore one of the honours must be with South. Unless
it's a doubleton, West isn't interested for a 4–3 heart split
can't hurt him. And if South has a doubleton, going up with
the ace will BLOCK the suit. Should South unblock, by
throwing his honour under the ace, the ♡ 9 will become a
stopper. Should he play low, North will be unable to cash
his hearts when he comes in with the ♣ A. The honour in
South's hand will bar the way.

QUESTIONS

(83)

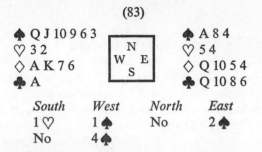

♠ Q J 10 9 6 3
♡ 3 2
◇ A K 7 6
♣ A

♠ A 8 4
♡ 5 4
◇ Q 10 5 4
♣ Q 10 8 6

South	West	North	East
1 ♡	1 ♠	No	2 ♠
No	4 ♠		

North leads the ♡ 6 against West's 4 ♠. South wins with the ace and returns the ◇ J. West wins with the ace.
What card should declarer play at trick three?

(84)

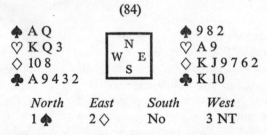

♠ A Q
♡ K Q 3
◇ 10 8
♣ A 9 4 3 2

♠ 9 8 2
♡ A 9
◇ K J 9 7 6 2
♣ K 10

North	East	South	West
1 ♣	2 ◇	No	3 NT

North leads the ♡ 3 against West's 3 NT.
(a) In which hand should declarer win the first trick?
(b) How should he continue?

(85)

♠ K Q 4 2
♡ A 2
◇ 8 7 5
♣ J 10 8 7

♠ 8 7 6 5
♡ J 7
◇ A K Q
♣ A K Q 6

North	East	South	West
1 ♡	Dble	No	2 ♠
No	4 ♠		

North leads the ♡ K against West's 4 ♠. West wins.
What card should declarer play at trick two?

QUESTIONS

(86)

♠ K		♠ A 10 8 3 2
♡ A Q 10		♡ 5 4 3 2
◇ 6 5 4 3 2		◇ A
♣ 5 4 3 2		♣ 8 7 6

North/South vulnerable:

East	South	West	North
No	No	1 ♣	Dble
4 ♠	No	No	Dble

At favourable vulnerability, West makes an outrageous third hand suit psyche and an unsuspecting partner jumps to 4 ♠ over North's double. North doubles again and leads the ◇ K.

What should the North-South hands be to allow West to make his contract?

(87)

♣ A J 10 9 8 7		♠ K Q
♡ A K J		♡ Q 4 3 2
◇ K 2		◇ 7 6 3
♣ K 2		♣ 7 6 4 3

North opens a trump against 4 ♣. Declarer leads a diamond from dummy to his king, and loses the trick to North's ace. Another trump comes back, South following.

(a) Which East-West cards should make up trick three?
(b) How does declarer continue at trick four?

ANSWERS

(83)

♣ A. *Marks* 5

The play of the ◇ J, which is surely a singleton, indicates that South, with a quick entry, can ruff a second diamond. This suggests that his trumps are K x x and that after coming in with the king, he intends to give North the lead with a heart. To foil this plan declarer cashes ♣ A, crosses to dummy with ♠ A and leads ♣ Q, expecting South, on the bidding, to produce the king. On this declarer throws his second heart, exchanging one loser for another and severing communications between defenders. When South comes in with the ♠ K he will have no means of giving North the lead. His hand is probably something like:

♠ K x x ♡ A Q J 10 x ◇ J ♣ K x x x.

(84)

(*a*) Dummy 1

(*b*) ◇ 2 towards the closed hand. 4

Declarer doesn't need the diamond finesse, because if it is right, he can afford to lose two diamond tricks—so long as he gives up the first one to North, who can do no harm. The danger lies in allowing South to come in with the ◇ Q, at trick two, while North still has the ◇ A. A spade through the ♠ A Q, at this stage, could wreck the contract. If, however, declarer leads a low diamond from dummy, South is most unlikely to go up with the queen. Declarer's play constitutes a gentle confidence trick, which will often gain and rarely lose.

(85)

♠ 2. 5

It is clear on the bidding that North must have the ♠ A. Leading up to the king from dummy cannot, therefore, gain. Conversely, playing low can gain but cannot lose, whatever the distribution. If the spades break 3–2, declarer will lose two tricks, and no more, whether he plays the deuce before the king or vice-versa. But playing low will make all the difference when North has the singleton ace.

(86)

The full deal could be:

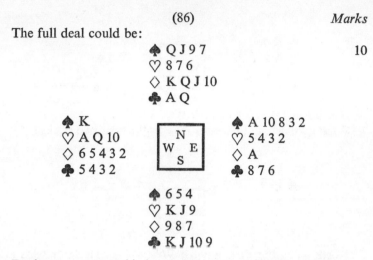

♠ Q J 9 7   10
♡ 8 7 6
◇ K Q J 10
♣ A Q

♠ K
♡ A Q 10
◇ 6 5 4 3 2
♣ 5 4 3 2

♠ A 10 8 3 2
♡ 5 4 3 2
◇ A
♣ 8 7 6

♠ 6 5 4
♡ K J 9
◇ 9 8 7
♣ K J 10 9

Declarer crosses to his hand three times with the aid of a double finesse in hearts and each time ruffs a diamond in dummy. South does not follow to the fourth diamond, but cannot overruff dummy's ♣ 8. West ruffs dummy's last heart with the ♠ K and leads his fifth diamond. If North ruffs with an honour, dummy throws a club and makes the last two tricks with ♠ A 10.

(87)

(a) ♠ A and ♠ K.   4
(b) ♠ J.   1

If dummy had no more entries declarer would lead a club at trick four and he would make his contract, so long as North didn't have both aces in the minors. Good odds, but declarer can do better still. He draws trumps and leads hearts, overtaking the jack with the queen. If the hearts break 3–3, there is no need to take any further risks. If the suit doesn't split evenly, there is still time to play South for the ♣ A. By testing three plays in the right order declarer gives himself the maximum chance of success.

QUESTIONS

(88)

♠ K 4
♡ A K 3 2
◇ 5 4 3 2
♣ 10 9 2

♠ 5 3 2
♡ 5 4
◇ A K Q
♣ A K J 8 7

North leads the ◇ 6 against West's 3 NT.
What cards should declarer play to the next two tricks?

(89)

♠ 10 7
♡ 7 6 5
◇ K Q J
♣ A K 7 6 4

♠ A 4 3
♡ A 2
◇ A 10 9 3
♣ 10 8 5 2

North leads the ♠ K against West's 5 ♣. Declarer wins and takes two rounds of trumps. On the second round North throws a heart.

Which cards should declarer play from his own hand and from dummy to the next two tricks?

(90)

♠ 8 5
♡ K J 9 8 7
◇ J 6 5
♣ A Q 7

♠ 10 7 3
♡ A Q 10 6
◇ A 7 3 2
♣ K J

North leads the three top spades against West's 4 ♡. Declarer ruffs.

Which East-West cards should make up trick four?

94

(91)

```
♠ Q J 10 9 8          ┌─────────┐          ♠ A 7 6 5 4
♡ A K Q               │    N    │          ♡ J 10 9
◇ A J 10              │ W     E │          ◇ K 3 2
♣ A J                 │    S    │          ♣ K Q
                      └─────────┘
```

North leads a heart against West's 6♠.

How should declarer play trumps? Should he or should he not finesse?

(92)

```
♠ Q 9 8 5             ┌─────────┐          ♠ A 7 6 4 3
♡ A K Q               │    N    │          ♡ J 10 9
◇ K Q 6 2             │ W     E │          ◇ J 10 5
♣ K Q                 │    S    │          ♣ A J
                      └─────────┘
```

	West	East
	1♠	4♠
	4 NT	5♡
	6♠	

North leads a heart against West's 6 ♠.

What card should declarer play at trick two?

(88)   *Marks*

The ♣ A and ♣ K.   5

Declarer needs no more than four club tricks for his contract, but he must try to keep out South since a spade from
him through the ♠ K 4, might prove fatal. If North has the
guarded queen of clubs declarer's play will cost a trick which
he can afford to lose—so long as he loses it to North. If
South has the guarded queen of clubs, it will make no difference. But if South has a *doubleton* queen, laying down the
ace and king will bring home the contract while a finesse
might lose it.

(89)

The ◇ K, then the ◇ J, overtaking with the ace.   5

Since he must lose a trump and a heart, West cannot afford
to lose a spade and must try to get rid of it quickly on the
fourth diamond. The danger is that South may have a
doubleton and will ruff on the third round. To dissuade him
declarer resorts to deception. He overtakes the ◇ J and
leads the ◇ 10, creating the impression that he has a doubleton himself and is attempting a ruffing finesse or else that he
is hoping to drop the queen. If South is taken in and lets the
third diamond go, West crosses to dummy with the ♡ A
and parks his spade,

(90)

The ◇ 5 and the ◇ A.   5

The only hope of avoiding two diamond losers is to find
one of the defenders with a doubleton king or queen. After
eliminating clubs and drawing trumps, that defender must
be thrown in. With only black cards left he will be compelled to concede a ruff and discard. Such will be declarer's
plan, but he mustn't give it away too soon. If defenders
see him strip the hand they will become alive to the danger
and the player with the doubleton honour may be able to get
out of the way by throwing it under the ace. So as not to
arouse his suspicions the ◇ A should be played as early as
possible.

ANSWERS

(91)

No finesse.   5

The odds favour a finesse, for if the trumps split 2–1 the king is twice as likely to be guarded as to be bare, and if they are divided 3–0 only a successful finesse can avoid the loss of a trump trick. There are, however, other considerations. Declarer can eliminate hearts and clubs and lead a trump, endplaying the defender with the king. Unless the trumps are 3–0 he will be compelled to concede a ruff and discard or to save declarer a guess in diamonds.

(92)

The ♠ Q.   5

Since there is an unavoidable loser in diamonds declarer cannot afford to give up a trump trick—yet there is a certain trump loser! The only hope, therefore, is to hoodwink the defence. On the bidding, North may place West with five spades, if not with six, and he may decide not to cover the queen in the hope that declarer will play for the drop. For this psychological play to succeed the trumps must be divided 2–2 and North must have the king but not the jack. It is not a very good chance, maybe, but it is the only one.

QUESTIONS

(93)

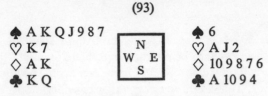

♠ A K Q J 9 8 7
♡ K 7
◇ A K
♣ K Q

♠ 6
♡ A J 2
◇ 10 9 8 7 6
♣ A 10 9 4

North leads the ◇ 5 against West's 7 ♠. Declarer wins with the ◇ K and plays the ♠ A. North throws a heart.

(a) What East-West cards should make up trick three?

(b) What East-West cards should make up trick four?

(c) Assuming the best distribution for declarer and the best defence against him, can the contract be made?

(94)

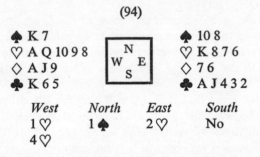

♠ K 7
♡ A Q 10 9 8
◇ A J 9
♣ K 6 5

♠ 10 8
♡ K 8 7 6
◇ 7 6
♣ A J 4 3 2

West	North	East	South
1 ♡	1 ♠	2 ♡	No
4 ♡			

North leads the ◇ K against 4 ♡. Trumps break 2–2.

(a) When declarer plays clubs, which card should he play first?

(b) If the first defender follows with the ♣ 7, which card should declarer play from the other hand?

QUESTIONS

(95)

♠ K 2			♠ A Q 4 3
♡ A Q	N		♡ 10 4
◇ A 6 3 2	W E		◇ 6 5 4
♣ Q 10 9 8 5	S		♣ K 4 3 2

North leads ♠ 10 against West's 3 NT.
(a) In which hand should declarer win the first trick?
(b) Assuming that the first defender plays low, which East-West cards should make up trick two?

(96)

♠ K Q 10 9 8 7			♠ J 2
♡ A 5 4	N		♡ 3 2
◇ 5 4	W E		◇ K Q J 3 2
♣ 3 2	S		♣ A K 5 4

North leads ♣ Q against 4 ♠.
What East-West cards should make up trick two?

(97)

♠ K Q 10 9			♠ 8 7 6
♡ A 3	N		♡ Q 4
◇ J 9 2	W E		◇ A Q 10 5
♣ 5 4 3 2	S		♣ A K Q J

North leads the ♡ 6 against West's 3 NT. Declarer plays dummy's queen.
(a) If South puts up the ♡ K and declarer wins, what card should he play at trick two?
(b) What card should declarer play if the ♡ Q holds the first trick?

ANSWERS

Marks

(a) ◇ A and ◇ 7   2
(b) ♡ 7 and ♡ J.   7
(c) No.   1

To catch South's ♠ 10 declarer must reduce his trumps to South's level and then play from dummy. This requires three entries to dummy and only two are available. A third entry may materialize if the heart queen is with North. Having cashed the ◇ K, declarer leads the ♡ 7 away from the king. If North is inspired and puts up the queen, all is lost. But not many Norths will be so brilliant, especially at trick four. If the ♡ J holds, declarer ruffs a diamond, enters dummy by overtaking his ♡ K with the ♡ A and ruffs a second diamond. He now has the same number of trumps as South. The ♣ K comes next, then the ♣ Q overtaken with the ♣ A —and the lead is in dummy. Declarer sits with ♠ K Q J 9 over South's ♠ 10 5 4 3 and all is well.

But be careful. If South throws a club on the third round of diamonds, declarer should play clubs before overtaking the ♡ K. South's discard must determine the order of play.

(94)

(a) The ♣ 2.   2
(b) ♣ 5.   6

Declarer's main concern is to keep out South so as to prevent a spade lead through his king. He doesn't mind losing a trick to North who can do no harm. After drawing trumps, ending in dummy, declarer should lead the ♣ 2. South may play the ♣ 7. If so, declarer should duck for there is no club below the seven in opponents' hands and North will have to overtake. If South's club is higher than the seven, West goes up with the ♣ K and plays another to the ♣ A. He must not finesse because if North has the queen, the finesse is unnecessary, and South may have a *doubleton* ♣ Q.

100

ANSWERS

(95)

(a) Dummy.   2

(b) ♣ 2 and the ♣ 10.   3

Declarer needs three clubs only for his contract, so he can afford to lose two clubs—providing that the first one is not lost to South. A heart from South through declarer's A Q, before the clubs are set up, might wreck the contract. It is 'natural' to allow the opening lead to run up to the ♠ K, but since it is essential to play the first club from the table, it is wiser to win trick one in dummy.

(96)

The ♡ 2 and the ♡ 4.   5

(1) If declarer leads, mistakenly, a trump, the ace will be held up the first time, taken the second time and the attack on clubs will then be resumed, knocking out dummy's entry to the diamonds.

(2) If declarer tries to set up diamonds at trick two, the ace will be held up until the second round. The club entry will then be driven out as in (1) and unless the diamonds break 3–3 declarer will be in trouble.

(3) The defence have no answer to a low heart from both hands at trick two. If trumps are led, declarer has time to set up two diamond tricks. If trumps are not led, his tenth trick will be a heart ruff.

(97)

(a) ◇ 9.   1

(b) ◇ A.   4

If defenders clear their hearts at trick one, the contract will depend on the diamond finesse. Should West be careless, however, he may go down even if the finesse succeeds. To catch North's ◇ K, which may be guarded three times, West must lead the ◇ 9, *not* the ◇ J.

If the ♡ Q holds, declarer must play the ◇ A from dummy at once. He can now make certain of nine tricks without the diamond finesse and he cannot return safely to his hand in order to take it.

101

(98)

♠ K 10   ♠ 7 6 3
♡ A Q 8 3 2   ♡ 4
◇ K 5   ◇ A Q 10 8 7 6
♣ 5 4 3 2   ♣ A K Q

North leads the ♠ Q against West's 3 NT. South plays the deuce, and ♠ K wins.

Which card should declarer play to trick two?

(99)

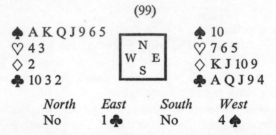

♠ A K Q J 9 6 5   ♠ 10
♡ 4 3   ♡ 7 6 5
◇ 2   ◇ K J 10 9
♣ 10 3 2   ♣ A Q J 9 4

North	*East*	*South*	*West*
No	1 ♣	No	4 ♠

North leads the three top hearts against West's 4 ♠. Declarer ruffs, goes one down and tells everyone how unlucky he is.

(a) What card did the unlucky declarer play after ruffing the third heart?

(b) Which card would a lucky declarer have played?

(100)

♠ K Q 6 5   ♠ A 10 8 7
♡ K 7   ♡ A Q 4 2
◇ A J 6   ◇ K Q 10
♣ K 7 5 2   ♣ A 4

North leads the ♡ J against West's 7 ♠. West wins with the ♡ K and plays the ♠ K. South throws a club.

(a) Assuming a favourable distribution of the other three suits, can the contract be made despite the 5–0 trump break? If so:

(b) give the shape of North's hand.

ANSWERS

Marks

A club. 5

If the diamonds break 3–2 there is no problem. But South may have ◇ J x x x, and if so, declarer will have only eight tricks on top. The heart finesse gives him an extra chance, but he can do better still by first testing the clubs. The odds are against a 3–3 break (only a 36 per cent chance), but it costs nothing to try it—so long as you do it at once, before parting with the ◇ K.

(*a*) A trump. 2
(*b*) The ◇ 2. 3

It is so easy to draw trumps—and to kill the contract at trick one. As soon as North shows up with the three top hearts, declarer knows that he cannot have the ◇ A, as well, for he passed as dealer. He is unlikely to have the ♣ K either, but that is unimportant. At trick two declarer finesses the ◇ J, losing to South's ◇ Q, maybe, and winning the trump return (South's best play) in dummy. Now the ◇ K is played and the ◇ 9 follows, unless South goes up with the ◇ A. Either way, declarer parks two clubs on the diamonds.

It's easy—so long as declarer retains the ♠ 10 as an entry. Impossible if he doesn't.

(100)

(*a*) Yes. 1
(*b*) North's shape should be: 5–3–3–2. He could have:

♠ J 9 4 3 2   ♡ J 10 9   ◇ 9 8 7   ♣ Q J 4

At trick three declarer leads a low trump finessing against North. He then plays off his winners in the side suits—two hearts, three diamonds and two clubs. Dummy's last heart is ruffed with the ♠ Q and North, having trumps only left, is compelled to under-ruff. Declarer's last two cards are the ♠ 6 and the ♣ 5, while dummy has the ♠ A 10 over North's ♠ J 9. The lead is *through* North.

Part Three

Well, have you answered the quizzes in PART TWO or did you suspect a trap? If you did, try the next fifty quizzes first, then go back to PART TWO. No matter in which order you do them, you will return a higher score on your last fifty quizzes, for your dummy play is improving as you go along.

But don't forget to count your winnings. Measure your progress and try these quizzes again in, say, six month's time, reversing the order in which you now tackle PARTS TWO and THREE. You will win again. You will win by more. But by how much more? That is an imponderable to be weighed carefully—next time round.

QUESTIONS

(101)

♠ Q J 10
♡ A
◇ A K Q J 4 3 2
♣ 9 2

♠ K 9 3
♡ 7 6 5
◇ 10 9
♣ A Q J 10 8

North leads the ♡ K against West's 6 ◇.
What card should declarer lead at trick two?

(102)

♠ A Q J 8 7 6 3
♡ A Q 2
◇ — —
♣ K 3 2

♠ K 10 9
♡ 6 5 4 3
◇ Q 10 2
♣ A Q J

North leads the ◇ K against West's 6 ♠. Declarer ruffs.
(a) Assuming that trumps break 2–1, can declarer make certain of his contract? If so . . .
(b) which trick will he lose? Specify the East-West cards.

(103)

♠ A K Q 10 2
♡ A J 10
◇ 6 5 4
♣ A K

♠ J 9 4 3
♡ 7 4 3
◇ A 3 2
♣ 5 4 3

North leads the ◇ K which declarer ducks, then the ◇ Q against West's 4 ♠. West wins and finds the trumps split 2–2
(a) Which card should declarer lead at trick five—after two diamonds and two rounds of trumps?
(b) What will be the last five cards in the East-West hands?
(c) Which card will declarer play at this point?

QUESTIONS

(104)

♠ 1098765   ♠ A K Q J
♡ A J 10   ♡ 4 3 2
◇ A K   ◇ 3 2
♣ A K   ♣ 5 4 3 2

North led the ♣ 10 against West's 6 ♠. Declarer led a trump and South showed out. North turned up with the king and queen of hearts and declarer went one down. West complained of bad luck and East complained of bad play.

(*a*) Who was right?

(*b*) Could declarer have made certain of his contract, and if so, where did he go wrong?

(105)

♠ J 10 9 8 7   ♠ A K Q
♡ A J 10   ♡ 4 3 2
◇ Q J 10   ◇ 4 3 2
♣ A K   ♣ 9 8 4 2

North leads a diamond against West's 4 ♠. Defenders take the ◇ A and ◇ K and the third trick is won by declarer's ◇ Q.

(*a*) What card should declarer play at trick four?

(*b*) What cards should he play at tricks five and six?

(*c*) Can declarer make certain of his contract?

(101)   *Marks*

♣ 9.   5

It looks as if the contract will hinge on the club finesse, but declarer can give himself an additional chance by taking it immediately. If it fails, South may return a heart. Should declarer first draw trumps, North, if he has the ♠ A, may have a chance to signal.

(102)

(*a*) Yes.   1

(*b*) ◇ Q and ♡ 2.   4

Declarer will lead the ace and another trump, ruff the ◇ 10 and play off the clubs, ending in dummy. The stage will now be set for playing the key card, the ◇ Q, on which the ♡ 2 will be thrown from the closed hand. North, who is marked with the ◇ A on his opening, will be compelled to lead a heart into declarer's A Q or to concede a ruff and discard.

This is an example of the LOSER-ON-LOSER technique. Declarer must lose a heart, even if the finesse is right. He prefers to lose a diamond instead, because this puts North on play—when he has no trump left and after the minors have been eliminated from the East-West hands.

(103)

(*a*) ♣ A.   1

(*b*)   3

```
        ♠ Q                        ♠ 9
        ♡ A J 10      ┌─────┐      ♠ 7 4 3
        ◇ 4           │  N  │      ◇ 3
        ♣ — —       W │     │ E    ♣ — —
                      │  S  │
                      └─────┘
```

(*c*) A diamond.   1

If South wins and leads a heart, declarer will insert the ten. North will be compelled to return a heart into the A J or to concede a ruff and discard. If North wins the third diamond the defence will collapse quicker still. The key to the play is to ELIMINATE the clubs before losing the lead—THROWING IN—the defence. Note that unless the first diamond is ducked, South may be able to come in *twice* to play hearts through West's A J 10.

108

ANSWERS

(104)

Marks

(*a*) Partner was right, as usual. 5

(*b*) Trick two. 5

Declarer should not have led a trump since he needed *all* dummy's entries to ELIMINATE the clubs. After cashing the ♣ A (the ♣ K having been played at trick one), declarer crosses to the table twice with the ♠ A and ♠ K to ruff clubs. He lays down his two top diamonds, goes over to dummy a third time with a trump and leads a heart, inserting the ♡ 10 from his own hand. North can choose between conceding a ruff and discard or playing into declarer's heart tenace. The 3–0 trump break is vaguely disagreeable but immaterial.

(105)

(*a*) ♣ A. 1

(*b*) ♣ K; then a trump. 2

(*c*) No (not quite). 2

Declarer plans a *partial* elimination. After laying down the ♣ A K, he crosses to dummy with a trump, ruffs a club and returns to dummy with another trump. Then he leads a heart, inserting the ten. If North has no more black cards, he is compelled to play a diamond—conceding a ruff and discard—or to lead a heart into declarer's tenace.

Maybe North can EXIT with a spade or a club. If so, declarer has lost nothing. There is still a trump entry to dummy to lead hearts again. Declarer cannot make certain of his contract—but he can improve his chances.

QUESTIONS

(106)

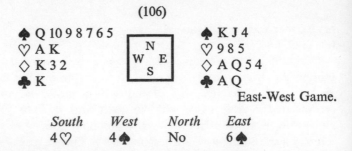

♠ Q 10 9 8 7 6 5   ♠ K J 4
♡ A K   ♡ 9 8 5
◇ K 3 2   ◇ A Q 5 4
♣ K   ♣ A Q

East-West Game.

South	West	North	East
4 ♡	4 ♠	No	6 ♠

North leads ♡ 9. Declarer is unlucky and goes one down. Then he realizes that the contract is unbreakable.

(a) At which trick did declarer go wrong? What did he do?

(b) How could he have made certain of his contract?

(107)

♠ 9 8   ♠ Q J 10
♡ A K Q 8   ♡ J 10 9
◇ A J 10 9   ◇ K 4 3 2
♣ K 3 2   ♣ A 7 6

North leads the ♠ 3 against West's 4 ♡. South wins with the ♠ K, plays the ♠ A, to which North follows with ♠ 2, and continues with the ♠ 7.

What card should declarer play?

(108)

♠ 2   ♠ A K Q
♡ A K 3 2   ♡ Q J 10
◇ A 7 6 5 4 3 2 ◇ 8
♣ 8   ♣ A 6 5 4 3 2

North leads the nine of diamonds. South plays the ten and West the ace. Declarer plays next dummy's three top spades—discarding two diamonds—and then the ace and deuce of clubs.

(a) What is the contract?

(b) What card will declarer play from the closed hand on the deuce of clubs?

QUESTIONS

(109)

♠ K Q 8 7 6 5 2
♡ — —
◇ K 3 2
♣ K 3 2

♠ J 10 9 4
♡ K J
◇ 5 4
♣ A 8 7 6 5

After North has opened the bidding with 1 ♡, West becomes declarer in 4 ♠. North leads the ace and a small trump.

(*a*) In which hand should declarer win the second trick?

(*b*) What cards should be played from the closed hand and from dummy to the third trick?

(110)

♠ K 9 3
♡ A 9 3 2
◇ A K Q 9
♣ 9 3

♠ 7 6
♡ J 5
◇ 7 6 4
♣ A K Q 8 4 2

North leads the ◇ 2 against West's 3 NT. South plays the ◇ 8 and ◇ 9 wins.

(*a*) What East-West cards should make up trick two?

(*h*) Which East-West cards should make up trick two if declarer exchanged ♠ 9 for the ♠ 10?

(106)

(*a*) Trick two. 1

He doubtless led a trump. South won with the ace and gave his partner a heart ruff.

(*b*) Declarer should have led the ♣ K. Overtaking it in dummy, he should have continued with the ♣ Q and discarded his ♡ A (or K). Then—but not before—he should have led trumps. 4

It should be obvious to declarer as soon as he sees dummy that however sketchy South's 4 ♡ opening may be, he cannot have fewer than seven hearts and also the ♠ A. North's ♡ 9 must, therefore, be a singleton and he will ruff a heart— if declarer gives him the chance. Why should he?

(107)

A diamond. 5

The ◇ 10 is probably the best card. The J is a little ostentatious, but either is better than a club. Presumably North will ruff the third spade and it will be a great help to declarer if he can be persuaded to find for him the ◇ Q. Dummy's fourth diamond will later take care of the club. The ◇ 10 is a psychological discard which will often gain and seldom lose.

(108)

(*a*) 4 ♡. 2

(*b*) The ♡ K (or A). 3

The play shows that declarer is expecting trumps to yield five tricks through cross-ruffing. He will trump two clubs in his own hand with the ace and king and three diamonds in dummy. The danger is that during the cross-ruff an opponent may discard spades and later ruff one. Declarer begins, therefore, by cashing his side-suit winners—always the preamble to a cross-ruff.

In 6 ♡ declarer would have to make four ruffs in his hand. He would play the ♣ A at trick two and ruff a club with the deuce of trumps at trick three, before entering dummy with a spade to ruff a second club with the ♡ 3. The cross-ruff would follow as before.

ANSWERS

(109)

(*a*) Dummy.

(*b*) ♡ K.   5

Declarer must try to set up dummy's clubs without letting in South from whom a diamond might prove fatal. Expecting to lose the trick to North, declarer will throw a club on the king of hearts. On regaining the lead he will play the king, ace and another club, ruffing in his hand. Later he will dispose of two diamonds on two good clubs.

If South turns up unexpectedly with the ace of hearts, declarer ruffs, enters dummy and throws his club on the ♡ J.

The plan will not work if the clubs split 4–1, but it is the most promising line of play.

(110)

(*a*) ♣9 and ♣A.   3

(*b*) ♣9 and ♣2.   2

The Safety Play is to duck a club at trick two in case the suit splits 4–1. In (*a*) declarer cannot afford it, because if North has the ♠ A and South comes in with a club, the contract will be in danger. The 4–1 club break will occur only 28 per cent of the time, while the ♠ A will be on the wrong side as often as not. Declarer would be wrong, therefore, to run the bigger risk so as to avoid the lesser one.

With ♠ K 10 3 in (*b*) declarer can afford the Safety Play. If North covers the ♣ 9, declarer *ducks* in dummy—in case the suit breaks: N: ♣ 10   S: ♣ J 7 6 5.

II   113

QUESTIONS

(111)

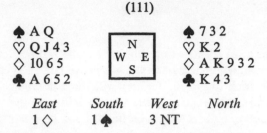

♠ A Q
♡ Q J 4 3
♢ 10 6 5
♣ A 6 5 2

♠ 7 3 2
♡ K 2
♢ A K 9 3 2
♣ K 4 3

East	South	West	North
1 ♢	1 ♠	3 NT	

North leads the ♠ 9 to the king and ace, and declarer crosses to dummy with the ♢ A.

What card should declarer play from dummy at trick three?

(112)

♠ 4 3
♡ A
♢ Q 8 7 6 5
♣ K Q J 6 2

♠ A Q 2
♡ 5 4 3
♢ K 10 3 2
♣ A 10 3

North leads a heart against West's 5 ♢.

Assuming that declarer plays correctly, how many tricks will he make? North has the A 9 of trumps and South J 4.

(113)

♠ A K 3 2
♡ A 4 3 2
♢ 5 4
♣ A 3 2

♠ 5 4
♡ 6 5
♢ A K Q 10 3 2
♣ 6 5 4

North leads a spade against West's 3 NT. Declarer wins and leads a diamond to which North follows with the six. The contract goes one down and West complains bitterly of his bad luck.

What diamond did declarer play from dummy at trick two?

114

QUESTIONS

(114)

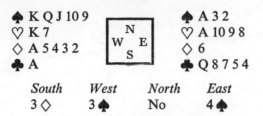

♠ K Q J 10 9			♠ A 3 2
♡ K 7		N	♡ A 10 9 8
◊ A 5 4 3 2	W	E	◊ 6
♣ A		S	♣ Q 8 7 5 4

South	West	North	East
3 ◊	3 ♠	No	4 ♠

North leads the ♣ 6 to the 4, 10 and ace.
What card should declarer lead at trick two?

(115)

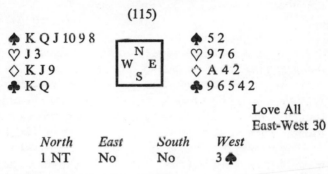

♠ K Q J 10 9 8			♠ 5 2
♡ J 3		N	♡ 9 7 6
◊ K J 9	W	E	◊ A 4 2
♣ K Q		S	♣ 9 6 5 4 2

Love All
East-West 30

North	East	South	West
1 NT	No	No	3 ♠

North bids 1 NT (12–14) and after two passes, West, whose
side has a part-score of 30, bids 3 ♠.

North leads the ♡ 2 to his partner's king and ace, wins the
club switch with the ace and returns another club to declarer's
queen. Drawing trumps, declarer finds North with the A 7 6.

What card should declarer lead after drawing trumps?

(111)   *Marks*

♡ 2.   8

This is a race between declarer and the defence. Can West make nine tricks before North-South make five? West's first impulse is to set up the diamonds, but this will only yield eight tricks—assuming the likely 3–2 break—and before a ninth trick can be developed South will clear his spades.

The ♡ 2 solves the problem. If South, who must surely have the ♡ A for his bid, plays low, West takes his trick and goes for the diamonds. If South goes up with the ace, West has nine tricks—three hearts and two tricks in each of the other three suits.

(112)

Eleven tricks only.   5

A poor player will make one more. He will lead a trump to dummy's king and drop the jack on the next round. As the cards are, all will be well. But should North turn up with ◇ A J x and South with ♠ K, he will go down, for he cannot stand a spade through dummy—yet. He must first clear the trumps. Then he can throw dummy's ♠ Q 2 on his clubs. The correct play is to finesse the ◇ 10 at trick two. Let South make his jack, even if it is a singleton. He can do no harm. Whatever he returns, declarer will clear trumps and live happily ever after.

(113)

The ◇ 10 (surely not one of the tops).   5

Evidently West knew something about safety plays—but not enough. Playing the ten ensures five tricks and the contract against a 4–1 break. Playing low ensures the contract against *any* break. If South wins (with the singleton seven maybe) all is well. The suit cannot break worse than 4–1 and neither defender will have more than three diamonds left. But South may show out. Now playing low to North's six at trick one brings its just reward. Declarer will lose the trick, but on the next round he will take the marked finesse against North's jack, making five diamond tricks and his contract.

ANSWERS

(114)

Marks

The ◇ 2.   5

The bidding and the opening lead make it clear that North has no diamond. If declarer leads the ace, it will be ruffed and he will be one trick short of his contract. If South is allowed to win a diamond trick—with the seven perhaps—declarer will make his ace later. Meanwhile, he will ruff a diamond with the ace of trumps and collect ten tricks: five trumps, two hearts, the ace of diamonds, the ace of clubs and a diamond ruff.

Note that if, at trick three, South returns a club, declarer will throw a diamond and his contract will be safe even if trumps break 5–0.

(115)

◇ J.   5

Declarer can see 20 points in the East-West hands and South has shown up with 7—the ♡ A K. North must, therefore, have the rest, including the ◇ Q. To catch that queen declarer leads the ◇ J, intending to run it unless North covers. If he does, the trick is won with the ◇ A and a finesse is taken against the ◇ 10. South may have that ten, but he cannot have the queen.

Declarer may still go down for North may have both the ◇ Q and the ◇ 10, but by backing the possible against the impossible he is on to a good bet.

117

QUESTIONS

(116)

♠ A 7 6
♡ A 10 3 2
◇ A 7
♣ A K 3 2

♠ Q J 8
♡ Q 4
◇ K 10 9 8 6 3
♣ 5 4

North leads a spade against West's 3 NT. The contract looks almost unbeatable—by the defence. Declarer, however, can beat himself in two ways.

(a) What is the first mistake he is liable to make?

(b) Having overcome the first hurdle, what other lapse could he have?

(117)

♠ A K Q 10 9
♡ 9 8 4
◇ K 7
♣ Q 10 6

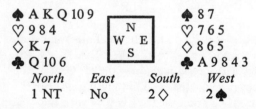

♠ 8 7
♡ 7 6 5
◇ 8 6 5
♣ A 9 8 4 3

North	East	South	West
1 NT	No	2 ◇	2 ♠

North bids 1 NT (12–14) and West becomes declarer in 2 ♠. North leads the ♡ Q, then the ♡ J, which South overtakes with the king. He takes the ♡ A and switches to ◇ J through West's K (trick four). North makes the ◇ A Q and leads a third diamond. Trumps break 3–3.

How should declarer play the clubs?

QUESTIONS

(118)

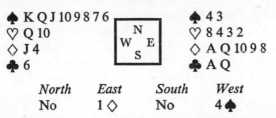

♠ K Q J 10 9 8 7 6   ♠ 4 3
♡ Q 10   ♡ 8 4 3 2
◇ J 4   ◇ A Q 10 9 8
♣ 6   ♣ A Q

North	East	South	West
No	1 ◇	No	4 ♣

North leads the ♡ K, the ♡ A and a third heart which declarer ruffs. Back in the lead with the ♠ A, North persists with a fourth heart (trick five).

(a) What card should declarer lead to the next trick?
(b) Which will be the last three cards in the East-West hands?

(119)

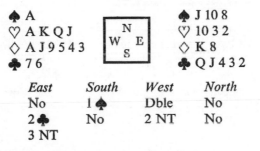

♠ A   ♠ J 10 8
♡ A K Q J   ♡ 10 3 2
◇ A J 9 5 4 3   ◇ K 8
♣ 7 6   ♣ Q J 4 3 2

East	South	West	North
No	1 ♠	Dble	No
2 ♣	No	2 NT	No
3 NT			

North leads the ♠ 7 against West's 3 NT.

What cards from the East-West hands should make up the first two tricks?

ANSWERS

(116)

(a) Many a declarer, playing automatically, will go up with   3
one of dummy's honours at trick one. South will hold up
his king (if he has it) and West will discover a few seconds
later that he has lost a vital entry to dummy's diamonds.
He should play low from dummy to the first trick, win
with the ace and leave the Q J intact in dummy as a certain entry.

(b) A thoughtless declarer might fail to take a safety play in   2
diamonds. He should lay down his ace and finesse on the
second round, making sure of five tricks even if North
should have ♢ Q J 4 2.

If South has those diamonds, it's unlucky, but there is no
need to be unlucky the rest of the time.

(117)

He should lead the ♣ Q.   5

North must have the ♣ K for his bid and the only hope is
that South has a singleton J. North's 1 NT could be:

♠ J x x   ♡ Q J x   ♢ A Q x   ♣ K x x x

Of course, the chances are that West will go one down, but
he has nothing to lose and must play for the only distribution
that can help him.

(118)

(a) ◇ 4.

Marks
5

(b)

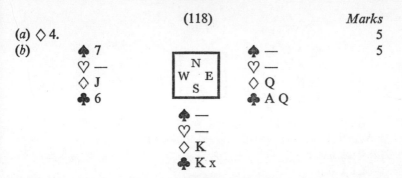

```
        ♠ 7                      ♠ —
        ♡ —         ┌─────┐      ♡ —
        ◇ J         │  N  │      ◇ Q
        ♣ 6         │W   E│      ♣ A Q
                    │  S  │
                    └─────┘
                    ♠ —
                    ♡ —
                    ◇ K
                    ♣ K x
```

5

On his last trump declarer will throw dummy's ◇ Q. If South doesn't throw his ◇ K, declarer will *know* that the ♣ K will drop on the ♣ A. There are two points to bear in mind:

(1) North, who passed, has shown already ♠ A and ♡ A K. He cannot have another king. Therefore, South has both and there can be no question of finessing.

(2) Declarer must play off the ◇ A *unblocking* the suit, so as to make his ◇ J a threat against South's ◇ K. This play —the Vienna Coup—must be made at once, at the sixth trick.

If declarer plays one more trump, he will be unable to get back to his hand (without touching clubs) to lead out the trumps.

(119)

Trick One: ♠ J and the ♠ A.

Trick Two: ◇ 3 and ◇ 8.

2

3

The bidding and the lead combine to pinpoint the ♠ K Q 9 with South. Not knowing—as you and I do—that West's ♠ A is bare, South will surely cover dummy's ♠ J. Now the 10 8 will be a stopper—so long as North is kept out of the lead. West takes a deep unnatural finesse in diamonds to lose a trick to South, who can do no harm. Declarer isn't out of the wood yet. The diamonds may break badly and it's possible, though unlikely, that North may produce the ♣ K. But at least declarer has given himself every chance and more often than not he will make his 3 NT.

(120)

♠ A K 2		♠ 4 3
♡ A K 2	N	♡ 5 4 3
◇ K	W E	◇ A Q 5 4 3 2
♣ K Q 6 5 4 2	S	♣ A 3

North opens a spade against West's 6 NT. West wins.
Which East-West cards should make up:
(*a*) trick two?
(*b*) trick three?

(121)

♠ K 9 4		♠ A 10 3
♡ K Q 10 9 8 7	N	♡ A 4 3 2
◇ 5	W E	◇ A J 8
♣ A 10 3	S	♣ K 9 3

At favourable vulnerability, North opens 1 NT, East doubles
and South rescues into 2 ◇. East-West assume rashly that
North's 1 NT was an outrageous psyche and West finishes up
in 7 NT. North leads the ◇ K. West admits on seeing dummy
that he was wrong to suspect North of psyching. He tables his
hand, however, and claims thirteen tricks despite—or rather because of—North's opening bid.
(*a*) Which will be dummy's last six cards?
(*b*) Assuming that North clings on to his ◇ Q to the bitter end,
which thirteen tricks will West make?

(122)

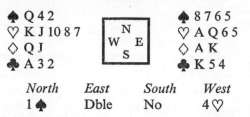

♠ Q 4 2   ♠ 8 7 6 5
♡ K J 10 8 7   ♡ A Q 6 5
◇ Q J   ◇ A K
♣ A 3 2   ♣ K 5 4

North	East	South	West
1 ♠	Dble	No	4 ♡

North opens the ♠ K to which South follows with the ♠ 3.

(a) Which card should West play?

(b) If North switches to a diamond at trick two and if trumps break 3–1, can declarer make certain of his contract? If so, how (or by means of which card) will he make his tenth trick?

(123)

♠ K J 3   ♠ A 9 2
♡ A K 4 3 2   ♡ 10 9 8 7
◇ 6 5   ◇ 4 3 2
♣ 4 3 2   ♣ A K J

North leads the ◇ K, ◇ Q and ◇ J against West's 4 ♡. Declarer ruffs and draws trumps in two rounds (North had Q 6).

(a) What cards should declarer play from his own hand and from dummy to the next (sixth) trick?

(b) Had North opened the bidding with 1 NT (12–14), would it make any difference to declarer's play?

ANSWERS

(120)   *Marks*

(*a*) ◇ K and ◇ 2.   0
(*b*) ♣ 2 and ♣ 3.   10

There would be no problem in a GRAND SLAM, for declarer couldn't afford to contemplate ill-luck. In a SMALL SLAM he tries to guard against bad distribution. What if both minors break unkindly? He gets rid of his ♠ 2 and ♡ 2 on the ◇ A Q, but then finds that he must concede a club. The defender with the fourth club happens to hold the fourth diamond, too, and all is lost.

To retain an entry to the two diamond tricks in dummy, declarer concedes the first trick in clubs without running the risk of losing a diamond as well.

The SAFETY PLAY costs nothing—in a six contract—and is a safeguard against bad breaks in two suits.

(121)

(*a*) ♠ A 10   ♡ — ◇ J ♣ K 9 3 or   5
    ♠ A 10 3 ♡ — ◇ J ♣ K 9.
(*b*) Six hearts, one diamond, three spades and three clubs.   3

Since East-West have 28 points between them, North must have all the outstanding honour cards—♠ Q J ♡ J ◇ K Q ♣ Q J. After seven cards have gone (six hearts and one diamond) North will need to keep not six but SEVEN cards; the ◇ Q and the Q J x in each of the black suits. Declarer will press on with whichever suit is unguarded. Say that North throws a club; declarer will lead the ♣ A, the ♣ K and the ♣ 10, and North will be squeezed a second time—in spades and diamonds. It is axiomatic that a squeeze yields one trick only. Here it yields two. Why? Because there are, in effect, two squeezes, one following the other—a PRO-GRESSIVE SQUEEZE.

124

ANSWERS

Marks

(*a*) The ♠ 2.   1

Clearly South's ♠ 3 is a singleton, for with a doubleton
he would have played his higher card first, and he cannot
have three spades. If declarer false-cards automatically,
playing the ♠ 4 and concealing his deuce, he will be send-
ing out a signal on South's behalf against himself.

(*b*) Yes. A ruff and discard or the ♠ Q.   4

Declarer draws trumps, cashes dummy's second diamond
and leads out three rounds of clubs. If South wins the
third club he must concede a ruff and discard. If North
takes the trick, he must either do the same or lead a
spade, allowing declarer to make his queen.

Bad defence? Certainly. North should have continued
spades instead of switching to a diamond, but then declarer should always be on the alert to profit by the errors
of the defenders.

(*a*) ♣ 2 and ♣ A.   4

(*b*) None.   1

Declarer should play the ♣ A, the ♣ K, then the ♣ J. A
finesse can lose but cannot gain, for if North has the ♣ Q,
the contract is unbeatable anyway. Winning the third club
trick, he would be END PLAYED, compelled to concede a
ruff and discard or to lead a spade into the K J.

If South has the ♣ Q the finesse will lose, so nothing can
be gained by taking it. But observe what happens. South
returns another club and the contract now depends on the
finesse against the ♠ Q. If, however, South wins the *third
club*, he cannot lead another (or a diamond) without conceding a ruff and discard. So he has to open up the spades
himself and unless North has both the ♠ Q *and* the ♠ 10,
declarer is home. He has two chances instead of only one, for
if the ♠ 10 drives out the ♠ A, the finesse against the ♠ Q
is still available. Also, South may have a doubleton ♣ Q.

The bidding is immaterial. A red herring? Yes, perhaps,
or more likely, a red whitebait.

(124)

♠ A 10 9　　　　　　　　　♠ 3 2
♡ A K　　　　　　　　　　♡ 5 4 3 2
◇ A 7 3 2　　　　　　　　◇ 5 4
♣ Q 9 8 7　　　　　　　　♣ A K 6 5 4

North opens the ♡ Q against West's 3 NT. South follows with the ♡ 6. At trick two declarer leads the ♣ Q to which all follow.

(a) Can anything go wrong? If so, what can it be?

(b) What card should declarer lead at trick three?

(125)

♠ A 3　　　　　　　　　　♠ J 10 7
♡ 8 7 3　　　　　　　　　♡ A K 2
◇ A J 10 8 6 5　　　　　◇ Q 9 7
♣ 5 3　　　　　　　　　　♣ A Q 8 4

East	South	West	North
1♣	1♠	2◇	No
3◇	No	3 NT	

North leads the ♠ 8.

If South has the ◇ K, all is well, but what if South's hand is:

♠ K Q 9 6 5　　♡ Q J 10 9　　◇ 3　　♣ K J 10?

North would then have the ◇ K and three spades.

What chance can declarer give himself against such a distribution?

(126)

♠ K 4 3　　　　　　　　　♠ 6 5
♡ A 4 3　　　　　　　　　♡ K 5 2
◇ K 6 5 4 3　　　　　　◇ A 2
♣ K 9　　　　　　　　　　♣ A Q 10 8 6 3

North leads a heart against West's 3 NT.

(a) In which hand should declarer win the first trick?

(b) What cards should he play from the East-West hands to the next trick?

126

QUESTIONS

(127)

```
♠ K 3                    ♠ 7 4 2
♡ A 7 6          N       ♡ K 9 8
◇ A J 5 2    W       E   ◇ K 4 3
♣ A K Q 3        S       ♣ 7 6 5 4
```

North leads the ♡ Q against West's 3 NT.

(a) Should declarer win the first trick or duck?

(b) Which suit should declarer play after he has finished with clubs?

There is nothing fiendish about the hand and the clubs break 3–2.

(128)

```
♠ K 7                       ♠ A 6 5 3
♡ K Q 7 6 5 4 3 2    N      ♡ —
◇ — —            W       E  ◇ Q 10 7 4 3 2
♣ A K 6              S      ♣ 10 3 2
```

North leads the ◇ K against West's 4 ♡. As West ruffs with the deuce, the ♡ 3 drops accidentally alongside. Being superstitious, West refuses to pick it up. Fate, he says, intended it that way and it might bring bad luck to thwart her.

What will be the effect of yielding to superstition?

Is playing the 3 ♡ at trick two likely to:

(a) Cost a trick?

(b) Turn to declarer's advantage?

(c) How could the division of the trump suit affect the answers to (a) and (b)?

(124)

(*a*) Yes, the clubs can be BLOCKED.　2

(*b*) The ♡ K.　3

On the face of it, declarer has nine tricks, but if the clubs break 3–1, the suit will be blocked. The fourth club trick will be taken in the closed hand and there will be no way back to dummy.

To free the fifth club in dummy declarer must somehow get rid of one of his own. Thinking ahead, he takes his ♡ K (the ♡ A was played at trick one) *before* playing his second club. Now, if he finds that the clubs split 3–1, he leads a heart from dummy, discarding a club and UNBLOCKING. Even if North started with six hearts he can do no more than take four tricks. The contract is safe.

(125)

Declarer should play *low* to the first trick.　5

Deception is his best hope. The ♠ J is played from dummy and when South covers, declarer *plays low*, pretending to have a third spade. If South believes him, and there is no reason why he shouldn't, he is unlikely to lead away from his other honour. If he does anything else the contract is, of course, unbreakable.

(126)

(*a*) Dummy.　2

(*b*) A low club from dummy and the ♣ 9 from the closed
hand.　3

To make sure of his contract declarer needs five club tricks only, so he can afford to lose one—but only to North, who can do no harm. A spade switch from South might prove fatal and some of the time the clubs will break 4–1, the ♣ J x x x being with South.

ANSWERS

(127)

Marks

(*a*) Declarer should win the first trick.   1

Since the question of severing communications between opponents does not arise, a hold-up would serve no purpose.

(*b*) Hearts.   4

The ♡ A is played and unless South shows out, declarer leads a third heart putting North on play. He cannot have more than three hearts to cash—South having followed twice—and he must then present declarer with his ninth trick by leading a spade or a diamond. But declarer must show foresight by not cashing his fourth club. He will need it, as well as a diamond, to throw on North's hearts. Dummy, of course, throws spades and retains a club.

(128)

(*a*) No.   1

(*b*) It might.   1

(*c*) ♡ A bare with either defender would be a feather in Fate's cap.   3

If the trumps break 3–2 it will make no difference whether declarer plays the ♡ K, then the ♡ Q and finally the ♡ 3 or whether the process is reversed. Whatever he does, he will lose two tricks. But some of the time (28 per cent) the trumps will break 4–1. If so, three trump tricks must be lost—unless the ace is bare and declarer brings it down on the ♡ 3. Then he will lose two trump tricks only. Fate pointed the way to gaining on the swings without losing on the roundabouts.

QUESTIONS

(129)

♠ A K		♠ 9 7 5 4
♡ K Q J 10 8 7 5	N	♡ 4 3 2
◇ K 7 3	W E	◇ 8
♣ K	S	♣ 7 6 5 3 2

North leads the ♣ A against West's 4 ♡ and switches to a trump. South wins with the ♡ A and returns the ♠ J.
What card should declarer play at trick four?

(130)

♠ K Q J 7 6 5		♠ 4 3
♡ 5	N	♡ A 4 3 2
◇ Q J 9	W E	◇ A K 8
♣ 4 3 2	S	♣ A 6 5 4

North leads the ♡ K against 4 ♠ by West. Declarer goes up with dummy's ace and loses the ♠ K to North's ace. The diamond return is won in the closed hand and the ♠ Q follows. South shows out.

(a) How can defender still bring home his contract?
     Which ten tricks can he hope to make?

(b) Fill in a hand for North which will allow West to make 4 ♠.

(131)

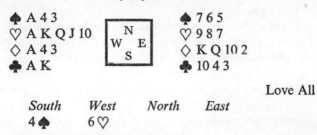

♠ A 4 3
♡ A K Q J 10
◇ A 4 3
♣ A K

♠ 7 6 5
♡ 9 8 7
◇ K Q 10 2
♣ 10 4 3

Love All

South	West	North	East
4 ♠	6 ♡		

North leads the ♣ Q to West's ♣ A. Declarer draws trumps, finding North with four and South with a singleton.

Which East-West cards should make up the next three tricks?

(a) The sixth?

(b) The seventh?

(c) The eighth?

ANSWERS

(129)

Marks

The ◇ K.   5

Declarer has eight top tricks and needs two diamond ruffs for his contract. One trump is still out and his only hope is to surrender the inevitable diamond loser to the defender who cannot return that trump.

If declarer leads a low diamond either defender can win it, so of course it will be taken by the one with the trump. Playing the ◇ K gives opponents no choice. Half the time, no doubt, the defender with the ◇ A will have the trump, return it and kill the contract. But half the time the trump will be in his partner's hand.

(130)

(a) Declarer must try to ruff three hearts with his low trumps,   2
scoring: five trumps; one heart; three diamonds and one club.

(b) ♠ A 10 9 8   ♡ K Q J 10   ◇ 7 6 5   ♣ K J.   3
North must have four hearts, three diamonds and one club. His last card is immaterial. Declarer must cross to dummy three times to ruff hearts. So long as his entries to dummy—◇ K and ♣ A—are not ruffed and the three low hearts are not over-ruffed, all is well.

ANSWERS

(131)   *Marks*

(*a*) ♣ K and ♣ 4.   1
(*b*) ♦ 3 and ♦ K.   1
(*c*) ♣ 10 and ♠ 3.   8

Clearly North has no spades or he would have led one. At trick five (after one club and four trumps) declarer leads the ♣ K, a diamond to dummy's king and the ♣ 10 on which he throws a spade. If South follows to the third club, he cannot have more than two diamonds, so declarer leads the ♦ A and finesses against North's ♦ J. If South shows out on the ♣ 10, he must have three diamonds and declarer plays accordingly.

South is known to have seven spades and one heart and therefore five cards in the minors. Count the clubs and the diamonds will count themselves.

What if South has a singleton club? Then he must have four diamonds. Inevitably, he will be squeezed in spades and diamonds—after declarer has lost a club to North.

ALTERNATIVE SOLUTION   10

At trick six declarer plays a low spade from both hands, paving the way to a double squeeze. After nine cards have been played—five hearts, two spades and two clubs—North will have to keep a club and South will have to keep a spade. Neither defender will have room for four diamonds.

Yes, the 6 ♡ bid was a wild gamble and had the contract proved to be unmakeable, partner would have been justified in saying 'tut, tut' or words to that effect. But since twelve tricks can be made, it's declarer's job to make them. (*Take 10 marks for either solution, but not 20—even if you found both.*)

(132)

♠ K 3
♡ A K 7 6 5
◇ A K Q J 10 9
♣ — —

♠ A
♡ 4 3 2
◇ 3 2
♣ A K 9 8 7 6 5

North leads a spade against West's 7 ◇.

How can declarer give himself a reasonable chance of making an unreasonable contract?

What should be the last five cards in the East-West hands?

(133)

♠ 3 2
♡ K 9 6 5 2
◇ A K Q
♣ J 10 9

♠ K 5 4
♡ 8 7 4 3
◇ 4 3 2
♣ A K Q

West is declarer in 4 ♡.

(a) What card should declarer play at trick two if North's opening lead is the ◇ 10?

(b) What card should declarer play at trick three if North opens the ♠ A and continues with the ◇ 10?

QUESTIONS

(134)

♠ A K 3 2
♡ 2
◇ A 7 6 2
♣ K 9 8 3

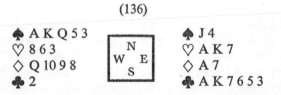

♠ Q J 10 9
♡ A 5 4 3
◇ K Q 3
♣ A 6

(a) What is the maximum number of tricks that can be made in any contract?
(b) Which tricks will declarer make?

(135)

♠ A
♡ A Q J 10 3
◇ K J 9 6 5
♣ A K

♠ 3 2
♡ K 9
◇ 8 4 3 2
♣ 7 6 5 4 3

West is in game. North leads the ♠ K.
(a) At trick two declarer leads the ◇ 5. What is the contract?
(b) At trick two declarer leads the ♡ 3 to dummy's ♡ 9. What is the contract?

(136)

♠ A K Q 5 3
♡ 8 6 3
◇ Q 10 9 8
♣ 2

♠ J 4
♡ A K 7
◇ A 7
♣ A K 7 6 5 3

North leads the ♡ Q against West's 6 ♠. Declarer wins. What card should he play from dummy at trick two?

ANSWERS

(132)

Marks

♡ A K 7 6 5　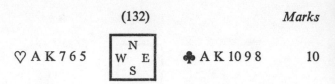　♣ A K 10 9 8　　10

Taking the top clubs, when declarer is in dummy at trick one, can serve no purpose, for two winners cannot dispose of three losers. The psychological effect of not taking the ♣ A K may, however, prove of considerable value. Opponents will assume that declarer must have a club. Would he cut himself off from dummy otherwise? If the club honours are split, say Q x x with one defender and J x x with the other, each in turn will expect his partner to have a doubleton. Clinging on to his three clubs, he will unguard the hearts. In the five-card ending each defender will have three clubs. Neither will have more than two hearts and declarer's five hearts will all be good as the result of a PSEUDO-SQUEEZE. Of course, it is no certainty, but it's by far declarer's best chance.

(133)

(a) ♠ 2.　　　　　　　　　　　　　　　　　　　　　　2

Until declarer finds out whether he has one spade loser or two, he will not know how to handle the trump suit. If South has the ♠ A, over dummy's K, he will be able to afford one trump loser only. He will then lead a heart from dummy, hoping to find South with the doubleton ace, for that will be his only hope. If the ♠ A is with North, West will be able to afford two trump losers— but not three. Then he will play.

(b) ♡ 2.　　　　　　　　　　　　　　　　　　　　　　3

This will cost a trick—which he can afford—if South has ♡ A x. But it will ensure the contract against a 3–1 split with the singleton ace in North's hand.

ANSWERS

(134)

(*a*) With spades as trumps declarer can make all thirteen   2
tricks on a DUMMY REVERSAL.

A spade is the least convenient lead. Declarer wins in
dummy, plays the ♡ A and ruffs a heart (three tricks).
He leads a diamond to dummy's queen, ruffs another
heart, goes back to the table with the ◇ K and ruffs
dummy's last heart with his own last trump (nine tricks).
With the ♣ A he returns to the table and draws trumps
—three rounds if a trump was opened. That brings declarer's total to eleven. The last two tricks are the ♣ K
and the ◇ A. The contract is made even against a 4–1
trump break. The thirteen tricks are:

(*b*) Four trumps (in dummy); one heart; three heart ruffs   3
(in the closed hand); three diamonds and two clubs.

(135)

(*a*) 4 ♡.   3

Declarer must set up his diamonds and is prepared to
lose three tricks—so long as he retains trump control.
But he cannot afford to be forced twice—which is what
will happen if he draws trumps. Even one round could be
fatal if the defenders come in three times and press on
with spades.

(*b*) 5 ◇.   2

This time declarer prefers to play trumps from dummy and
he is not afraid of being forced.

(136)

The ♣ 3.   10

Declarer needs four club tricks, but he must allow for the
probable 4–2 break in clubs and in trumps. Since he cannot
afford to ruff two clubs, he ducks the first time, and ruffs a
second club as soon as he regains the lead. Now he draws
trumps—four rounds if need be—and scores twelve tricks
with: five trumps, four clubs and three red cards.

QUESTIONS

(137)

♠ A Q 10 4		♠ 7 2
♡ A Q 9 8	N	♡ 10 4 3
◊ K 3	W E	◊ 10 9
♣ 9 8 2	S	♣ A K Q 7 4 3

North	East	South	West
1 NT	No	2 ◊	Dble
No	3 ♣	No	3 NT

North leads the ◊ A, then the ◊ J.

(a) Can any distribution, consistent with the bidding, defeat the contract?

(b) What mistake would a careless declarer be likely to make?

(138)

♠ — —		♠ A 10 4 3 2
♡ K Q J 10 9	N	♡ 3 2
◊ A Q 9 8	W E	◊ K 4 3
♣ A Q 10 2	S	♣ K 5 3

North leads a trump against West's 6 ♡. South plays the ♡ A and continues with the ♠ K.

(a) Which card should declarer play from his hand?

(b) What should be the four-card end position?

QUESTIONS

(139)

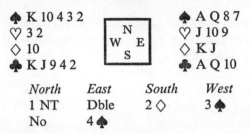

♠ K 10 4 3 2
♡ 3 2
◇ 10
♣ K J 9 4 2

♠ A Q 8 7
♡ J 10 9
◇ K J
♣ A Q 10

North	East	South	West
1 NT	Dble	2 ◇	3 ♣
No	4 ♠		

North leads the three top hearts against West's 4 ♠.
What card should declarer play after ruffing the third heart?

(140)

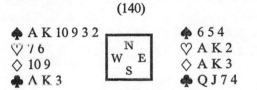

♠ A K 10 9 3 2
♡ 7 6
◇ 10 9
♣ A K 3

♠ 6 5 4
♡ A K 2
◇ A K 3
♣ Q J 7 4

North leads the ◇ Q against West's 6 ♠. Declarer wins and
leads a trump. South throws a club.

Is the contract doomed or is there still hope? If so, how should
declarer proceed and what should be his last three cards?

(141)

♠ A K Q J 10
♡ 3 2
◇ 4 3 2
♣ A K 6

♠ 9 8
♡ A K J 8 7 6
◇ — —
♣ J 5 4 3 2

North leads the ◇ K against West's 6 ♠. Declarer ruffs in
dummy.

What East-West cards should make up trick two?

(137)   *Marks*

(*a*) No.   1

Unless South has all four missing clubs the contract is in no danger, and since North bid 1 NT, South cannot have four clubs.

(*b*) He might lead the ♣ 2 at trick three.   4

Give North ♠ J 10 6 5 and follow (*b*) through. On the ♣ 2 North plays the ♣ 5, dummy the ♣ A and South shows out, revealing the 4–0 split. Next time the ♣ 9 is covered by the ten and won by the ♣ K. But on the third round North plays the ♣ 6 on the ♣ 8 and whatever West does it's his last club trick. The eight *blocks* the suit.

Now try the ♣ 9, in place of the ♣ 2, at trick three. Again North plays the ♣ 5 and dummy the ♣ A. The second time the ♣ 8 is covered by the ♣ 10 and the ♣ K wins. But on the third round North leads the ♣ 2 through the J 6 *up* to dummy's Q 7 and all is well. Since only this division of the clubs could beat him, declarer should have allowed for it from the first.

(138)

(*a*) ♡ 9.   3

(*b*)   5

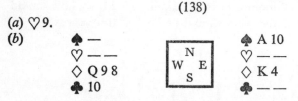

	♠ A 10
♠ —	♡ — —
♡ — —	◇ K 4
◇ Q 9 8	♣ — —
♣ 10	

Declarer cannot tell at trick two how the minor suits will break and meanwhile the ♠ A can wait. After drawing trumps, declarer leads the ♣ A and the ♣ Q—in case the J drops—then a third club to dummy's king. If the ♣ J is still out, the ♣ 10 is thrown on the ♠ A. The contract succeeds if *either* minor breaks 3–3. Had West discarded, instead of ruffing, at trick two, he might easily have thrown the wrong card. Note that even if both minors break badly, declarer still has a chance of making his contract on a squeeze.

(139)

The ♠ K.   5

Declarer is concerned solely with a 4–0 trump break and only South can have a void since North bid 1 NT. The ♠ K is led from the closed hand and if South shows out, declarer finesses twice, against the jack and against the nine. Had South bid 1 NT, declarer would have played the ♠ A first, finessing against South's J (J 9 6 5), if North showed out.

(140)

The contract may still be made despite North's ♣ Q J 8 7. Declarer's last three cards should be: ♣ K 10 9.   5

Declarer must shorten his trumps twice, so as to have the same number as North. He cashes his top cards in the red suits and ruffs one heart and one diamond (he could ruff a club if he had reason to believe that North had four clubs). So long as North does not over-ruff declarer at any stage, the contract is safe. From ♣ K 10 9, when three cards only remain, declarer leads the ten and North is end-played in trumps.

(141)

The ♣ 2 and the ♣ 6.   5

Even two diamond ruffs in dummy would bring the total to eleven tricks only. Declarer would still need the heart finesse to bring home his contract. For this line of play he requires two entries in the closed hand—one to lead a second diamond for dummy to ruff and another to draw trumps before taking the heart finesse. The clubs must, therefore, stand up twice. And if they do, declarer needs nothing more—neither a second diamond ruff, nor the heart finesse. At trick two he ducks a club. If the defence persist with diamonds, he ruffs, comes back to his hand with a club and draws trumps. If the defence switch to hearts, declarer comes to his hand with a trump. Either way dummy's clubs will take care of his diamond loser(s).

QUESTIONS

(142)

♠ A   ♠ J 9
♡ K Q J 10 9 8 7   ♡ A 5 4
◇ A Q 2      ◇ 5 4 3
♣ 5 4   ♣ A K J 3 2

North leads the ♠ K against West's 6 ♡. Trumps break 2–1. Having drawn trumps with the ♡ K and ♡ Q how should declarer play to:
(*a*) trick four?
(*b*) trick five?
(*c*) trick six?

(143)

♠ J 9 2   ♠ A Q 10 3
♡ K Q J 3   ♡ 5 4 2
◇ A 2   ◇ 4 3
♣ A K Q J   ♣ 5 4 3 2

North leads a club against West's 3 NT.
(*a*) Which suit should declarer lead at trick two?
(*b*) Which card?

(144)

♠ A 10 9		♠ 8 7
♡ K J 10 9 8 7	N	♡ Q 6
◇ 7	W E	◇ A 8 5 4
♣ 10 9 3	S	♣ A Q J 4 2

North leads ◇ K against West's 4 ♡.
Which East-West cards should make up trick two?

(145)

♠ K 4 2		♠ 7 5
♡ Q	N	♡ A 4 2
◇ A 9 8 4 3 2	W E	◇ K Q J
♣ 7 6 5	S	♣ A K 4 3 2

North	*East*	*South*	*West*
1 ♣	Dble	No	3 ◇
No	4 ◇	No	5 ◇

North leads the ◇ 6 to dummy's king. South follows.
What East-West cards should make up trick two?

(146)

♠ A Q 10		♠ 9 8 7
♡ K Q	N	♡ 6 5 4 3
◇ Q J 10 9 8 7 6	W E	◇ A K
♣ A	S	♣ 6 5 4 3

North leads a club. Declarer, who is in a game contract, plays
a diamond to the table and:
(*a*) leads a spade;
(*b*) leads dummy's second diamond.
What is the contract in each case?

ANSWERS

(*a*) ♣ K.   1
(*b*) ♣ A.   2
(*c*) ♠ J and ♢ 2.   2

Declarer plays off the ♣ A K and leads the ♠ J, discarding his ♢ 2—a loser-on-loser play. North must now commit suicide but he can choose his weapon:

(*a*) a spade will present declarer with a ruff and discard.

(*b*) a diamond will run up to declarer's major tenace.

(*c*) a club will set up a club trick in dummy.

If North leads the ♣ Q, it will be ruffed. If he leads a low club, the ♣ J will hold or else South will produce the ♣ Q and the suit will have broken 3–3. The ♡ A remains as an entry in dummy.

(143)

(*a*) Hearts.   2
(*b*) The ♡ J.   3

The spade finesse offers a 50–50 chance while the odds are nearly 2–1 against a 3–3 break in hearts. After a lucky club opening, however, declarer has time to try both. But the hearts must come first. If the spade finesse fails and a diamond is shot back, it will be too late to try the hearts.

A 50 per cent chance plus another worth 36 per cent looks pretty good, but declarer can do better still. The ♡ J as early as trick two may catch North napping. Holding A 8 7 6, perhaps, he may play low. If he does, declarer has his ninth trick and can switch to spades to make certain of the others. The finesse no longer matters.

Marks

The ♠ 8 and ♠ 9.   5

If, to stop a spade ruff, the defence switch to trumps, declarer will have time to set up his clubs. If the ace of trumps
is not led at trick three, declarer will ruff a spade. Either way
he will not lose more than three tricks—one spade, the ace
of trumps and perhaps a club.

Note that declarer cannot afford to take the club finesse
at trick two. With ♣ K x x South will play low the first time,
go up with the king on the second round and give North a
ruff.

(145)

♡ 2 and ♡ Q.   8

The danger to the hand lies in losing a club to South who
can kill the contract by leading a spade through the king.
Expecting North to have the ♡ K for his opening bid, declarer leads a low heart to his queen. A club will then be
discarded on the ♡ A and the clubs will be ruffed out (if
they split 4–1 there's no hope, anyway), without letting
South in.

Yes, 3 NT is a much better contract, but not so easy to
reach. Meanwhile, West should concentrate on 5 ◇.

(146)

(*a*) 5 ◇.   4
(*b*) 3 NT.   1

There are only two possible game contracts. The best,
though by no means the easiest to reach, is 3 NT. On a club
lead declarer must take his nine tricks at once. He has no
time to lose and promptly sets about the diamonds.

In 5 ◇ declarer cannot afford to lose two spades, since
he has an inescapable heart loser. If North has both the
♠ K and the ♠ J, there's no hope but if the honours are
split, declarer can make certain of his contract by taking two
finesses. One or the other will succeed. He must, therefore,
use both his entries to dummy to finesse the spades.

QUESTIONS

(147)

♠ A K J 9 2		♠ 7 5
♡ 5 4	N	♡ A K 3 2
◇ 5 4	W E	◇ A K 3 2
♣ Q 7 6 5	S	♣ A 3 2

North	East	South	West
1 ♡	Dble	No	2 ♠
No	2 NT	No	4 ♠

North leads ♡ Q against West's 4 ♠.

What should be declarer's plan of campaign and which ten tricks will he try to make?

(148)

♠ ♠ — —		♠ J 10 9 8
♡ K Q 9 8 7 6 5	N	♡ A J 10
◇ A 4 3	W E	◇ 6 5 2
♣ K Q 9	S	♣ A 10 2

North leads a club against West's 6 ♡. West's king wins.

Which East-West cards should make up:

(a) trick two?

(b) trick three?

(c) On what will the contract depend?

(149)

♠ A 10 9 8 7 6　　　　　　♠ K Q
♡ 10 9 5　　　♡ K Q J
♢ K J 9　　　　　　　　　♢ A Q
♣ 5　　　　　　　　　　　♣ A K Q J 10 9

North leads the ♡ A, then a diamond against West's 6 ♠.
Declarer wins with the ♢ A and continues with the king and
queen of trumps. On the second round North throws a diamond.
Which East-West cards should make up the next two tricks?

(150)

♠ A J 10 8 4　　　　　　　♠ K 7 6 5
♡ 7 8　　　　　　　　　　♡ Q 10 3
♢ A Q 2　　　　　　　　　♢ 5 4 3
♣ K J 4　　　　　　　　　♣ A Q 5

North	East	South	West
No	No	No	1 ♠
No	3 ♣	No	4 ♠

North leads the ♡ 9 against West's 4 ♠ and finds South with
♡ A K J.

How should declarer play trumps?

ANSWERS

(147) *Marks*

Declarer should try to ruff *three red cards* in the closed hand, making: five trumps; the ♡ A K; the ◇ A K and the ♣ A. 8

Winning the first trick with the ♡ A, declarer should lay down his ♠ A K, dummy's ◇ A K and ruff a third diamond with the ♠ 2. If North does not over-ruff, he is nearly there. Crossing to dummy with the ♡ K he will ruff a third heart with the ♠ 9 and going back with the ♣ A he will play the key card—dummy's last heart. If South ruffs with the ♠ Q, West will throw a club. If South plays any other card West will ruff. Either way the ♠ J will score the tenth trick.

So long as South has two hearts and North has three diamonds—or two diamonds and only two trumps—all will be well. North could have: ♠ Q 10 8 6 ♡ Q J 10 9 ◇ Q J 10 ♣ K J and the contract could still be made.

(148)

(*a*) A trump to dummy. 0

(*b*) ♠ J. 3

(*c*) The contract will depend on finding South with two of the three top spades. 2

Declarer intends to throw a diamond on the ♠ J (unless South covers) and to lead spades twice more from dummy, ruffing twice and setting up the fourth spade. But he must be careful with his entries for he will need all four. He cannot afford a second round of trumps before leading the ♠ J.

(149)   *Marks*

(1) The ♣ A and ♣ 5.   2
(2) ♣ K and ♠ 6.   3

To catch the unfinessible ♠ J, declarer must shorten his trumps so as to have no more than South. He leads a club and ruffs a club, enters dummy with a heart and ruffs a second club. This leaves him with ♠ A 10 and South with ♠ J x. Crossing to dummy with a diamond, declarer leads clubs until South—having nothing left but trumps—is compelled to ruff in front of him. This trump-reducing play, in which declarer ruffs dummy's winners, is known as a GRAND COUP. To succeed, a GRAND COUP requires adequate entries in dummy—enough to shorten declarer's trumps and one more to give dummy the lead at the crucial moment, e.g., if declarer has three more trumps than the defender sitting under him, he will require *four* entries in dummy.

(150)

Declarer should lay down the ♠ A, in case of a singleton queen, then run the ♠ J.   5

South has shown up with 8 points already (♡ A K J) and he *must have* the ◇ K. Otherwise the contract is unmakeable. He cannot have ♠ Q x (or ♣ Q x x) as well or he would have opened the bidding. Declarer must, therefore, assume that the queen of trumps is with North.

This book is for *Helen Perelman,*
who Makes Things Happen,
with special thanks to *Elizabeth Rudnick,*
Queen of the LFC.

- 1 -

stealth freak•ies \ 'stelth 'free-keez\ *n* : a feeling that comes before dread, i.e., when you just feel a little bit sick, before you realize that anything is wrong, or that your whole life is about to change for the worse, or something else equally bad

"You aren't taking this seriously, Allie," said my best friend in the world, Tamara Thompson. "This is the kind of thing that can make or break your whole year." She crossed her arms over her chest, frowning at me from her seat in my desk chair.

It was actually kind of funny to see her sitting there in the chair that I hardly ever use. I mean, I use the chair—but only to throw clothes on. Of course, that might have to change soon, I thought as I looked at my messy desk. It was covered in glitter and a few half-ripped-off photos from magazines I had accidentally glued to the top while making a collage last year. There was a pair of dirty socks sitting next to the stapler, and a withered old apple core that must have been

about as old as I was hanging out by a dust-covered cube of Post-its. Glick.

Tam picked an ancient plastic toy horse off my desk, turned it over in her fingers, and set it down again. I had developed an obsession with ponies in first grade, and immediately started collecting toy horses and begging my mom for a pony for Christmas. But Mom said no way. Instead I got a soccer ball. That was why my walls were covered in soccer posters and the collages I had made of Mia Hamm and David Beckham. My bookshelves were crowded with ribbons and trophies from tournaments. Plus, I'd won MVP three years in a row.

It's weird how—when you have stuff long enough—you just stop seeing it. All of that junk had been there for years, but suddenly, I was embarrassed by my plastic horses, my messy desk, and my even messier room. I can't start sixth grade this way, I decided, mentally vowing to clean the place up that night.

"School starts tomorrow," Tam went on, as though we hadn't spent the past three months talking about how nervous and excited we were about middle school. See, Tam and I were headed

to a "magnet" school for the so-called "smart" kids. I'm not really sure how that happened, but Tam claims it had to do with some test we took in the second grade. Personally, I think it probably had more to do with my dad calling the school board and threatening to unleash holy heck if I didn't get into the program, but whatever. The point is: almost all of the other kids we knew were headed to Twin Pines Middle School, while we were headed to Grover Cleveland. "So what are you going to wear?" Tam asked seriously.

"I don't know," I told her. "Jeans?"

Tam gave her curly black hair a toss and let out a frustrated "Grr." Tam is my best friend, but we're way different. She's always been the prettiest girl in the class, and she always dresses really well—she's just good at that kind of stuff. Like right now, for example. It was a summer Sunday, and she had on a bright blue tank and a tan skort, both of which looked brand-new. If I'd put on that outfit, I would have gotten a stain on the front within five minutes.

"*I'm* going to wear a skirt," Tam said, twirling in the desk chair.

"I don't even own a skirt," I told her. "None that fit, anyway."

"What about the khaki one?" Tam suggested.

Wow. Tam was right. I *did* have a khaki skirt . . . somewhere. My stepmom, Marci, had given it to me—proving beyond a reasonable doubt that she doesn't know me at all. I'd worn it once, like, two months before. Feeling kind of impressed that Tam knew my clothes better than I did, I walked to my closet and flipped through the hangers. "Not here." My eyes moved to my bed. I had a dim memory of kicking it under there after Sally Chin's birthday/Fourth of July party.

Catching my look, Tam slid off the desk chair and peered under the bed. "Oh my God," she said, as if I had a dead body under there. I mean—what's the big deal? I thought. Hasn't she ever seen a hidden mountain of junk before? In case it isn't blatantly clear, I'm not exactly into cleaning, and neither is my mom. There was so much fossilized crud under that bed, I could have turned it into a natural history museum exhibit.

Tam pulled out a plastic mug filled with

bluish mold. "Allison Louise Kimball, what is this?" she asked, doing a really killer imitation of my dad.

I flushed a little. "Um . . . milk?" I guessed, although the stuff in the mug wasn't even liquid anymore.

Tam jumped away from the mug, which clunked on the floor. "Gross!" Still, I guess the mass of junk was kind of fascinating, or something, because she put her hand under the bed again and fished out a pair of sunglasses wrapped in a giant lint ball.

"I've been looking for those!" I said, grabbing the glasses. Oh, glick. The linty junk was kind of greasy. Actually, Tam was right—this was really gross.

"What's this?" Tam asked. I winced as she scraped an ancient, dust-covered notebook across the dirty floor under my bed. Tam blew some of the dust off the cover. "LFC," she read aloud. "Allie," Tam said with a grin, "do you know what this is?"

I cringed as she flipped it open to the first page. "Living proof that we used to be major

dorks?" The LFC Club had been Tam's idea. LFC stood for Look for Clues, and it was supposed to be like the Baby-sitters Club, only without the babysitting. Once a week, the members would meet by the swings at recess to discuss the "clues" we had been looking for—evidence that the guys we were crushing on liked us back. There were only three of us in the club, so the reporting never took very long. It was kind of like being a very lame spy.

"'October fourteenth. Chris G. asked Allie if he could use her pen,'" Tamara read aloud.

I snorted. Chris Gibson was a guy a grade above us who I used to have this mad crush on. One day, while we were at recess, he asked me if he could borrow a pen. I said, "Sure," but when I reached for my backpack—I don't know, I picked it up by the side, or something. Anyway, every-thing spilled out into this big patch of dirt, and Chris was, like, "Never mind," and that was the last time I ever talked to him.

Anyway, the fact that Chris asked me for a pen was considered by the club to be a major clue that he was into me. Just to show how very far

into la-la land we were, I will tell you that it was recorded in the notebook in *red* pen, with hearts around it.

Smiling, Tam continued to flip through the notebook. "'Heather J. is a complete snig, and keeps squeeling whenever Brian B. makes his rat face,'" Tam read aloud. "'She totally likes him.'" There was a star by the word *snig*, and then a definition: "snobby pig who likes to squeel."

"Please destroy it," I begged. "I don't want anyone to know that I couldn't spell *squeal*."

Tam giggled. "I'd forgotten that you were nuts about vocabulary words back then."

Actually, I'd been making up words ever since Ms. Ratner's third-grade class. She always made us look up words in the dictionary when we didn't know the meaning. And that was when I realized that sometimes you needed just the opposite—you had a meaning, but there wasn't a word to fit it. So I started making up my own vocabulary. The truth is, I still do it.

Tam kept reading. "'Renee and Tam think—'"

"Alli-i-ie!" My older brother, Lionel, has this annoying way of shouting my name that makes it

sound like something heavy has fallen on his foot. It gets on my nerves.

"What?" I screamed.

My door popped open, and Lionel stuck his raggedy head inside. His hair is the same color as mine—dark red—but his is straight instead of curly. His eyebrows flew up when he saw Tam. Lionel has always said that Tam was way too cool to be my best friend. "Hey, Tam."

"Hi, Lionel."

"Greetings, Prime Minister of Jerkistan," I put in. "What do you want?"

Lionel's eyes clouded over as he glanced at me. "I want you to stop touching my stuff." Lionel is two years older, and I was *not* happy that we were about to be in the same school again, starting tomorrow. "Where's my iPod?"

"How should I know?" I gave my hair a toss and leaned back on my elbows.

Lionel gritted his teeth. "Because you took it."

"No, I didn't."

"Then where is it?" Lionel's face was starting to turn red, a sure sign that he was getting mad.

"Maybe it's in your pigsty of a room," I said. "Look under your trough." I just said that to bug him. The truth is, Lionel is way neater than me. I mean, he organizes his socks by *color*. His CDs are alphabetized. He reads his comic books once, then seals them in plastic bags. I'm telling you, he's sick.

Lionel gave this little lunge toward me, and I screeched, "Mom!" which normally would have been completely pointless—Mom likes to let us "work out our own differences"—but she happened to be walking down the hall at that very minute.

"What's going on?" Mom demanded, poking her red head into my room. She has the most beautiful hair. It's really red—not brownish, like Lionel's and mine—and it falls in even waves instead of rising in a ball of frizz. "Oh, hi, Tam. I didn't realize you were over." Mom smiled, her gray eyes crinkling at the edges.

"Hi, Ms. Fine." Tam is superpolite around grown-ups.

You're probably wondering why Mom and I have different last names. It's because Mom went

back to her maiden name after my parents got divorced. In a way, it's kind of weird to have the same name as my dad, who lives in another state, instead of Mom, who I see every day. But I didn't get to choose my last name when they split up, and I knew that Dad would freak if I changed it now, so I just stuck with Kimball.

"Lionel, you left your iPod in the back pocket of your jeans," Mom said, holding it out. "I found it in the laundry."

Lionel took it, his face burning. I gave him a smug little smile as Mom held out the phone to me. "Dad wants to talk to you."

I took the phone and retreated to my desk while Lionel showed Tam his iPod. Mom dug around in my closet for my laundry.

"Dad?" I said into the receiver.

"Hi, sweetheart." Dad's voice is a warm rumble. When I was little, I used to love it when he read stories to me. My dad is huge, and I would cuddle next to him before he tucked me in. I didn't even really care which story he chose—just hearing his deep growly voice made me feel safe. "I wanted to say, good luck tomorrow."

10

"Thanks. I guess I'm a little nervous."

"Don't be," Dad said. "Just give them your best smile." This is typical Dad advice. He used to be a marine, and isn't afraid of much. "Do you have a pretty dress?"

I sighed. I love my dad, but he always acts like I'm about four years old. I guess it's because I *was* four when he moved to Ohio. "I think I'm just going to wear jeans."

"Jeans?" I could hear the frown in his voice.

"Well," I hedged, "maybe my white pants." I should have known. Dad is the only person in the world who cares about how I dress even more than Tam does.

"Pants? Don't you think you should get a little dressed up for the first day of school?" I knew he was thinking of the skirt Marci had given me.

"My white pants are dressy," I said.

Dad sighed. "Okay. Well, have a good first day. I want a full report. Would you put your mother back on the phone?"

"Okay," I told him. "Bye, Dad."

"Yes?" Mom said, cradling the phone between

her ear and her shoulder as she scooped up my laundry—which had somehow landed all around my basket instead of in it. "Howard, I think pants are fine." There was a pause, then Mom said, "I think she should wear what she wants." She blew her bangs out of her face, and rubbed her neck the way she does when she's feeling stressed. Phone conversations with my dad usually have that effect on her. "Lionel's here, would you like to speak to him?"

Lionel bounded off the bed and grabbed the cordless. "Hey, Dad!" he chirped. He and Dad get along great. They're on the same wavelength, somehow. Mom picked up the laundry basket and followed Lionel out the door.

"So, what did your dad think you should wear?" Tam wanted to know.

"A dress," I told her. "But he's a dad—he doesn't know anything."

Tam nodded. "Allie," she said slowly, "what if everyone at Grover Cleveland is mad cool, and I look like a nork?"

I actually laughed at that. "Look—Lionel goes there, and he's a major nerd. Besides, you can always hang with me."

"But we only have one class together," Tam pointed out.

I sighed. That part was true. "Well, there's before school, and after. And we have the same lunch." I picked up the dusty old LFC notebook. "Look, if we could stay friends through this," I said, holding up the notebook, "we'll stay friends through sixth grade."

"Best friends," Tam corrected. She held out her hand. On the index finger of her right hand was a slim blue enamel band that we had bought together over the summer.

I put my hand over hers, showing her that I was wearing my friendship ring, too. "Yeah, best friends."

Tam took the notebook and flipped through it again. "You know, you should keep another notebook this year. A record of middle school."

Actually, that wasn't such a bad idea. I had high hopes for sixth grade. Everyone warned me that it was much harder than elementary school, but it also seemed like more fun. More grown-up, or something. "Okay," I said, pulling out one of the clean new notebooks that Mom had bought for

me. It had soccer balls on the front and crackled as I opened it.

"A soccer notebook?" Tam asked, smiling a little.

Hmm, I thought, looking down at the cover, is it babyish? "Are you saying that you think the soccer notebook is lamer than the pink-with-red-hearts LFC notebook?" I asked.

"Good point," Tam admitted. I slipped a pen with blue sparkly ink out of the cup on my desk and sat on the bed beside her.

One day till sixth grade, and Tam is afraid of looking like a nork, I wrote. My handwriting hadn't gotten much better than it was in the third grade, I'm sorry to say.

"Better explain what a nork is," Tam said, pointing to the page.

I nodded and wrote in the definition.

———◦———

nork \'nork\ *n* : someone beyond both nerditude and dorkdom; a dweeb squared.

But that's not going to happen, I added to the notebook. *Allie is going to wear white pants, as her khaki skirt has disappeared into the Bermuda*

Rectangle known as her room. Then I flipped it closed, picked up the heinous, dust-covered LFC notebook, and placed them both side by side on the shelf. I turned to Tam and smiled.

She smiled back, but for some reason, the stealth freakies crawled down my spine.

It's just nerves, I told myself. This year is going to be great.

After all, I had my best friend. What else did I need?

- 2 -

blarg \\'blarg\\ **1:** *v* to insult rudely and loudly, to diss beyond normal diss-dom **2:** *n* an insult that leaves you feeling like the biggest nork that ever walked the face of the planet

"Take three steps back and don't tell anyone you're my sister," Lionel said the minute we arrived at the bus stop.

"Why?" I demanded, hitching my nearly empty book bag higher onto my shoulder. "Because you're too cool to be seen with me?"

"No—because you look like Strawberry Shortcake." Lionel smiled smugly.

I looked down at my outfit in horror. I was wearing my white pants and a pink T-shirt. Ohmygosh, I thought, wondering what I had been thinking when I got dressed that morning. You can't just go around wearing pink and white when you have a curly mop of red hair and freckles. People mock you.

But it was too late now, and stupid Lionel

knew it. That was why he had been so quiet at the breakfast table. He didn't want to blarg my outfit in time for me to change.

Did I mention that my brother is an evil genius?

Thankfully, Tamara walked up to the bus stop at that very moment.

"Tell me that I don't look like Strawberry Shortcake," I begged.

Looking my outfit up and down, Tam gave me this sort of *Gee I'm really sorry* wince, and said, "Lots of people *like* shortcake."

Lionel laughed from his place three paces away, and I sighed. That's the thing about Tam— she never lies to save your feelings. Sometimes I wish she would.

The bus pulled up with a rattling shudder and the doors sighed open. I stepped aboard and looked around, thinking, Who are all of these people?

I knew that Grover Cleveland Middle School was huge—I'd seen it when Mom and I had to drop off Lionel for chess club—and I knew that kids from lots of different elementary schools

went there. But somehow, I wasn't ready for a busload of strangers.

Lionel headed toward the back where his best friends—Jed and Sammy, the Nerdtastic Duo—were saving him a seat.

Tam found us seats in the center as the doors closed and the bus started to pull away.

Just then, a voice shouted, "Hold up! Hold up! Sto-o-o-o-op!" Someone banged on the side of the bus, and we jerked to a stop. The doors hissed open, and my friend Justin Thyme (I swear that's his name—Justin's dad is a huge joker) scrambled aboard. Breathing hard, Justin flashed the bus driver a huge grin and said, "Okay, you can go now."

The bus driver glared as the bus doors slapped closed. Justin flailed a little as the bus lurched forward, then recovered and started down the aisle.

"As usual, you're Justin Thyme," I told him as he took the seat in front of mine. My standard joke. Everyone's standard joke. With a name like that, you'd think he could try to be punctual once or twice in his life. "Nice entrance, by the way."

"I like to make an impression," Justin joked, flipping his hair like some Hollywood starlet.

"Hey, Justin," Tam said from her seat across from mine.

"Oh, hey, Tam," Justin said. He looked down at his backpack quickly, and moved it from the seat to the floor. Then he moved it up again. He opened his mouth like he was about to say something, but nothing came out. He just smiled at me.

Okay, that was slightly weird. Justin is usually really funny and fun to hang with. He lives two doors down, and we play soccer sometimes. But guys (including Justin, I guess) tend to get shy around Tam. Have I mentioned that she's really pretty? Sometimes, it can be kind of annoying.

I looked at her. She was wearing this cute yellow tank and a blue-and-yellow-flowered flippy skirt. Her long black hair curled around her face, and her dark eyes looked bigger than usual. I realized suddenly that she was wearing makeup.

I felt like an even bigger nork than I had before.

Why didn't I let Tam choose an outfit for me yesterday? I wondered.

The bus shuddered to a stop and we picked up three enormous eighth graders and a kid with frizzy brown hair, who looked like he was probably in sixth. The eighters bounded to the back, while the frizzy-haired kid looked around, then sat down in the front row.

You know how you can sometimes spot the class nerd a mile off? I had no doubts—this was the guy. It wasn't like he looked like a total weirdo, or anything—no Star Trek T-shirt, no Coke bottle glasses, no headgear. But his shirt was this really ugly shade of puce. And his leather shoes were the lace-up kind . . . and I could tell he was wearing them with sweat socks. Plus, he had a Snoopy pin on his backpack.

My outfit was a tragic mistake, but this guy's clothes were Nork City, USA.

A loud burst of laughter came from the back of the bus, and I turned around to see Lionel high-fiving one of the huge eighth graders. I frowned.

Since when is my brother cool? I wondered. I mean, he's a nork. Isn't he? I thought. But I was

starting to realize that he had sort of "cooled it down" since hitting middle school. His clothes, for example. Untucked plaid over too-large khakis. They blended right in. And his hair was shaggy in the way that all of the guys' hair seemed to be shaggy. Middle-school camouflage.

I turned back toward the frizzy-haired kid again. What did my brother know that this kid didn't?

With another rumble and growl, the bus pulled up to the front of the school, which was even bigger and more prisonlike than I remembered. I had to stifle the groan as I looked out the smeary bus window. Everyone was dressed up for the first day of school. All of the kids looked older, and half of them had clearly had their clothes shipped to them from MTV. Everyone was clustered in groups, and each little pack seemed to have its own dress code. Some of the groups were familiar. For example, the mathletes, with their enormous backpacks, were standing on the concrete front steps. The student government types, in their preppy, well-ironed khakis, were standing near the big tree on the front lawn. And

the tough kids—ripped jeans, concert T-shirts, messy hair—were over in the far corner. But there were other groups at Grover Cleveland, ones I didn't know. I felt like I had entered some kind of wildlife special. You know, one of the ones in which the innocent seal gets eaten by a grizzly bear.

Perfect, I thought. Frizzy-Haired Kid and I will fit right in. We'll be the seals.

"How many classes do we have together, again?" Tam whispered nervously as she eyed the school.

"One," I said miserably.

"I guess it's time to start the first day of the rest of our middle-school life," Justin said as he slid into the aisle.

Yeah, I thought as I stood up. Time to join the other wild creatures of the sixth grade.

———◆———

glom•mers \'glom-ers\ *n* : **1:** girls who cling to each other in groups **2:** friends who never go anywhere without each other, like they're tied together with invisible string

Tam and I had to split up to find our lockers and

homerooms. Then I sat through English, Spanish, and math in kind of a daze. Mostly we played "getting to know you" games, collected our books, and wrote down lists of supplies we'd need for the class while the teacher made a permanent seating chart. It was strange—I'd never had to play a "getting to know you" game in class before. In elementary school, I'd always known everyone. They were just the kids from the neighborhood— the same kids I'd been going to school with since kindergarten. But here, I couldn't remember a single person's name.

Well, except for Orren Kendall, aka Frizzy-Haired Kid. Since my last name is Kimball, so far I was seated next to Orren in every single class. I bet people thought we were swapping fashion tips.

When the bell for fourth period rang, I breathed a sigh of relief. Finally, science. My class with Tam. I pressed my books to my chest and kept my head down as I headed down the hall. I didn't have anyone to walk with during the passing periods, and it was embarrassing—especially since I kept getting lost and

wandering around with this totally fake *I swear I know where I'm going and besides I have friends they're just not in this class* look on my face. But that was about to change—for one period, at least.

But when I walked into science, Tam was already seated at a lab table with someone else—a girl with long blond hair. It took me a moment to realize who it was . . . and then the world seemed to tilt on its axis.

Renee Anderson.

I caught my breath. Oh, no, I thought. Nononononononono. My heart pounded in my ears.

"Allie!" Tam cried, waving me over.

Why is Tam sitting with her? I wondered frantically. My head felt like it was wobbling, balloonlike, on top of my neck as I walked toward their lab table.

"Allie, look who's here!" Tam cried, as though it was perfectly normal that she was seated with the person who had been her own archenemy for three years. "Renee is in five of my classes!"

"Oh," I said, trying to smile. "That's . . . that's great."

"Hello, Allie," Renee said.

Ugh. Even the way she said *hello* instead of *hi* made me want to barf.

Okay, I should back up. Renee used to be our friend. In fact, she used to be the LFC's third member . . . until things blew up. I'll admit, it was partially my fault. It was my stupid idea that we start a slam book. I thought that—since there were only three of us—we would all just write nice things about each other, and then we'd feel great and everybody would be happy. But under Tamara's "face" section, Renee wrote "kind of flat." I didn't think it was such a big deal, but Tam was *furious*. She stopped talking to Renee, and I didn't want to stop hanging with Tam . . . so I stopped talking to Renee, too. Then Renee became best friends with Hallie McDermott, and the two of them became glommers. They just latched on to each other, and then the two of them went everywhere together, like Tweedledum and Tweedledee, and that was the end of that.

Over the years, it had somehow morphed

into this "We hate Renee" thing. And then Renee had a different teacher for fifth grade, so we never really saw her much.

"Pull up a chair," Tam told me now.

All *three* of us are going to be lab partners? I thought. Oh, glick—where's Hallie when you need her? But Tam didn't seem to be kidding, so I grabbed a chair, which let out a wild squeak as I dragged it across the floor.

"Um, excuse me," said the teacher from the front of the room. She was tall and thin, with sparse brown hair and too much blue eye shadow over pale blue eyes. If the chalkboard was to be trusted, her name was Mrs. Larsen.

I pointed to myself. "Me?"

"Yes. Please don't move the chairs." She fixed me with that strange ice-blue stare.

"We just wanted to have three at this table . . ." I started.

"Two at a table," Mrs. Larsen said. "There's an empty seat at the back."

Her tone sounded final, so I turned to Renee. She knew that Tam and I were best friends. She had to move.

"See you after class," Renee told me, flipping her blond hair over her shoulder.

My heart fluttered like a frantic butterfly. This was my only class with Tam—and I wasn't even going to get to sit with her? I stared at Tam, who shrugged helplessly and glanced at the teacher, who was still giving me the blue–eye shadow glare.

That was it. I didn't have a choice. I made my way to the back of the class.

Oh, no. I had to take a deep breath to keep myself from groaning. Naturally, the only seat open was the one next to Orren Kendall.

He didn't even look up as I plopped into the chair next to his.

Great.

———◆———

stink•prise \'stink-priz\ *n* : something unexpected and unwanted, like a pair of dirty underwear in your Christmas stocking

Why didn't you save me a seat in science? The question had been ringing in my ears all day. But I hadn't asked it. Not yet. I just couldn't—it freaked me out too much. Did it mean that Tam was mad at

me, or something? But that didn't make sense. So then, what? The whole thing made me so crazy that I just kept quiet.

Besides, even if I had dared to ask, I hadn't had a chance. Renee sat with me and Tam during lunch. And after school, the minute Tam and I sat down on the school bus, Justin—who seemed to have gotten over his shyness—started chattering up a storm. So I had to wait until we got off for any privacy. Justin waved and walked toward his house with Jim Donelly, and Lionel sprinted way ahead of us. By the time I had a chance to talk to Tam in private, I really didn't know how to bring it up.

"So," I said brightly as we fell into step next to each other, "did you hear that announcement they made in homeroom? First soccer practice tomorrow." Tam and I had been on a league team together the year before. "We should join. Then we can hang on the team, and go to the big sports banquet at the end of the term." The Cleveland sports banquet was held twice a year, and I guess it was a huge deal. Everyone who played a sport got to go.

"Yeah . . ." Tam's voice sounded kind of . . . wispy. Like a thin strip of cloud across a bright blue sky.

"You want to meet me before?" I asked. "We can warm up together."

Tam squinted as she looked into the distance. "I was thinking of maybe . . . going out for cheer squad."

"Cheer squad?" I stopped in my tracks.

"Yeah." Tam looked apologetic. "I mean, soccer is your thing, Allie. I've never been very good."

"That's not true!" I said, even though it was true. Tam had actually kicked the ball into the wrong goal during one game. It kind of worked out, though, because the other team started laughing so hard that we managed to score on them. "You won't even know anyone on cheer squad," I pointed out, my heart fluttering.

"Well . . . Renee is going to try out, too."

"Is Hallie trying out?" I asked. I know, that was kind of mean. But I was feeling kind of mean. Having Renee in my life again was kind of a stinkprise.

"Hallie's going to Twin Pines," Tam said.

Twin Pines Middle School. That figured. That was where almost everyone we know was going.

"Allie," Tam went on quickly, "I just wanted to tell you that I'm so sorry about science. The thing is, when Renee told me that Hallie was going to Twin Pines, I felt kind of bad for her. And Renee doesn't know anyone at Cleveland, either, so we got to talking in homeroom, and . . . It's just—we walked together from Spanish class, and when I got into science, I didn't see you. . . . So Renee and I sat together. I really thought we'd be able to have three to a table. . . ." Tam's voice trailed off when she saw my glazed expresson.

I nodded, even though *I* would have saved the seat. I wouldn't have made her sit with a norky lab partner. But Tam really did look sorry, and I have to admit that I was kind of relieved. So she wasn't mad at me. She had just made a mistake. Anyone can make a mistake.

"Look, don't be upset about soccer," Tam said, taking my hand. Her blue friendship ring pressed against my fingers. "We'll still get to hang,

and we'll still go to the banquet together, okay? Cheer squad goes, too."

"Okay," I said. But I couldn't help feeling that it just wouldn't be the same.

- 3 -

jock•iss•i•ma \jok-'iss-i-ma\ *n* : an excellent female athlete

I sat on the bench, pulling on my cleats and trying not to be utterly obvious as I looked around, sizing up the other players. The Cleveland team—the Tigers—had a reputation as total jockissimas.

A tall girl with a long brown ponytail and hazel eyes loped down the field. She was slim and superfast, like one of those greyhound racing dogs. With a whiplash move, she cut left, then slammed the ball into the net. Holy guacamole, I thought.

"Jack!" A girl with a wide smile waved to the tall girl and trotted out onto the field.

Jack? I thought. What kind of name is that for a girl?

"Hey, Elena!" Jack shouted.

I hadn't seen either of these girls in any of my classes, so I figured that they were older—seventh

or eighth grade. Another group of about ten girls was running a kicking drill at the other goal. I figured anyone brave enough to hang out on the field must be a returning team member. Everyone else was warming up on the sidelines.

Jack and Elena squared off, with Jack trying to get the ball to the goal. Even with her lightning-fast moves, she wasn't having much luck against Elena. Jack cut left, then right, but Elena dogged her every step. Finally, Elena managed to steal the ball. She grinned at her own cool move.

I couldn't help smiling, too. Elena had coarse brown hair that hung around her round face in scraggly waves and dancing black eyes.

"Not bad for a sweeper," Jack said, clapping Elena on the shoulder.

Oh, no, I thought, groaning mentally. Sweeper was my position.

Even though I knew the Tigers were a great team, I'd been secretly hoping that I would get to start this year. I get antsy just sitting around on the bench—I always want to play. But I'd definitely be second string to Elena.

But there wasn't enough time to feel really sorry for myself, because just then the coach came out and blew her whistle.

I finished tying up my cleats and trotted over to where the coach was standing. She was short and powerfully built, with dark brown skin and warm brown eyes. Her hair was streaked with gray, but other than that, she looked really young.

"Okay, everyone!" the coach called as the team straggled over. "My name is Andrea Connors. Some of you know me from seventh-grade earth science, and some of you know me from last year, and some of you don't know me at all. So I'm going to pass this around." She held up a clipboard. "Everyone, please write down your name, your favorite position, your e-mail address if you have one, and your phone number."

I looked around. There had to be at least thirty girls standing around. In a way, that was good, because we had enough people to practice against each other with a full team on each side. But in a way, it was bad, because I had a feeling I'd be doing a lot of benchwarming.

"Not everyone will get to start in a game," Coach Connors went on, "but everyone will get to play." The clipboard came around, and I wrote down my information. I hesitated a minute over the favorite position category. But I knew I'd have tough competition no matter what position I chose, so I just scribbled "sweeper" and passed the clipboard to the next girl.

The coach ran through the usual coach speech about how we were going to work hard and have a great year, and blah-blahdy-blah. I was trying to listen to what she was saying, but I couldn't concentrate—I was too eager to get out on the field. The grass was fresh and green from a summer without trampling, and the sun was hot. Finally, Coach wrapped up. Someone handed the clipboard back to her. "Sarah Simmons, take goalie, blue team," Coach announced. She looked up at the short-haired African American girl who stepped forward, smiling shyly. "Welcome back, Sarah," Coach said. "Jacqueline Wallace: right wing, blue team. Good to see you, Jack." The greyhound-like girl went to stand with Sarah. "Sally Chin," Coach said, and I craned my neck to

see. I knew Sally! I hadn't seen her since early July, and I hadn't noticed her because she looked different—her hair was braided in cool cornrows and she was tan. But it was her. We weren't best buds, or anything, but at least she was a familiar face.

"Sally," the coach said, "take left wing, blue. Allie Kimball: striker, blue team."

Striker? Oh, great. My stomach felt like it was full of greasy caterpillars. I hate playing any of those scoring positions, but striker is the worst. "Uh, Coach Connors?" I said, raising my hand. "I think there's a mistake. I wrote down *sweeper*."

"You're striker today," Coach said without looking up. "Kristin Dallman, you're sweeper, blue."

I sighed and trudged over to join my team-mates as Coach ran through the rest of the positions. Sure enough, Elena was the sweeper for the red team.

"Everyone, take two laps, then head out onto the field," Coach announced.

I settled into a jog, dreading taking the field. Just what I didn't want—to be second or third

string in a position I hated. I was actually starting to wish that I had gone out for cheer squad, which is kind of hilarious, given that I had totally twisted my ankle the last time I attempted a cartwheel.

Actually, there had been about five minutes earlier in the day when I truly considered joining the cheer squad. Renee and Tam and I had eaten lunch together out on the patio, and they were talking about the cheers they were going to do for the tryouts, which weren't until the following week. Tam had made up her own cheer, the start of which went something like, "Tigers growl and Tigers bite! Let's go, Tigers! Fight, fight, fight!"

"You may not want to say, 'Tigers bite,'" Renee pointed out. She took a delicate sip of her soda.

Tam looked horrified. "Oh, no! I didn't even think of that."

"Hmm . . ." I said, biting into the fudge brownie my mom had packed into my lunch. "What about 'Tigers growl and Tigers roar! They'll use you to mop the floor!'"

"That's good," Renee told me. She seemed

kind of surprised. "Tam, use that. Why aren't you trying out for the cheer squad, Allie?"

I shrugged. "Because I don't want to break my neck."

"Seriously?" Renee asked. "But you're so coordinated. You're great at sports, right?"

"Yeah," Tam agreed, grabbing my hand. "Come with us, Allie."

I felt this warm glow in the pit of my stomach, like I had just drunk a huge cup of hot chocolate. Renee isn't so bad now, I thought. Actually, she was kind of cool. And I guess I felt flattered that she and Tam thought I'd make a good cheerleader. I even pictured myself with the pom-poms and everything. But cheerleading . . . well, you have to wear a skirt. Besides, Renee was only half right. I'm coordinated—on the soccer field. But cartwheels and roundoffs and junk like that—forget it. "I think I'll stick with soccer," I said finally.

Tam looked disappointed, but not surprised. She knows I'm a soccer girl.

"Oh, well. Less competition for us, right Tam?" Renee had said. And that was that.

I felt someone tap me on the shoulder, snapping me back to the present. "Hey!" Sally said, giving me a brilliant grin.

"Hey, Sally!" Our footfalls fell into the same rhythm as we headed into the last curve of the second lap. "I didn't know you went here."

Sally rolled her eyes. "Please. This place is so huge, your best friend could go here and you'd never know it!"

"Tell me about it," I agreed, feeling silent relief that at least I had lunch and science with Tam.

Once we were finished with our laps, we scrambled to our places. The ball was kicked off, and it immediately headed our way.

Instinctively, I trotted back to protect our goal. A skinny girl with long blond hair was streaking toward Sarah, the goalie. I cut in front of Skinny and managed to steal. Looking around for someone to pass to, I spotted Jack, and kicked the ball her way. She tore down the field, and I trotted after her. It took me a minute to register that I was the striker—I was supposed to be at the other end of the field! I raced toward the red goal

just in time for Jack to pass the ball back to me. I had a perfect shot—wide open. My heart nearly exploded out of my chest. Don't screw this up! I thought as I took the shot.

And missed.

I *missed*! Someone dig a hole for me to hide in, I thought as I stared at the ball. This is why I'm a sweeper.

"Kimball!" Coach shouted from the sidelines. "Move it!"

That was when I realized that I had stopped dead in my tracks, while the game had kept going. Elena had the ball, and she was driving it toward the center of the field. I took off after her.

Elena dodged downfield, past two girls trying to defend her. She slammed the ball toward her team's right wing —not in time. Sally intercepted and passed the ball to me.

Oh, God, why does everyone keep passing to me? I thought desperately. I just wanted to get rid of it, so I took the open shot to Jack. She headed it into the goal.

Score!

"Dallman, Kimball, Boynton, Kirikalis, Wallace,

take a rest!" Coach Connors called from the side-lines. "Jackson, Smythe, Laird, Khan, Anderson, sub in!"

That was it. My turn was over. I had to go sit on the sidelines.

Fighting the urge to run up to Coach Connors and tell her that I was a much better player than it seemed, I jogged to the sidelines and flopped on the grass.

"Hey," Elena said, flopping next to me. "What's your name?"

I looked behind me, but there wasn't anyone there. "Allie," I said.

"I'm Elena Kirikalis." The girl leaned back on her elbows and flexed her feet. "It's always rough to come back after the summer. I know I'm going to hurt tomorrow."

"Yeah," I agreed, feeling kind of shy. In a way, sitting with a seventh grader made me feel like less of a nork. And in a way it made the norkitude worse. "Were you on the team last year?"

"Yeah."

"And she has Connors for life science, too," Jack added, trotting up on the tail end of our

conversation. "Which means she'll need earplugs for the rest of the year."

Elena grinned. "I love Connors," she said. "Even if she yells a lot."

Jack rolled her eyes. "I hear Connors is the toughest science teacher in the school. I'm hoping that I get Rawlings next year." Then she smiled at me. "Hi, I'm Jack."

"Allie." I adjusted my weight on the soft grass below me. "Wait—you're in sixth?" I asked Jack. "How do you guys know each other?"

"League team," Elena said with a smile.

"That was a nice steal you made, by the way," Jack said, turning to me.

I rolled my eyes. "Nice goal, too," I said sarcastically.

Elena shrugged. "We're all rusty."

I gave her a weak smile. It was a nice thing for her to say, even though she and Jack didn't look too rusty to me.

"Ladies," Coach Connors shouted at us. "Less chatting, more watching. You can learn from your teammates."

I sighed and turned back to face the game.

Yeah, I thought as I watched the girls darting across the field, I have a lot to learn.

———◦———

ac•ci•diss \'aks-e-diss\ *n* : an accidental insult, the kind that slips out when you have something else on your mind

"Hey, Allie," Justin said as I slipped into the seat across from him. There was only one bus in the afternoon for kids who played sports, and it wasn't as nice as the morning bus. Fossilized gum was stuck between the ridges of the antislide rubber lining the aisle, and the backs of the seats were lined with graffiti. "Where's Tam?"

"Cheer squad hasn't started yet, so I'm riding solo."

"Thanks a lot," Justin said.

I winced at my accidiss. "Sorry—you know what I mean."

"So how'd it go?" he asked.

"Horror movie," I told him. "You?"

"More like a screwball comedy. Some of the guys are having a little trouble working together. But I think I did okay. What happened to you?"

"The coach put me in as the striker. The rest

of the team is really great, and I looked spaztastic."

Justin nodded gravely. He knows how I feel about scoring. Way too much pressure. "There were a couple of really good guys on my team, too—Stuart Jackson and Chris Gibson. Remember Chris? They made the rest of us look pretty bad. But you still have to have eleven on a team, so I think . . ."

This was where I tuned out. Chris Gibson. Of course I remembered him. He was the guy I'd crushed on for all of third and fourth grade. The guy from the LFC. The thought of his blue eyes made my heart give a little stutter. So he was here. At Cleveland. I'd forgotten that he and Justin used to be friends.

The bus hissed to a stop and I saw a frizzy head retreat from the front row.

"I wonder what sport he plays," I said idly, watching Orren from the bus window.

"Who? Orren?" Justin peered out the window as the bus started up again. "He plays soccer. Wing. Pretty decent, too."

"Really?" I asked. For some reason, I found that kind of hard to believe.

The bus lurched to a stop. "This is us," Justin said, and I followed him off the bus. Justin walked to a bike rack and undid the lock on his blue ten-speed.

"You rode your bike to the bus stop?" I asked him. "It's only four blocks away."

The corners of Justin's mouth curled into a smile. "I was running a little late this morning—needed all the help I could get. Need a ride?"

I grinned. "On that thing? With you? No, thanks."

"Come on, I'm an excellent driver," he said, but I shook my head. "Have it your way. I'll see you tomorrow." He gave a little wave and rode off.

I sighed. Ugh, I thought, tomorrow. More middle-school fun.

"How did it go?" Mom asked the minute I walked into the kitchen.

"Don't ask." I grabbed a cookie.

Mom nodded and gave me a hug. "It's always hard to come back after the summer. Do you want to help me chop some veggies?" she asked, turning back to the counter.

I slung my book bag on the floor and said,

"Sure." I washed my hands and reached for the knife, peering at the open recipe on the counter. Veggie lasagna—one of my many faves. Mom hates cleaning, but she loves cooking. And that's the better deal, as far as I'm concerned. Plus, she runs her own design firm out of our house, so that means that she's always home to make dinner.

I washed some parsley and was just starting to chop it up when the phone rang. I pulled the receiver from the wall and cradled it against my shoulder while I chopped. Multitasking is a skill I've picked up from Mom, who is always doing about fifteen things at once.

"Allison, how's the new school going?" It was Dad's voice. Besides, he's the only person on the planet who calls me Allison.

"Oh—great," I lied. "I've got this really smart lab partner in science." Actually, that part was true. It turns out that Orren Kendall is a serious brain. He doesn't talk much, but he always seems to know the answers to everything.

Mom passed me a washed green pepper, and I sliced it in half.

"What about soccer?" Dad asked. "Is there a team?"

"Mmm," I said. I don't know why, but I just couldn't bring myself to tell Dad about practice. I guess I really was afraid that I wouldn't start. And then I'd have to tell him I was a benchwarmer. I just . . . didn't want to tell him. "I'm not so sure about that."

"Well, find out," Dad insisted. "Sports are a great way to make friends."

Yeah, as long as you don't stink, I added mentally.

"So, listen, I'm calling because I'm coming to town in a few weeks."

"You are?" I asked, putting down my knife. Dad comes through pretty regularly because of business—he's in sales. But still, only, like, once every couple of months. Lionel and I always have a great time when he comes over—it's way more fun than visiting Dad at his house. Dad is remarried to the most boring woman in the world. Marci and my dad bicker a lot, and when she's alone with me or Lionel, she can't talk about anything but my baby brother, Daniel, who is three.

Luckily, Daniel is really cute and funny. Otherwise I think I'd go crazy.

"Yeah, I was hoping that you and Lionel and I could go out to dinner."

"That would be great!" I said eagerly.

"So don't make any plans for Tuesday, October twenty-fourth. We're going out."

"Okay," I told him. "Give Daniel a kiss for me."

"Sure," Dad said. I knew I should ask to speak to Marci, but I just couldn't make myself do it. Luckily, Dad let it go. "Is Lionel there?"

"Oh, yeah, I'll go get him." I covered the receiver with my hand and turned to my mom. "Dad is coming on October twenty-fourth," I told her. "He wants to take me and Lionel out to dinner."

Mom rolled her eyes and frowned slightly. "You'd think he'd check with *me*," she grumbled, but she circled the date on the wall calendar and wrote, *Howard out w/kids.*

I ran up the stairs and busted into Lionel's room. He was lying on his bed, listening to his iPod, but he sat up when he saw me. "Get out!" he shouted.

"Dad's on the phone, tumbleweed-hair," I said, eyeing my brother's serious case of bed head. "I'll be happy to tell him that you're too busy to talk—"

Lionel grabbed the phone from my hand and pointed to the door. Then he turned his back on me. "Hey, Dad," he said into the receiver.

I stuck out my tongue at his back and went downstairs.

Dad is coming, I thought as I trotted down the steps, grinning. At least now I had something to look forward to.

- 4 -

pe•cool•iar \peh-'cool-yer\ *adj* : something (or someone) both cool and strange at the same time

"This microscope is defective." I pressed my
eye against the telescopey-thing and adjusted
the crank on the side. "Unless we're supposed to
be studying blurs."

"I think maybe you've got to adjust it the
other way," Orren said shyly.

I scooched back and let him take over.
He sort of slithered the slide around, then turned
the crank. Sighing, I looked over at Tam and
Renee. They were pointing to their microscope
and giggling. God—what is so funny about a
microscope? I wondered, gritting my teeth. I
glared at my microscope. Tell me a joke, I thought
at it. Be funny.

But the microscope didn't do anything.
Orren was still peering into it. "There you go," he
said finally, clearing the way for me.

I peeped in. "Hey," I said, "that looks like—something." Actually, what it looked like was one of my dad's blueberry pancakes. Kind of squiggly at the edges, and full of weird-looking blobs. "How did you do that?" I asked.

"I have a microscope at home," Orren admitted. "It was a Christmas present from my grandmother," he added quickly, which made things a little bit better. I mean, at least he hadn't saved up his allowance for it. "Want to see something cool?"

Hmm, I wonder what *cool* means in dorkese, I thought. I shrugged. "Okay."

Reaching up, he plucked one of the hairs from his frizzy head and placed it on a microscope slide. Then he adjusted the microscope and backed away. "Take a look."

I lifted my eyebrows at him. "That's not cool," I informed him. "That's gross."

"Yeah," Orren said, laughing and blushing slightly, "but check it out."

Well, I guess it could be some worse bodily product, I thought, leaning over to peer in.

I hate to say this, but that hair really was kind

of amazing. First of all, it didn't look like a hair. It looked more like a long, twisty pinecone, or a gnarled tree limb covered in rough bark.

"You know," Orren said, like it was perfectly normal that I was looking at a blown-up image of his hair, "if you shrunk the earth to the size of a pool ball, it would seem just as smooth as a pool ball is, and vice versa." This was typical Orren information. He'd started talking a lot more lately, and he was always saying things like: "If a lobster loses a claw or an eye, it can grow another," or "Slugs have four noses!" You know— interesting. But weird. He's one pecooliar dude, I decided.

A peal of laughter cut through the room. I looked up. It was Tam.

"Tamara," Mrs. Larsen said, "are you finished with your lab?" Her eye shadow was green today, and I found it extremely disturbing. Very Wicked Witch.

"Not quite," Tam replied in a sweet voice.

"Well, then. I suggest you quiet down and focus on your work."

Once Mrs. Larsen turned her back, Tam

swatted Renee on the arm, and the two bent over their lab work. But their shoulders were shaking with laughter. Jealousy slithered into my stomach and coiled there like a snake.

Just then, the bell rang, and I started packing up my bag. I felt a pang of relief as Tam hurried over with Renee dragging behind her. Part of me had worried that they might just walk off without me. Tam waited until Orren took off, then draped herself over my lab table. "I am so sorry that you're stuck with him," she said in this serious voice.

"He's not that bad," I said, thinking about how Orren had adjusted our microscope, and everything.

Renee cocked an eyebrow. "Not that bad? Please. All of his shirts are weird shades of green, and he likes Snoopy."

"And his hair makes him look like he just got hit by lightning," Tam added.

"You know, he actually put one of his hairs under the microscope," I confessed.

"Eewww!"

"Girls," Mrs. Larsen said, frowning at us from

the front of the room. "Don't you have to get to class?"

She was right—two minutes to the bell. I grabbed my book bag, and the three of us beat it out of there.

"Girls, I need you to leave so I can smear more green chalk dust on my eyelids," Renee cooed in this flutey voice once we were halfway down the hall.

Tam and I cracked up. I couldn't help it. Renee was just too good with a put-down.

---

su•per•no•va \soo-per-'no-va\ *n:* someone who's so hot, he could melt your brain just by standing near you

I could hear Coach Connors's voice in my mind— like an annoying echo—as I trotted over to the other practice fields to meet Tam. She still had me stuck on striker, and, again, I had missed a goal early on during practice. Then, since I didn't want to mess up anymore, I just kept passing to Jack. Jack didn't miss goals.

I thought I'd kind of played it off, but Coach took me aside after practice. "Kimball," she said, pinning me with those intense brown

eyes, "you've got to get aggressive. Strikers strike."

That's why I want to sweep! I thought. Sweep!

"You've got the speed, and you've got the accuracy when you're passing," Coach went on. "You just need to work on your confidence." Then she squeezed me on the shoulder.

Like it was just that easy.

I needed to talk to Tam. This whole school was starting to get to me. But when I rounded the science building, I saw that the other practice fields were nearly empty. The guys' soccer team was packing up, and the cheer squad was nowhere to be seen.

I stood there for a while, totally confused. What happened? I wondered. Did Tam go home already? But I had talked to her at lunch, and she'd said that she would meet me after practice so we could ride the bus together. . . .

Looking around, I spotted Justin packing up his gear. "Hey," I called.

Justin looked up and grinned. "Hey!"

"You seen Tam?"

"Uh . . . I don't know." His face was a little red. Is he blushing? I wondered.

"She was supposed to meet me here," I said, trying not to smile. Does Justin have a little crush on Tam? I wondered. Is that why he's blushing?

"Oh, uh . . . wait a minute. Yeah. I think I saw her walking toward the parking lot with Renee." Justin shoved his cleats into his bag. "Why?"

"Oh . . . nothing," I hedged. Did Tam go home with Renee? I wondered. It sure sounded like it. I looked down at the friendship ring on my hand, feeling confused.

"Allie!" a voice called. I turned and saw Jack standing with Elena and Chris. My heart thudded in my chest in a very familiar way. Chris looked the same. Well . . . maybe a little more gorgeous.

I have no memory of walking over to join Jack and Elena, but I must have done it, because I found myself staring up into the golden flecks in Chris's blue eyes. He's such a supernova, I thought, feeling my face flush.

"Allie, this is my cousin Chris," Jack said.

For a moment, I wasn't sure that I'd understood what she said. "Your cousin?"

"My *baby* cousin." Jack grinned. "I'm two months older."

My head was swimming. Jack was Chris's cousin? But she didn't go to my elementary school. . . . Then again, why should she have? I wondered. She probably lived across town. I wish someone had clued me in earlier. "Hi," I said lamely.

"Hey," Chris said. His voice was velvety warm and soft.

"We're going out for ice cream," Elena piped up. "Do you want to come?"

I hesitated. On the one hand, eating ice cream with Chris was a bona fide dream come true. On the other hand, I thought of all of the things that could go wrong: I could spill something on myself, I could look like a pig, I could get a drip or a sprinkle on my face and not know it. . . . Besides, there was the whole Tam mystery. We were supposed to meet up—what if she was sitting on the bus, waiting for me? Actually, the thought made me a little panicky. She could be waiting right now, I realized, wondering where I am, and getting mad. "Sorry, guys," I said finally, "I have to pass."

"Next time," Jack suggested.

"Definitely," I told her.

"Hey, Allie, you coming?" Justin called.

"Yeah. Hold up a minute!" I turned back and said, "I'll see you guys later," but it was Chris I was looking at. I couldn't help it. I tried to tear my eyes away, but they wouldn't seem to go anywhere else.

"See you," Jack and Elena chorused as Chris gave me a nod.

I couldn't wait to tell Tam about this.

———◆———

men•tion•i•ac \'men-shun-ee-ak\ *n* : someone who keeps mentioning the same thing over and over and over . . .

"Mom!" I shouted as I walked in the door. "I'm ho—"

I bit off the last part of my sentence. There was chanting coming from the living room. I looked to the right and saw my mom, Mrs. Wilkerson from down the street, and Eileen Ohara—my mom's best friend—sitting cross-legged on the floor.

Grimacing, I tiptoed through the family

room toward the kitchen. I'd forgotten it was Wednesday. Yoga night.

Lionel grunted at me as I slung my backpack on the floor. I was starving, so I reached for the other half of his patriot. That's what we call an American cheese sandwich in my house. But he just slapped my hand away and sort of let out this growly snarl, so I headed for the fridge. I grabbed the orange juice and swigged from the carton.

Lionel watched me. "Do you know how many germs you carry in your mouth?"

"Do you know how many dorky facts you carry in your brain?" I retorted, taking another swig. I screwed the cap back on the OJ. "Did any-one call for me?" I asked, thinking of Tam. She hadn't been on the bus, after all. Mom always leaves a note on the fridge if anyone calls, but Lionel usually blows it off.

"Yeah, but I told the mental institution that I didn't know where you were," Lionel retorted. "You owe me one."

I rolled my eyes.

Just then, the chanting stopped, and some flute-and-chime music came on. Mom had picked

up this CD at some world music fair, and said that it helped her "de-stress." Personally, it made me want to claw the walls. When I want to de-stress, I put on loud music and dance around my room like crazy. That tinkly stuff just drives me nuts.

"Downward-facing dog." I could hear Mom's voice from the other room. She's been taking yoga classes since she was a kid in the 1970s, and she gets up and does her routine every morning. Now she teaches an informal class on Wednesday for any of her friends who want to learn. "That's good, Helen," she told Mrs. Wilkerson. "Now bend your knees and give a big stretch back. Good. Now, three-point. Lift your right leg."

I heard a grunt, then a thud as Mrs. Wilkerson toppled over.

Lionel sighed. "Why can't I live in a normal family?" he asked the ceiling. Then he trudged out of the room.

I grabbed an apple and followed him. "Hey, Peebles," I said to my cat, who was curled up on my bed, asleep. I leaned over her and gave her a kiss on the head, then stroked the fur between her ears. Peebles gave a sleepy "Brrowr . . ." and

shifted slightly, but she didn't open her eyes. She's kind of lazy, but I love her anyway.

Settling down at my desk, I booted up my computer and crunched into the sweet tartness of my apple. I checked my e-mail. There was a "Welcome to the Tigers" e-mail from Coach Connors. I skimmed the e-mail, which gave a list of names and phone numbers of the team members, as well as a schedule of games and practices. But there was nothing from Tam. She wasn't on my IM buddy list, either, so I decided to give her a call.

She picked up on the third ring. "Hello?"

"Tam? It's Allie."

"Hey! How was practice?"

"Great. How 'bout you?"

"Oh, it was so fun," Tam said brightly. "We're making up a new cheer, and the coach came up with this really cool move where—okay, we stand in a group of three, and two people plant their feet and flip the third one over. I'm one of the people who gets flipped. I keep ending up with my hair in my face, but I think it's going to look really great when we work out the kinks."

"Sounds cool," I said, and it really did. Of course, if I ever tried a move like that, I'd end up with gravel permanently implanted in my face. But that's why I'm a soccer player, not a cheerleader. "Just wear your hair in a ponytail."

"Yeah," Tam agreed. "That's what Renee said she was going to do."

"So, uh, did practice get out early, or something?" I asked, trying to ignore Renee's name. Tam was becoming a bit of a mentioniac when it came to Renee, and it was starting to bug me. "I looked for you before I got on the bus. . . ."

"Oh, yeah. Renee said that her mom could take us home after practice, so I just went with her," Tam said, like we'd never made plans to hang out together or anything.

I was starting to think that maybe we *hadn't* made plans. I mean, maybe I'd misunderstood. Maybe it was just an *I'll catch you later* kind of deal. I didn't want to blow the whole thing out of proportion. Besides, we were hanging out right now, kind of. "So, uh, I rode home on the bus with Justin." I kicked off my shoes and lay back against my pile of pillows. "I think he has a megacrush on someone."

"Who?" Tam asked. She loves gossip.

"Someone whose name rhymes with Stamara Stompson."

"Me?" Tamara squealed. "Really? How do you know?"

"He asks about you a lot." Besides, I added mentally, every guy has a crush on you. I nudged Peebles with my foot. She meowed in protest, then got up. Stepping onto my stomach, she tucked herself, sphinxlike, onto my belly. "So, what do you think?"

Giggling, Tam admitted, "He's okay. Kind of short. But there's lots of cute guys at Cleveland. Especially the older ones."

"Mmm," I said, even though I didn't think Justin was short at all. He was at least two inches taller than Tam. But it didn't seem worth arguing about, so I just changed the subject. "Guess who I talked to at boys' soccer practice today."

"Who?"

"Chris Gibson."

"Ohmygosh," Tam said. "Did he ask you for a pen?"

"Ha, ha."

Tamara giggled. "Just kidding. So—was he as cute as ever?"

"Supernova," I said, grinning. Peebles stared at me with calm yellow eyes, as if this conversation was way below her intelligence. Which maybe it was. "He's my friend Jack's cousin."

"Who's Jack? Is he cute, too?"

I laughed. "Well, I guess you could say that, but Jack is a girl. She's on the soccer team."

"Oh," Tam said. "A Sweaty Betty." That was what a lot of kids called the Tigers, but there was something about the way Tam said it that kind of made it sound like she was wrinkling her nose or something.

"*I*'m a Sweaty Betty," I said, kind of hurt.

"Well, yeah, but you're normal."

I stared at the receiver. "What's that supposed to mean?"

"Oh, nothing. It's just that all of those Cleveland soccer girls are, like, superjocks."

"That's why they win," I told her.

"I guess." Tam didn't sound convinced.

Just then, there was a knock at my door and Mom stuck her head into my room. "Oof," I said

as Peebles jumped off my belly and darted through between Mom's feet and into the hallway. "Hold on," I said to Tam.

"Sweetie, dinner is in five minutes," Mom said.

"Okay," I told Mom. "I'll be down in a sec. Tam?" I said into the phone. "I've gotta go. Dinner."

"Okay," Tam said. "I'll see you tomorrow."

"Okay, see you on the bus," I said. "Bye." I clicked the OFF button and hauled myself off the bed toward the bathroom. But I paused in front of my bookcase.

I couldn't stop myself. I pulled down the old LFC notebook. I had to flip through it for a minute, but eventually I found the page I was looking for.

Reasons Allie likes Chris G.
1. His blue eyes
2. His blond hair
3. He has a nice smile
4. Seems smart

I snapped closed the notebook and put it back on the shelf. All of those things are still true, I told myself. Chris was exactly the same.

And so was my crush on him.

- 5 -

pre•dork•a•ment \ pre-'dork-a-ment \ *n* : a real dilemma—but only if you're a nerd—*see* NORK

Orren's eyebrows drew together in concentration as he used the small dropper to drip ammonia into a beaker of lavender-colored cabbage water. It was Thursday, lab day, and we were studying acids and bases. I sighed as he stared at our experiment, as though he thought he could make it do something interesting using the power of his mind.

But all that happened was that the liquid turned yellowish. Orren dipped a piece of pH paper into the liquid. Green. "Write that down," he commanded.

I rolled my eyes and obeyed. I let Orren do the labs because he was good at them, even though it drove me crazy that he was so slow and perfect about it. I was way too impatient to do the experiments correctly. Like when we had to study

polymers. I just dropped the sodium borate and the guar gum in the water and mixed it all up without waiting the exact amount of time between steps. When Orren complained, I'd said, "Hey—it's only science. It's not an exact science." Which Orren found infuriating.

After that particular experiment—which ended up producing liquidy goo instead of slime—Orren announced that he would do the labs, and I could write them up, which was fine with me. I had an easier time with writing than Orren did. He labored over every sentence, while words flowed out of me.

Just then, there was a giggle at the front of the class. Renee had put a piece of litmus paper in her mouth, and Tam was laughing as though that were the funniest thing that she had ever seen in her entire life. I glared at Renee, hoping that litmus paper tasted like barf.

Do I sound annoyed?

It just didn't seem fair that Tam and Renee were lab partners. After all, they already had four other classes together.

"Allie?" Orren peered at me from under

his Brillo-pad hair. "It's another base."

I was so zoned out that for a minute I actually thought he was talking sports. Then I remembered where we were, and scribbled the latest results on my notebook paper.

"Okay, that's it," Orren said. "I'll clean up while you get the results together."

I nodded and started copying what we had done onto a fresh sheet of paper as Tam let out a laughing shriek. Renee had dripped some goopy liquid soap on Tam's arm.

"Ladies," Mrs. Larsen said sharply, "do I need to separate you two?"

Hope squiggled through my body like milk through a curly straw. If they got separated, maybe I could be Tam's lab partner.

Tam and Renee looked sheepish, and muttered "No, ma'am." I noticed that they were only on vinegar, the fourth experiment in the lab. There were twelve in all. They were going to have to hurry if they wanted to finish.

There was a soft knock on the door, and Mr. Sykes, our social studies teacher, poked his head in. "Hi, everyone!" he said brightly. "I hope you

don't mind if I borrow your teacher for a few minutes. Linda?"

"Sure, Clarence," Mrs. Larsen said. I've always thought that hearing your teachers use each others' first names is completely freakish. "Class, when you're finished, please place your labs face down on my desk." Then Mrs. Larsen stepped out of the room.

Once she was gone, the class was completely silent . . . for about ten seconds. The sound built almost like an avalanche—the way the first little rock tumbles down, then the next, then a few more. . . . Suddenly the whole class was chattering away, and David Cho and Randy Jefferson had gone up to the blackboard to play hangman.

From my seat behind them, I could see that Tam and Renee were looking at a magazine. Orren was nearby at the slop sink, scrubbing out our beakers. Oh, well, I thought. It's probably better that Orren doesn't want to play games or act stupid. At least I'll get this lab done. I put the finishing touches on it just as Orren got back to our table.

"Basic Training for Acids," he read aloud over my shoulder. "Good title." He scanned the rest of the lab, and nodded. "Looks great."

I smiled dubiously. "You think?" I'd sort of expected him to wig out when he saw the title. But Orren had loosened up lately.

"Sure." Orren nodded at the paper. "Hand it in."

I smiled at him, and he smiled back. That was when I noticed something weird. I'd always thought that Orren's eyes were brown, but they weren't. They were dark green. It's just that you couldn't really tell, because his frizzy hair hid half of his face.

Plucking the paper from his hand, I headed up the center aisle toward Mrs. Larsen's desk. Just before I reached it, someone grabbed my hand.

"Hey!" I said, smiling brightly when I saw it was Tam. She didn't look happy. "What's wrong?"

"Allie, there's only three minutes until the bell," Tam said.

"I know." I looked over at Renee. "Do

you guys need some help with the lab?"

"We don't have time," Tam said. "I don't know what happened, we just, kind of lost track of time, and . . ." Tam glanced at the paper in my other hand.

Renee cut to the chase. "Can we borrow your lab?"

I stood there for a moment, feeling like something heavy had just whizzed past my head. Borrow my lab? She meant *copy*. My jaw tightened. Tam knows I've hated cheating ever since Tommy Samuelson copied my spelling test in the third grade, and when we both flunked, he went around telling everyone that I couldn't spell. Part of me couldn't believe she was even asking. Plus, I felt kind of mad. I mean, I'd been working all period—having a very boring time—while they'd been goofing around having fun. I ask you, is that fair?

Besides, this wasn't just my lab. It was Orren's lab, too. I didn't feel like I could just hand it over.

"Please," Tam whispered. She glanced at the door. "Before she comes back."

I looked down at Tam's hand in mine. Our fingers were interlaced, and our friendship rings were right next to each other. Oh man, I thought, what's the huge predorkament here? Just hand over the lab.

Glancing back at Orren, I saw that he was busily copying down the homework assignment. "Just don't let anyone see," I whispered as I slipped Tam the paper.

"Thanks," Tam said gratefully. "I owe you."

Renee smiled at me.

I headed back to my seat, feeling kind of glad that I'd handed over the paper. It was weird how doing the wrong thing actually kind of felt like doing the right thing.

I guess that's the way things work in middle school.

———◆———

an•em•o•ne \an-'em-o-nee\ *n* : someone who isn't exactly an enemy, but is just sort of hanging out, waiting to sting you

"Hey!" I said as I slid my lunch tray across the table next to Tam's.

"Allie!" Tam grinned, gesturing to the seat

next to hers. "Thanks so much for saving us today."

"Yeah, be sure to thank Orren for me," Renee said with a smirk. "And tell him that I think he's hot." Renee was really starting to annoy me. No *Thank you, Allie*, just a big old insult for my lab partner. She's such an anemone. "Why are you laughing?" Renee asked Tamara, who was giggling so hard that I thought ketchup was going to come out of her nose. "I'm totally serious. He's gorgeous. Stop laughing, I mean it!"

Tam was losing it.

"Hey, Tam," Renee went on. "Maybe we could double date. Me and Orren, and you and your boyfriend over there." She nodded toward this really overweight guy in the corner. He was eating green Jell-O. I don't know, something about the scene made me laugh a little, too, even though I felt bad about it.

"I don't know," Tam said, catching her breath. "I'm thinking of breaking up with him. I'm totally crushing on that guy at the head of the cafeteria line."

Renee and I both turned to look. The

guy was tall and skinny, and when he stepped forward, his movements were all jerky, like a marionette.

"Ooh, didn't I see him in *CosmoGIRL* magazine?" Renee joked, plucking a French fry from my plate. "As one of the Top Hotties? Hey, Allie, maybe you should go for Mr. Forks and Knives, over there."

I didn't even turn around—I knew who she was talking about. I could feel the smile wavering on my face. When we took our empty trays to the back of the cafeteria, there was a guy who collected our silverware and dropped it into a washtub. He had a flat face and close-set, almond-shaped eyes. I'm pretty sure he had Down syndrome.

I don't know; it seemed really wrong to make fun of him. But Tam and Renee were laughing, and I knew that if I said anything, I'd just sound like some kind of public-service announcement and they would tell me to chill out.

"I think I need a soda," I said, wanting to get out of there.

"Let us know if you spot any hotties," Renee said as I stood up.

"Yeah, don't go stealing our boyfriends!" Tam added.

I smiled weakly and headed toward the vending machine, hoping that they would have changed the subject by the time I got back. I arrived at the snack machines just in time to see Jack nearby with Elena . . . and Chris in all of his gorgeousness. I stopped in my tracks and nearly turned right around, but I was a split second too late.

"Allie!" Elena had spotted me.

"Hey!" Jack chimed in, waving. "Over here!"

"Oh, hey!" I said, as though I totally hadn't realized they were there. My heart was pounding in my ears. Act casual, I told myself as I walked over to their table. "Hey, guys," I said to Jack and Elena. "Hey, Chris," I said, all cool, like I just happened to remember his name.

"Sit down," Jack urged.

I plopped into a chair next to her, and directly across from Chris. I had an incredible view of his gorgeous blue eyes. Say something brilliant! I commanded myself. But what?

"Think you'll start in the game next week?" Jack asked me.

"I hope," I confessed, "but I doubt it. There's plenty of girls better than me."

"Lies," Elena said. "Allie's a great player," she informed Chris.

A burning sensation crept up the back of my neck, and I knew I was blushing again. That's a big problem for me. I blush all the time. "So, what's for lunch?"

"Don't ask me," Jack said, "I'm only eating the Tater Tots."

"They're just an excuse to eat ketchup," Elena said. "My favorite vegetable."

I turned to Chris. "Those fish sticks look delicious," I said sarcastically. They were covered in green glop. "Enjoying them?"

"Not really," Chris said seriously. "They aren't that good."

I sat there for a minute, wishing that I had a napkin to hide behind. He didn't get my joke, I realized. He must think I'm an idiot. And then I felt myself blushing again.

I opened my mouth to explain that I was

kidding, but Elena jumped in and said, "Person-ally, I really like to *savor* the cafeteria food. The complicated flavors are really . . ." She trailed off, searching for the right word.

"Revolting?" Jack guessed.

"That's it," Elena said, nodding.

"Like the desserts, for example," I agreed, joining the joke. "It takes a refined palate to enjoy just how bad butterscotch pudding can be."

Everyone cracked up, except for Chris. "I like the pudding," he said.

Oh. My. GOD! My jokes were bouncing off him like bullets off of Superman's chest! I felt like such an utter nork. Just then, the bell rang. I looked up at the clock, thinking, Fire drill? But no—lunch was over. I'd spent the whole time chatting with Jack and her gang—I hadn't even eaten anything! "I'll see you guys later," I said, shoving back my chair.

"See you," Jack said.

I hurried across the cafeteria to collect my backpack. I couldn't wait to tell Tam that I had just spent all of lunch hanging with Chris! But when I got back to the lunch table, Renee and Tam had

already left. Only my tray and my book bag were there.

And to make things worse, someone had eaten all of my fries. Renee sure does have a big mouth, I thought bitterly, in more ways than one.

style-o-me•ter \\'stile-o-mee-tr\ *n* : a measurement indicating just how fashionable you are—or, you know, are not

Soccergrl228: Hey! What ru up 2 2day?

tamtam14: family junk. Grandma. U?

Soccergrl228: oh, same. Have to help Mom with some stuff. Call me later?

tamtam14: won't be back until 2nite. Call u tomorrow?

Soccergrl228: cool. Bye. Have fun at Grandma's!

I stared at the blinking cursor on my computer monitor, feeling oddly empty, like a toothpaste tube that's been all squeezed out. It was Saturday, and I had nothing to do. There wasn't even anyone I could call. It seemed too weird to call some of my old friends from elementary school. Especially since it was so last minute. I couldn't see myself calling Julie or Mandy and saying, "Hey, I know we

haven't talked since before the summer, but I was wondering if you wanted to go see a movie in half an hour." The only person I could be that last minute with was Tam, because we spent almost every Saturday together. We didn't even have to make plans. Those were the plans.

But not today. Peebles, who was standing on my windowsill, let out a jaw-breaking yawn and then stretched until she was about a yard long, with her butt in the air. Then she sat down and gazed out the window. She looked as bored as I felt.

"I guess it's just you and me," I said to the cat. "And my school books." Oh, man, I thought. Am I seriously considering doing schoolwork on a Saturday? That's just sad.

I laced my fingers together and rested my chin on them, feeling a strange sense of cold anger in my stomach—as if I'd swallowed a whole Popsicle. I wasn't really sure why, though. Tam couldn't help it if she had to go visit her grandma. I was mad at myself—mad that I hadn't checked to make sure we had plans. But I was also kind of mad at Tam. She should have told me that she

wasn't going to be around. I felt kind of blown off.

"Allie?" Mom poked her head into my room.

"Yeah?" I didn't pick up my head from my desk.

Mom held up her keys and gave them a jingle. "I was going to go to the mall. I need a new skirt. Is there anything you need?"

I thought for a minute. "Some new cleats?" The sole on one of my old ones was starting to separate from the front of the shoe. It had tripped me up in practice a couple of times, and we had our first game next week.

"You want to come with me?" Mom asked.

I shrugged. "Sure," I said. "Just give me a minute."

Mom smiled, like she was really surprised. She knows that going to the mall is my idea of torture. But what the heck? I didn't have anything else to do . . . aside from social studies. "Take your time," Mom said. "I'll be downstairs."

I peeled off my pjs and went to wash my face and brush my teeth, deciding to skip the shower. It's Saturday, what do I need to be clean for? I

thought, although I did go for some deodorant. I pulled on my oldest, softest jeans and my navy Yale sweatshirt (a present from Dad, who went there), slipped on my scuffed brown clogs, and yanked my hair into a bushy ponytail. Good enough, I decided as I looked in the mirror. You know, for the mall.

———◦———

fash•ion pas•sion \fash-un-pash-un\ *n* : the kind of mania that comes over you when you are trying on clothes in a dressing room, and convinces you that you should immediately buy everything that isn't nailed down

The mall was just starting to get busy as Mom and I walked in at the second level. We started out in one of Mom's favorite boutiques. I waited in an overstuffed chair while Mom tried on a few skirts. She looked great in everything, of course. Mom is funny, because she's kind of a casual person, but she has a lot of dress-up clothes. She always looks really nice, even when she's just wearing her yoga pants and a fleecy pullover. And whenever she has to meet people for work, she gets dressed up in suits and high heels with a matching purse and

junk like that. It's almost like she was born with some good-clothes gene, or something. Tamara is the same way. I'm not.

I looked down at my old sweatshirt and ancient jeans that hadn't been washed in about three weeks. This is what I mean, I thought. This is my favorite outfit.

"What do you think of this, Allie?" Mom held out a sweater knit from blue and purple chunky yarn. "Want to try it?"

"Okay." Standing up, I yanked off my sweatshirt and pulled the sweater over my T-shirt. It was so soft—like being wrapped in a baby blanket, or a cloud, or something.

"That looks great." Mom spun me, so I could see myself in the full-length mirror.

"Wow," I said. The sweater did look good. I usually wear really baggy clothes, but this was a little more form-fitting—just enough so that you could see my waist. It had a V-neck and bell sleeves, and the color made my hair look more vibrant, and my brown eyes look really rich.

It's funny, I thought. This is the kind of sweater that Tam would wear.

I looked over at Mom, who was now frowning at my jeans. "I really like this sweater, Mom," I told her.

"Great—sold. Allie, sweetheart . . . maybe we should get you some more new clothes." Mom lifted her eyebrows, like she half expected me to tell her to get lost.

I turned back to face myself in the mirror, taking in my faded jeans with the hole in the knee and my scuffed-up shoes that looked like they'd been run over by a tractor. I was scoring about a negative one zillion on the style-o-meter. "You think I should get *new* clothes, when I've already got great outfits like this one?" I joked.

The edges of Mom's eyes crinkled up into a smile.

"Okay," I said, pulling the sweater over my head. "Let's do some shopping."

"I can't believe you talked me into buying a skirt," I said as Mom and I walked out of store number five zillion, three hours later.

"Two skirts," Mom corrected.

"Ohmygosh," I said, peering down at the

shopping bags in my hands. "I'd forgotten about the black one." Mom had helped me pick out a really pretty outfit—a hot-pink blouse and a long black skirt—for the sports banquet. I stopped in my tracks, biting my lip and feeling like a victim of fashion passion. "Maybe we should take one back," I said uncertainly.

Mom laughed. "The corduroy one isn't exactly a dress-up skirt."

"That's true," I admitted. I guess I was just feeling sort of overwhelmed by the sheer amount of stuff we'd bought. In addition to the two skirts and the blue sweater, I'd picked out a new pair of jeans, two funky pairs of pants—one pair of red plaid low-riders and a maroon velvet pair—two more sweaters, three shirts, a pair of chunky black boots, a completely cool pair of red suede sneaks, and yes, the cleats. Oh, and a new black backpack. We'd already had to go back to the car twice to dump stuff in the trunk.

"Okay," Mom said, scanning the stores nearby. "Is there anything else you need? A winter coat? Hats? A raincoat?"

Mom said something else, but suddenly her

voice blurred with the background noise of the busy mall. Because that was when I saw them. Tam and Renee. They were coming out of a store, giggling.

I froze.

"Allie?" Mom said, turning. She had walked a few steps ahead. "What's wrong?" She turned to where I was looking. "Isn't that Tam? Do you want to say hi?"

I felt light-headed, like I couldn't get enough air. I pressed my hand against my stomach, which felt nauseatingly hollow. "No," I said quickly.

Mom's eyebrows flew up.

"I—I don't want her to see my new clothes," I hedged. "I want to surprise her on Monday."

Mom looked like she didn't believe me, but I didn't feel like explaining that Tam had lied to me. Lied, so she could hang with Renee instead of me.

"It's okay," Mom said gently. We stood there for a moment, until Tam and Renee walked into another store. She wrapped an arm around my shoulder. "Let's go get some food. You'll feel better."

"Yeah," I mumbled, even though I wasn't

hungry anymore. The hollow feeling in the pit of my stomach stayed there.

Mom kissed me on the head. "It's okay," she whispered again into my ponytail.

But it wasn't.

———◦———

dis•pos-a-friend \ dis-'poze-a-frend \ *n* : someone easily tossed away, like a used Kleenex

I lay on my bed, absently stroking Peebles's fur. She was curled into a tight ball at my waist. Shopping bags were piled next to my bed, two of them propped on my desk chair. I hadn't unpacked a single thing. I couldn't motivate to move.

Why had she lied to me? I thought over and over. Why had she ditched me? Had I done something? Said something? Or was it just that Tam liked Renee better?

I remembered the time Janine Jackson had called me a pig in fourth grade. Tam got the whole class on my side, and Janine finally apologized to me out by the swings, so everyone could hear.

That's what it was like—having Tam as my

best friend. I felt safe. But now, I felt kind of like a dispos-a-friend.

I held up my right hand. The blue friendship ring sat there as always. Pulling it off for a moment, I noticed how pale the skin was beneath the band. I hadn't taken it off since the day I first got it.

"We have to promise to wear these all the time," Tam had said the day we bought the rings. After we left the store, we went to our favorite spot in the park—the sunny side of the hill near the picnic tables. We were lying on our backs, looking up at the clouds. "Then, whenever we look at them, we'll think of each other."

I had looked at Tam. There was a blade of brilliant green grass caught in her curly black hair, but I didn't bother picking it out. It looked kind of pretty there. "We'll be friends forever," I said.

"Best friends," Tam agreed.

But now . . .

The phone rang, snapping me out of my trance. For a minute, I didn't move. Then I got this crazy idea that it might be Tam. A split-second image of how great it would be to say *Get lost*

89

flashed through my mind, so I put my ring back on my finger, hauled myself off my bed, and picked it up.

"Hello?"

"Allie? It's Jack."

Jack? I was so surprised that for a moment, I didn't say anything.

"From soccer," Jack explained.

I laughed. "I only know one girl named Jack," I said. "Sorry, I was just—in the middle of something. What's up?"

"Do you want to hang out in the park and kick the ball around?"

I heard a mental echo of Tam's voice from the time when I had told her about Jack and she had said, "Oh, a Sweaty Betty," like she was sneering, and for a moment I hesitated. But then I decided, Oh, that's stupid. You're going to sit around alone because Jack is a jockissima? Jack is fun and I like soccer, and Tam is busy hanging with her snobalicious friend, anyway. "Uh—sure," I said finally. "When?"

"How soon can you get there?" Jack replied.

———◦———

bore•chid \ 'bor-kid \ *n:* someone who looks good, but doesn't have much personality—they're just there for show, like an orchid, or some other pretty flower

Twenty minutes later, I jogged onto the playing field at the edge of the park. I had exchanged my scrungy jeans for an equally scrungy pair of shorts, and was wearing my new cleats.

"Allie!"

I turned toward the voice and was surprised to see Justin rolling toward me on his bike. "Hey!" I called. "What are you doing here?"

"Meeting up with you to play some soccer," Justin said, squeaking to a stop. "Chris called me." Justin jutted his chin and I looked behind me.

Sure enough, Jack was walking toward me . . . with Chris, Sally, and Tom Fine. I didn't really know Tom, but I knew who he was—he'd been Chris's best friend for years. He was kind of cute, but he never really talked much—I'd always thought he was kind of a borechid. What is he doing here? I thought as the group headed toward me and Justin. What is *Chris* doing here?

My heart nearly stopped. What is the deal

with today? I wondered frantically. Is this National Don't Tell Allie Stuff Day, or something? Miserably, I thought about all of the cute outfits piled on the floor of my room. *And Chris has to see me in my holy, moldy Yale sweatshirt?* Not that I would really have showed up to play soccer in my new maroon velvet pants, but still. I might have combed my hair.

Jack waved and trotted over. "How about girls against guys?" she called.

Justin shrugged. "Why don't we mix it up?"

Jack grinned. "Okay—Sally, Chris, and Allie against you, me, and Tom."

"Fine." Justin grinned. "As long as Allie doesn't mind getting beat."

My brain had barely processed anything after the words *Chris and Allie*, but I managed to trot onto the field after Chris.

"I'll be goalie," Sally volunteered.

"I'll cover defense," Chris said. "Allie, you can handle the top of the field."

Great. I needed the practice, anyway. I was starting to accept the fact that Coach Connors wasn't going to switch my position. Her two star

strikers had graduated the year before, and she needed a fast runner in that position. Jack started out with the ball, and shot a quick pass to Justin, who headed toward our goal. Diving in, Chris made a quick steal, then side-kicked the ball to me. Nice move. I dribbled it up the field, trying not to wonder whether the way I ran looked stupid or not.

Chris cut away from Justin, and was open for a split second. But I felt really weird kicking it to him . . . I don't know, like I didn't want him to know that I was paying such close attention to him, or something. So I kicked the ball toward the goal.

Justin slapped it away like he was shooing a fly from a piece of pie. Easy.

"What was that?" Chris demanded. "I was open!"

"Sorry!" I called, wincing. Okay, he's your teammate, I told myself. You're *supposed* to be paying attention to him.

Justin tossed the ball back into play, and Jack took it. After a while, I managed to ease into the game. Chris became just another player, almost

like a shadow. In the end, I gave him a few solid passes, and managed to score a point on Justin— the only point of the game.

"This stinks," Justin complained once the game was over. "I demand a rematch."

"Let's go for another half an hour," Jack suggested.

Sounds good to me, I thought, as I snuck a glance at Chris. Personally, I could play all day, as long as he was on my team!

I wracked my brain for something clever to say as Chris and I took the field again, but drew a total blank. Oh, well, I thought. Does it really matter? Chris and I are playing soccer!

That was way better than asking me for a pen.

- 7 -

Dweeb•o•saur•us rex \ 'dweeb-o-saur-us 'reks \ *n*
[Fr. Latin *dweebus maximus* major loser and *rex* king]
1: emperor of the nerds. **2:** a geek large enough and
out-of-control enough to inspire fear in others

I walked down the hall thinking, What was I
thinking? My stupid new corduroy skirt was ruin-
ing my morning.

I should've changed. I knew it the minute I
walked into the kitchen. Lionel took one look at
me and nearly snorted a Froot Loop out of his
nose.

"Lionel!" Mom glared at him. Then she
smiled at me. "Allie, you look so pretty!"

Lionel coughed, still laughing through his
breakfast cereal.

"That's it," I said, turning to hurry back up
the stairs. I should've known that wearing a skirt
would make me look stupid.

"No—wait," Mom called. "Allie, you have to
be at the bus stop in three minutes."

I checked my watch. She was right. I was stuck in this dumb outfit. I mean, I'd really liked this outfit when I bought it, and I couldn't wait to put it on right away. But now it was looking like I'd made a major mistake.

"Oh, are we going to school?" Lionel asked. "I thought maybe we were going to church."

"They wouldn't let you in without an exorcism," I snapped, grabbing an apple.

"At least I'm not dressed like it's Halloween," Lionel shot back.

"Right—that's just your normal face, I forgot."

"Kids." Mom gave us this *Stop it right now!* frown. "It's late."

I sighed, and gave Mom a kiss on the cheek. Then I grabbed my lunch and my new black backpack and headed out the door.

Lionel and I didn't speak on the way to the bus stop. Which was fine with me. My stomach was squirming around like the inside of a dormant volcano that's about to erupt.

Wait a minute. Did I just think that? Whoa. That was very Orren.

Anyway, my stomach was queasy. I hadn't talked to Tam all weekend. She had never called after she went to see her "grandmother." I was kind of hoping to see her at the bus stop so we could make up and she could say something nice about my skirt so I wouldn't feel like such a Dweebosaurus rex, but she wasn't there.

Tam still wasn't there when the bus chugged and hissed to the curb. I trudged aboard slowly, hoping she would show up. I almost told the driver to wait, but then I remembered that I was mad at her, and just drooped into my seat and glared out the window.

The bus started to pull away, and I bit my lip. Could Tam be sick? Maybe something awful had happened. . . .

Oh, what do you care? another part of my brain screamed. Let her miss the bus.

But my heart was beating hard, and when someone banged on the side of the bus, I heaved a sigh of relief. I arranged my face into a frown as we jerked to a stop and the doors hissed open. I wanted Tam to know that I was mad.

"Thanks, Mrs. Lipscomb!" a cheery voice

called as the late passenger scrambled aboard. "I could never make it to school without you."

I rolled my eyes. It wasn't Tam. It was Justin.

"Hey!" Justin said brightly as he sort of flopped into the chair in front of me. "Where's Tam?"

"Good question."

"Oh my God," Justin said, eyeing my outfit. "Is it Picture Day?"

"I just felt like wearing a skirt," I snapped. "Why is that such a big deal?"

Justin held up his hands in mock surrender. "Sorry, sorry. It's just not something you see, you know . . . ever. It looks . . . nice," he added lamely, but it was too late. I snorted.

He sank into his chair in confusion and I scowled out the window for the rest of the ride.

So those were the cheerful memories of my morning that flashed through my brain as I walked down the hall toward my locker.

Someone put a light hand on my shoulder, and I jumped.

"Ohmygosh, Allie!" Tam said, spinning me around and giving me a huge smile. "You look

great! Wow—cool new backpack," she added, checking it out. "I almost didn't recognize you."

Ugh. Was that supposed to be a compliment? "Thanks," I snapped. "Missed you on the bus."

"Oh, Renee and I are carpooling now," Tam explained. "Her mom takes us to school, and my mom picks us up after practice. It's way better than the bus," she added, rolling her eyes.

Thanks for telling me! I thought. Rage started to bubble in my chest. "Hmm," I grunted, fuming. "So—did you have a good time with your grandma this weekend?"

"Yeah," Tam said smoothly. "So, uh, where did these clothes come from?"

I folded my arms across my chest. "From the mall," I said, my voice dripping poison, "on Saturday."

I think I've told you that I blush at basically anything. Well, Tam is the opposite. She never blushes . . . but she was blushing now. "Oh." Her voice was a squeaky sigh.

"Yeah. I saw you there." My voice was wavering, but I forced myself to go on. "Why didn't you just tell me the truth?" I swallowed

hard, annoyed with myself. I wanted to be angry, but now that Tam was standing in front of me, I just felt hurt.

Tam turned an even brighter shade of red. "It's just—I know you hate the mall," she said in a rush. "You know, you usually just wear whatever and dress like a guy—"

"Thanks," I snapped. Accidiss? I wondered. Or deliberadiss?

Tam winced. "Sorry," she said. "But, you know—what I mean." She cleared her throat and went on. "So when Renee asked if I wanted to go shopping, I thought, well, I'd better not tell Allie because she might feel like she has to come along, and then she'll be miscrable. So I just made up a story. . . ." Tam's voice trailed off. "I was worried you'd be mad."

"I was mad," I told her. "I am mad."

Her dark eyes clouded over. "Well, I'm *sorry*, but you hate shopping."

I ask you—is that the point? But I didn't have time to say that out loud, because the bell rang.

"Fine," I said. The truth was, I just wanted this conversation to be over so that things could

go back to normal with me and Tam. "Apology accepted," I added, even though I wasn't really sure that Tam had apologized.

"Good." Tam's serious face broke into a smile. "And you really do look great."

Not like a guy? I thought. But I didn't say that. What I said was, "See you in science."

Tam nodded. "See you."

Now I only had four minutes to get to my locker and homeroom. I turned to hurry down the hall, but just as I did, the world jolted. Literally. Flailing like a crazed Tickle Me Elmo doll, I tripped and fell face-first onto the fake-granite hall floor.

I looked behind me accusingly to get a look at the guilty foot. Someone's toes were about to get stepped on.

"Allie? I'm so sorry!" Chris, who had been crouching to peer into his bottom locker, stood up and rushed over to help me. "Sorry about that," he repeated as I straightened my clothes. "Jack always says that I have huge feet." He gave me an apologetic smile.

My heart went bonkers. "Oh, well," I said

breathlessly, "maybe you have a future as a clown."

Chris looked confused. "I'm really more into math and stuff."

I giggled nervously as my face flushed. Didn't he realize that was a joke?

"I like your sweater," Chris said.

Say thank you! I commanded myself. But the words wouldn't come out.

The one-minute warning rang.

"Well, I guess I'll see you later." Chris turned and headed down the hall.

"See you." My voice was a whisper, and I knew Chris hadn't heard me as he disappeared into his homeroom. Oh, well, I thought as I turned and hurried toward my class. At least he liked my outfit.

———◆———

Mil•ky Way \'mil-kee 'way\ *n* : someone who looks hard on the outside, but actually has a soft marshmallow center

"So the pH blah-blahdy-blah . . ." Mrs. Larsen was droning on once again. Her voice has this strange quality; sometimes it sounds like a vacuum cleaner.

My eyes were open, but I could hardly concentrate on her words.

Orren, on the other hand, was staring at her like she was spewing the secrets of the universe, writing down every word.

I tuned back in once Mrs. Larsen looked up at the clock. "We only have a few minutes left, so I'm going to pass back the labs from the other day. Most of you did very well." Picking up a stack of papers, Mrs. Larsen started walking around the room. She whispered something to each pair of students as she handed over the papers.

I drummed my fingers on the black marble lab table, feeling antsy. "Nice work," she whispered as she handed the paper back to Stephen and Vickie, who sat in front of us.

I sat up straighter, eager to see how we had done.

The smile dropped from Mrs. Larsen's face as she handed me the paper. "Please see me after class," she said in this weird robot voice.

My stomach soured. Oh, no.

Orren frowned and looked at me. "What did she say?" he asked.

"She said we should see her after class," I told him. I flipped over the paper, and there it was. A big red zero.

"Zero?" Orren's face turned white. "My parents are going to kill me."

I could feel myself blushing like a tomato. I swallowed hard, but I just couldn't bear to tell him that this was all my fault.

Why do I have to be so lousy at cheating when everyone else is so good at it?

The bell rang and Orren and I trudged to the front of the room while everyone started buzzing and thumping books closed, gathering things for their next class. Renee and Tam were already standing by Mrs. Larsen's desk. Tam looked as humiliated as I felt, but Renee's green eyes glittered like something cold and hard—a marble, maybe. Or a glacier.

Mrs. Larsen crossed her arms and sat back in her chair. "I have two identical labs," she said, looking at us, each in turn, "from two different lab tables."

Orren looked at me sharply. I looked at the floor.

"Well . . . we all did the same experiment," Renee hedged.

"Yes," Mrs. Larsen agreed, "but the wording of the labs is exactly the same. Down to the funny title."

"Funny title?" Tam repeated.

I looked up, and Tam's dark eyes stabbed into me.

"One of you, it seems, has a sense of humor," Mrs. Larsen said. "But since I don't know who copied whom, I have to give everyone a zero."

There was a beat of silence while we all let this sink in. A zero. As ten percent of our grade. Now the best any of us could hope for in the class was a B. I could almost feel the grade calculation happening in Orren's mind.

"Mrs. Larsen, isn't there something we can do?" I asked. "Some extra credit?"

"I don't offer extra credit to some students and not others."

"Well, maybe you could give everyone the chance to improve their lab grades," Orren suggested in a voice that was surprisingly calm.

Giving him a sideways look, Mrs. Larsen heaved a sigh.

Oh, please, please, I begged silently. Pleaseplease—pleasepleaseplease. Just let me do this and I will dedicate my life to stamping out cheating—

Finally, Mrs. Larsen pursed her lips, and nodded. "Okay," she said slowly. "Redo the lab by the end of the week, and I'll regrade it. But, in your cases, I'm taking twenty points off for being late," she added. "That means, even if it's perfect, the top grade you can get will be an eighty."

I expected Orren to protest that he hadn't even been involved in the cheating, but instead, he just said, "No problem."

"Thanks, Mrs. Larsen," Renee said.

"Yeah, thanks," I agreed. That was what I liked about Mrs. Larsen—she seemed like a toughie, but she was really just a Milky Way.

"You'd better hurry," the science teacher said. Students were humming past the door out in the hallway. "You'll be late for your next class."

Tam and Renee, who had already grabbed their backpacks, turned and left the room, but Orren and I had to scurry back to our lab table to collect our stuff.

"I'm so sorry," I whispered as I shoved my book into my backpack.

Orren didn't reply. He didn't even look at me.

I don't know why that bugged me. I mean, why should I care if Orren Kendall is mad at me? He's just a total nork who I got stuck with as a lab partner, right?

Right?

Then again, it was totally my fault that he had almost got a zero on a major lab. And I did feel really bad about it. I poked his arm, and he looked up.

"Orren," I said, "I am really sorry."

His green eyes were cloudy. "You gave it to them."

"Yeah," I admitted. "But they really needed it—they were about to get a—"

Okay, at least I had enough of a brain to stop myself before I said, "zero."

"Tam is my best friend," I finished lamely. Isn't she? I wondered. To tell the truth, I wasn't so sure anymore.

Orren pressed his lips together. Then he

hiked his backpack up onto his shoulder, and the anger seemed to drain from him. "It's okay," he said finally. "I probably would have done the same thing."

Suddenly, Orren looked kind of lonely. I felt sad as the meaning of his words hit me. He would have done the same thing . . . if he had any friends. "So, uh, do you want to meet up after school?" I suggested. "To work on the lab?"

Orren hesitated. "I have a soccer game today. So do you."

"Oh, right," I said. I'd completely spaced it. "Okay, how about tomorrow—after practice. Whoever gets out first can meet the other."

"Okay," Orren said hesitantly. Then again, more sure, "Okay."

I glanced at my watch. We were about to be seriously late. "Okay, see you," I said quickly and buzzed out the door.

"Allie!" Tam whispered furiously as I lunged out of the room. She had been waiting for me just outside the door. Grabbing my arm, she dragged me over to the lockers.

Orren glanced at us quickly as he raced out

of the room, but he kept on rolling toward our next class—history. I only had about ten seconds to get there, too. I could hear Tam's apology later. "Hey, look I gotta—"

"What were you thinking, putting a joke title on the lab?" Tam demanded.

I gaped at her, wondering if I'd just misheard. "What?"

"How was I supposed to know the title was a *joke*?" Tam hissed, her eyes flashing dangerously. "Why didn't you tell me that when you gave me the lab? Thanks to your sense of humor, Mrs. Larsen thinks we cheated, and Renee is really mad. God, Allie, why can't you just be normal?"

And then she walked away.

I tried to move, but I couldn't. I was too stunned. I just stood there, stuck in the ground like a streetlamp. Tam was mad—really mad. But this wasn't even my fault—it was hers! Still, I felt afraid. Tam was my best friend. Without her—what did I have? I was just a shadow. A ghost. A nothing walking between classes with no one.

The bell rang, snapping me out of my trance.

Great, I thought, starting to move. Now I'm late. And Mrs. Gibb made tardy students serve detention during lunch.

This day just kept getting better and better.

---

in•no•sense \'in-no-sens\ *n* : a question that is asked in an innocent tone of voice, but is really used to point out that what you're saying makes no sense at all

"Hey, sweetie," Mom said when I walked through the door later that night. "Good game?" She was sitting at the kitchen table, flipping through a recipe book. She does that sometimes—reads through recipes the way other people read novels.

"It was okay," I admitted as I plopped down in the chair across from hers. "We won." No thanks to me, though. Jack had scored the only goal. I looked down at the recipe Mom was reading, but my eyes barely registered the letters on the page. "So, uh, did anyone call for me?" I asked finally.

"Yeah," Mom said, and for a second I got this hopeful, fluttery feeling in my stomach until she added, "Dad called."

"Oh."

Mom lifted her eyebrows. I guess I'd sounded more disappointed than I'd meant to. "I mean, *oh!*" I corrected myself.

Mom closed her cookbook and looked at me. I squirmed. "Were you expecting another call?" she prompted.

"Not really," I said quickly.

"Mmm." Mom's gaze didn't shift. "It seems like Tam never calls anymore," she said finally.

"We're kind of in a fight," I admitted. "I think. I'm not exactly sure."

"Have you tried talking to her about it?" Mom asked gently.

"I can't just call her up and say, 'I'm mad at you,'" I snapped. I wasn't even sure why I was annoyed—I knew Mom was only trying to help. It's just that she was sounding a little like Coach Connors: be aggressive, be aggressive. Why do I always have to be the one who does all of the hard stuff? I wondered. "It's not that easy."

Mom nodded like she understood. "So, *not* talking to her is easier?" she asked.

I thought about it for a minute. That's so Mom. She uses this innosense act to make me

think. And now I had to confess that she had a point. "I guess not," I admitted. "It's just—it's so hard, you know?"

"Yeah," Mom said gently. "I know."

We were both silent for a while, and I could hear the seconds ticking by on the kitchen clock.

"I'd better call Dad back."

"Homework?" Mom prompted.

"Just a little," I admitted. "Can I call Dad first?"

"Of course," Mom said. She gathered up her books and stashed them away. "I'll be in the other room."

Getting up, I yanked the phone off the wall and punched in Dad's number.

"Hello?"

It was Marci's voice.

"Um, hi, Marci. It's Allie."

"Oh, hi, Allison," Marci said. Stress was giving her voice this tense twang. I could hear Daniel screaming in the background.

"How are you?" I asked. I always get into trouble if I just ask for Dad. I have to go through this charade of talking to Marci first.

"What?" Marci asked as Daniel's wailing grew louder. "I can't hear you."

"How are you?" I repeated, louder.

"Oh, fine," Marci snapped. "Look, I'm sorry but I can't talk now."

"Um . . . okay," I replied. "I was just returning—"

"Do you want to speak to your father?" Marci asked. Then, without waiting for my reply, she said, "Here you go."

"Bye. Good talking with—"

"Hello?" It was Dad. He must have been walking down the hallway, or something, because Daniel's screeching died away in the background.

"Hi, Dad," I said, taking a deep breath. Marci had really freaked me out—it was as if her stress had traveled directly into my ear through the phone wires, or something.

"Hi, Allison. How are things?"

"Ugh," I grunted.

"That bad?" Dad joked. "What happened?"

"Well, Tam and I are kind of in a fight," I admitted.

"I thought she was your best friend," Dad said.

That really bugged me. "She *is* my best friend," I insisted. "It's just—there was kind of this . . . misunderstanding."

"What about?"

I knew I couldn't tell Dad about the cheating, because he'd go Tilt-A-Whirl on me. "Well . . ." I hedged. "We both got bad grades on this science lab."

"How bad?" Dad asked.

"Well . . ." I hedged. "Right now it's a zero."

There was this big, fat, ugly silence until Dad said, "I see."

"But I can bring it up," I offered.

"Well, I hope you're going to do that."

I took a deep breath and thought, does he think I'm a total moron? "Of course I am."

"Because your grades are very important, Allison."

I rolled my eyes. "I know, Dad."

"You need to take this very seriously."

"I do take it seriously."

"Well, I think maybe you should be a little

more concerned about your science grade, and a little less worried about an argument with your friend."

I squeezed the phone tighter, regretting that I'd even brought it up. Once my dad gets something like this in his head, there's no getting it out. I mean, how could I make him understand that the grade was something I could fix, but that my friendship with Tam . . . well, I wasn't so sure? "Okay, Dad," I said finally. "Listen, I have to go do my homework, okay?"

"Isn't it a little late to be starting your homework?"

Grr! "I just have to finish up a few things. Give Daniel a kiss for me, okay?"

"All right, Allison. Let me know what happens in science."

"Okay. Night, Dad. Love you."

"Good night."

Sighing, I hung up. That conversation had stunk. I should have known better than to try to tell him about Tam. I really don't understand how Mom can seem to get the whole thing without my saying a word, while Dad doesn't get it no matter

how much I explain. I'll call him again after Mrs. Larsen regrades my lab, I decided. I grabbed my backpack and headed for the stairs.

Hey. At least my social studies textbook wasn't going to get on my back about my grades or about being my best friend. And I was pretty sure I could beat it at soccer.

That was something, right?

smile•ci•cle \'smile-si-kel \ *n* : a totally fake smile that gets frozen to your face and makes your cheek muscles hurt

I felt like a donkey, or some other pack animal, weighed down by my backpack and a sack full of clothes and soccer cleats as I made my way toward the boys' practice fields. I was still wearing my grass-stained practice clothes, but I had changed into normal sneakers.

As I rounded the rear of the science building, I saw that the guys were still out on the field, so I quickened my pace. Please please please, I begged silently, please don't let practice end before I get there. I scurried toward the fields while still trying to look as cool and nonchalant as possible.

I had been praying all through soccer practice that we would get out a little early so that I could meet Orren at the boys' fields. That way, I'd get to see Chris running around in his soccer shorts. I

squinted, and found him right away—he had the ball and was racing toward the goal.

A clammy chill passed over my body, and I felt like I'd stepped into a giant blob of Jell-O, or something. I caught my breath.

Cutting right, Chris took the shot. *Slam!* A rocket.

But not good enough. The goalie grabbed the ball as easily as if he were picking an orange off a tree. Man, I thought, nice hands.

Hey, I realized with a smile as the goalie kicked the ball back into play. That's Justin. I watched the ball bounce among the group of guys on the field, and I was amazed at how many of them I knew. Orren was out there, too. I smiled.

Orren had completely saved me in science class today. He'd been so intense about making sure that we both knew where and when to meet after school and what to bring that I barely had a chance to glance at Tam before class or after. Which was just as well. She'd spent the whole day ignoring me.

Hearing a giggle, I turned and saw two

girls sitting on the bottom step of the nearby bleachers. Curly black hair and glossy blond. Tam and Renee.

Suddenly, the blob of Jell-O that had held me rooted to my spot staring at Chris dissolved into a gooey, sticky mess. I felt nauseated.

This is kind of sick, but I'd actually been kind of glad that Mrs. Gibb had given me detention for being late the day before. That way, I could sit out lunch period in her classroom, rather than having to face Tam.

I guess I could have asked Jack if I could sit at her table, but I still felt kind of dumb doing that. I mean, it was one thing if she wanted to invite me. But I didn't want to look like some friendless loser in front of Chris.

I'd much rather look like a loser in detention.

But I couldn't let this go on forever. Tam and I had to make up eventually. Maybe I should try to talk to her, like Mom had said. . . .

I hesitated for another thirty seconds before I finally plastered a smilecicle on my face and decided to go over there.

"Hey, Tam," I said, climbing up the bleachers and sitting on the seat behind her. "Hey, Renee."

"Hi, Allie." Tam's voice was an empty puff, like a jelly doughnut with no jelly.

"Love your outfit," Renee said with this little smirk. Tam giggled.

"Oh, yeah," I said, blushing as I looked down at my dirty shorts and T-shirt. That's what I hate about Renee. She never says anything like, *You smell like a hairy armpit*, or *You're as ugly as a dinosaur's butt*, she just makes some kind of little comment so that you can't tell whether she likes you and is teasing you, or whether she hates your guts and is mocking you. And if you get all bent out of shape, she'll be like, "Chill out, I was just joking!"

"Are you here to see your boyfriend?" Renee asked.

Tam flashed her a warning look, and I was glad that she was finally annoyed by Renee. "Orren isn't my boyfriend. We're just going to the library to fix our lab."

"I wasn't talking about Orren," Renee shot back, giving her blond hair a toss. "I was talking

about Chris." She smiled, but only with one side of her mouth. "I can't believe you still like him, Allie. Do you still have your collection of little plastic horses, too?"

For a minute, I could feel the earth spinning in space. I opened my mouth to deny that I liked Chris, but it was too late—my face was red-hot. How did she know? I wondered. How could she have figured it out?

But the answer was staring me in the face. Tam had told her.

"It's funny that you still like him, Allie," Renee went on. "Because I don't think you're really his . . . type."

My face was burning so brightly that, looking back on it, I'm amazed that the people around me didn't end up with a nice tan. My eyes started to fill up, which only embarrassed me more. I couldn't believe I was almost crying because Renee knew about my crush. But it wasn't just that. I mean, okay, my crush on Chris was kind of hopeless. But it really hurt my feelings to think that Tam thought so, too—and that she and Renee had been laughing about it behind my back.

Just then, the coach's whistle blew, and I hauled myself off the bleacher seat. I had never been so grateful to be heading to the library in my life.

"Allie—" Tam called, but I didn't turn around.

———◦———

go Mup•pet \\'go 'mup-et\ *v* : to flail the arms wildly and let out a high-pitched scream, much like Kermit the Frog, Elmo, or Grover when they are spazzing out

"So how about, 'Acids Rock, Bases Rule'?" I suggested in my best library whisper. We had been working on our lab for about an hour, and we were almost done. A problem with Orren was that sometimes he kind of spaced out, and I had to repeat myself. Normally, that wouldn't have annoyed me, but I was still in a horrible mood over the Tamara thing. "Or we could go with, 'Covering the Bases.' Or maybe we shouldn't try to be funny at all. . . ."

Orren didn't reply. He was flipping through our textbook, trying to find more information on how pH was calculated.

I blew out an exasperated breath. "Your silence is very encouraging."

He still didn't say anything. I sighed, wondering whether his anger over our lab had finally kicked in. "Orren," I said. "Orren!"

Orren finally looked up. "Hmm? What? Were you saying something?"

The librarian looked over at us and frowned. Orren seemed to have forgotten he was in the library, and his voice was kind of loud.

I motioned for him to keep it down. "Are you okay?" I whispered. "You seem kind of out of it."

"Sorry." Orren shook his head. He sighed. "It's just that this is the first F I've ever gotten."

"On anything?"

Orren nodded.

I gaped at him. He'd never got an F. It didn't seem right. "You mean you've never flunked a pop quiz, or a homework assignment, or anything?"

Orren stared down at his textbook. "My parents freak out about my grades."

"Yeah . . . my dad is kind of like that."

"Really?" Orren looked surprised.

"But my mom always says that as long as I do my best, that's what's important."

"Nice mom."

"Yeah."

We sat in silence for a moment.

"You know the funny thing about getting this zero?" Orren asked suddenly, as though the thought had just occurred to him. "It really . . . it really wasn't that bad."

I smiled. "Don't get too used to it."

"Don't worry." Orren laughed, like the very thought was ridiculous. "It's just . . . I guess I thought my parents would totally lose it. But they didn't. I mean, they weren't happy. But they were okay."

I was actually kind of glad that Orren had told me about his parents. It sort of explained why he acted like the fate of the universe hung on each of our homework assignments, and why he would hiss "Yess!" and pump his fist every time he got a hundred on a quiz. It's amazing that you can sit right next to someone, and not ever really know what's going on in their brain.

Just then, a pair of hands covered my eyes, and someone with a fake French accent said, "Now you muz' guess 'oo eet ees."

"Pepe le Pew?" I suggested.

There were a few laughs, and someone said, "Close. Good guess."

That voice I knew. Jack. Which meant that the French voice had to be—"Elena."

"Jack, you gave it away," Elena griped as she pulled her hands away, then plopped into the seat next to mine. She grinned at Orren. "I'm Elena."

"Orren," he said.

"Orren, this is Jack," I said as she took the chair next to him.

"You play soccer with my cousin," Jack said.

"Yeah." Orren looked like he was shocked that she had noticed. "I see you after practice sometimes."

"What are you guys doing here?" I asked.

"Elena was over at my house," Jack explained. "Mom's dropping her off, but we're here to pick up Chris, since it's on the way."

"Speaking of . . ." Elena said, looking behind me.

I turned just in time to see Chris coming down the spiral staircase that led to the nonfiction section on the second floor. He smiled when he saw us. "Hey! It's the welcome wagon!"

"Minus the wagon," Elena joked.

I snuck a look at Chris. Jack was saying something, and his big blue eyes were fastened on her. He needed a haircut—one curl looped around the side of his ear, curling around his earlobe.

"—so are you, Allie?"

I snapped back to reality just in time to realize that everyone was looking at me. Jack had just asked me a question. "Uh, sorry," I admitted. "I was kind of on another planet for a minute. What?"

"I was just asking if we were all going to the sports banquet?" Jack repeated. "Coach Connors mentioned it at the end of practice."

"Oh, uh, sure," I said.

"I'll be there," Chris said, and my heart lurched like Frankenstein's monster. Thank God I said I'd be there! I thought. Maybe we'll all sit together!

"Okay, well, my mom's waiting, so we'd

better jet," Jack said. "See you later, Allie. Good meeting you, Orren."

"Bye," I said as Orren waved. I watched them leave for a minute. Well, I watched *Chris* leave. I couldn't tear my eyes away until the door closed behind him.

When I turned back, I saw that Orren was smirking at me.

I frowned. "What are you grinning at?"

He shrugged. "Nothing." He started flipping slowly through his science book, but he was still grinning.

I slapped my hand in the middle of his book so that he couldn't flip anymore. I waited until he looked up before I growled, "What?"

Orren lifted his eyebrows and sat back in his chair. "Someone has a crush," he said in this self-satisfied way.

He was so smug that it made me want to go Muppet on him. But I remained in control. "I don't know what you're talking about."

Orren leaned forward in his chair. "Look me in the eye and tell me that you don't like Chris."

I opened my mouth, but it was hopeless. "I hate you," I told him. "How could you tell?"

Orren shrugged. "Your eyes weren't following the conversation." He chuckled in this *I'm so smart* kind of way. Why did I have to get Sherlock Holmes as a lab partner? I wondered.

"Please don't tell."

"I never would," he said, all indignant, like the mere suggestion was an insult. "It's just funny . . . Chris doesn't really seem like your type."

I rolled my eyes, demanding, "Why does everyone keep saying that?"

"I have no idea," Orren admitted. "I don't even know what that means. But you just seem like you'd be weird together."

"I guess it's pretty hopeless," I admitted with a sigh.

"I didn't mean that—" Orren said, then stopped. "I don't know what I mean."

Silence settled over us.

"Okay," I said after a moment. "Let's finish the lab." I turned to our work, but a little worry mouse still gnawed at my heart. I looked Orren in the eye. "Promise you won't tell?"

"I promise," Orren repeated. His face was completely serious.

And for some reason, I believed him. It was really kind of depressing to think that I could trust Orren to keep a secret more than I could trust my own best friend.

pup•pet mas•ter \'puh-pet 'mas-ter\ *n* : someone who pulls all the strings and sometimes likes to jerk you around

"**M**om!" I shouted as I walked in the back door. "I'm h—"

"I'm right here, Allie," Mom said, and that was when I saw that she was sitting at the kitchen table . . . with Tam. Tam had a plate with half a brownie on it, and I was struck by how normal that seemed, and then I was struck by how weird it was that it should seem normal, because Tam hadn't been over to my house in weeks. She used to come over and hang out all the time . . . but that was last summer, last year. Not this year. Not since sixth grade.

"Hi, Allie," Tam said.

I dropped my backpack on the floor. "Hey."

There was this crushing silence, and Mom looked from my face to Tam's and then back again. "Well," she said finally, "Allie, I'll be upstairs if you

need me. Tam, it was great seeing you. Don't be such a stranger."

I was struck with this urge to say, *Yeah, Tam, don't be such a stranger.* But I just couldn't say it. I may have to be a striker on the soccer field, I thought, but I don't feel like striking right now.

Then Mom walked out of the room and we were alone.

I just stood there, leaning against the countertop, looking at Tam. I wasn't about to be the first one to speak. Mostly because I had no idea what I wanted to say.

"So," Tam said awkwardly, "did you get your lab done?"

"Yeah," I snapped. You did not come over here to ask to copy my lab, I thought, completely furious. If that's why you came over—

"Yeah, us too." Tam nodded, and looked back at her brownie. "It wasn't really that hard."

The adrenaline that had been pumping through my body left me feeling loose-limbed and light-headed. Well, at least she isn't here to cheat off my homework. "So—what are you doing here?" I asked.

Tam waited for a second. "Look, I'm sorry . . . about Renee."

Sorry that she's a complete witch? I thought. "What about her?"

"Just . . . she wasn't supposed to say anything," Tam said, her black eyes pleading. "I didn't mean to tell her about Chris, it just . . . slipped out."

"Is she going to go tell the whole school now?"

Tam shook her head. "I made her promise not to. She won't. I swear."

My chest felt tight. "She didn't have to be so mean about it," I said finally.

"She was just joking." Tam's voice was defensive.

Why are you letting Renee be your puppet master? I thought. But what I said was, "I didn't think it was funny."

Tam's eyes flashed darkly. "Well, she didn't mean anything by it," she insisted. "Besides, she has a point. You and Chris are kind of—"

I glared at her. "Kind of what?"

"It's just . . . he was never really more than a

dream, Allie," Tam said in this quiet voice, almost like she felt sorry for me. "Like having a crush on a movie star."

I knew what Tam was saying, but I thought she was wrong. Sure, Chris was older, but he *wasn't* a movie star. He was just a guy in our school. And he was someone that I hung out with . . . you know . . . sometimes. Kind of.

"I'm sorry." And Tam really did look sorry.

But that didn't make me feel any better.

Just to make the moment extra special, Lionel chose that second to walk into the kitchen. "Hey, Tamara," he said, stopping in his tracks when he saw her. "Long time no see." Turning quickly, I yanked open the fridge and peered inside so that he wouldn't see my eyes. Blinking hard, I grabbed the OJ, then kept my back to Lionel as I got a glass from the cupboard.

"Hey, Lionel," Tam replied. "What's new?"

"Not much. Ooh, look, Allie's actually using a glass," Lionel cracked. "Tam, have you been teaching Allie how to act normal?"

"Trying to," Tam said, and I swear, at that moment, I wanted to punch her, or scream, or

burst out crying. Anything. Anything would be better than this silent war, where everything had two meanings, and nobody said what they thought. Tam got up from her chair. "I've got to get home. Allie, I'll talk to you later?"

"Sure," I said.

Then Tam gave me a little wave as she walked out the back door, which closed with a slam. I put my empty juice glass in the sink.

Lionel looked at me carefully. "Are you okay?" Lionel asked. I must have looked pretty upset, because Lionel actually sounded worried.

"Fine," I croaked. But that was a lie.

I staggered out of the kitchen and upstairs to my room, fuming. Tam had waved good-bye with her right hand. She was wearing a ring, but it wasn't our friendship ring. I realized with a pang that I hadn't seen her wear it in weeks. It was as though it had disappeared.

Why? I wondered. Why? Okay, maybe I didn't dress as well as Renee, even with my new clothes, and maybe I wasn't into shopping and all that junk. But I'd never been into that stuff. I wasn't the one who had changed.

What is her problem? I thought as I flung my bag at the foot of my bed. We were friends. Best friends! She couldn't just treat me like some loser.

It was like what she was saying about Chris. Was it really so impossible to believe that he could ever be interested in me? Okay, sure, he was a golden god, and I was a . . . well, a sort of spazzy sixth grader. But he was also a plain old guy.

I need to show Tam that she's completely wrong about me, I realized. And suddenly, I had an idea. I would ask Chris to the sports banquet. I'd ask him, and he'd say yes, and then Tam would see that Renee was an idiot, and that she had me all wrong.

Peebles strutted into my room as I flopped onto my bed. "All I have to do is ask him." My cat jumped up next to me and she craned her neck to butt my hand with her head. "I mean, it's not like he's going to say no, right?"

Peebles blinked at me, and I scratched behind her ears. Purring, she stepped up onto my belly, poking me in the stomach with her little cat feet as she turned around three times and then lay down.

It's a start, I thought as I patted Peebles on the head. At least somebody believes in me.

———◆———

par•o•lies \ pa-'rol-eez \ *n* **1:** kids from parochial school **2:** uptight preps with no sweat glands **3:** girls whose hair stays perfectly braided, even while playing contact sports

"Get aggressive!" Coach Connors shouted as I flipped the ball to Jack for about the twentieth time that day. "You've got to take those shots, Allie!"

Why doesn't she just make a CD of one day's worth of shouting? I wondered as the other team's goalie—a tiny girl who reminded me of a jumping flea – blocked a tremendous shot and kicked the ball back into play. Coach always repeated herself with me: "Get aggressive! Get aggressive!" When was she going to figure out that I didn't *want* to get aggressive—that I wanted to do what I already knew how to do?

The other team tried a shot, and Elena headed it away from our goal just in time. The ball whizzed past my face. Luckily, Jack was all over it. She dribbled the ball downfield, toward the flea. I sprinted after her.

136

Jack was getting a lot of pressure from this blond French-braid girl defending her. We were playing the girls from Saint Agnes, and they were a lot tougher than they looked. You know the type: glossy hair, painted fingernails, and tiny gold hoop earrings. In a soccer game! When they jogged out onto the field in their superclean, fabric-softener-scented uniforms, I'd thought, See ya later, parolies.

Well, guess what? Saint Agnes must have been the patron saint of soccer, because these girls were kicking our butts. It was the second half, and we were down by two. It didn't look like we were getting anything past the flea.

I cut a hard right and ditched the lip-gloss queen who was defending me. In a flash, Jack snapped me the ball.

"Go for it, Allie!" Coach screamed.

Stop yelling at me! I thought. Gritting my teeth, I lined up my shot. Top corner. It was an impossible angle, but I had to try it.

Suddenly, I felt someone looking at me. After weeks of finely tuning my Chris compass, it was like I had some freakish sixth sense that told me

when he was nearby. Like now. Top of the bleachers, next to Justin. They were watching the game.

Ignore him! I thought as I took the shot. It was gorgeous, just where I wanted it . . . but no goal. That stupid flea jumped higher than humanly possible and nabbed the ball just before it went in.

"Allie, look alive!" Coach called from the sidelines.

Argh! I chased after the ball, pouring on the speed, but the other team had intercepted it, and I had to cut fast back toward our goal.

When did Chris get here? I wondered as I zoomed upfield. Could he possibly have been here for the whole game? Would he be here after? Maybe I could ask him then. *Chris, I was wondering whether you were going to the sports banquet,* I rehearsed as I chased after the ball. A quick pass across the field, and I had to stumble off in another direction. *Because I'm going,* I thought, *and so, like, maybe we could go together. . . .*

My heart was throbbing with the effort of the game, and with the fear of asking Chris to the

banquet. My knees felt like they were made of Silly Putty. I guess that was how the other team managed to kick the ball right through them.

Tell me he didn't see that! I thought. Okay, that last move actually made me mad. I lunged after the ball and went after it like it was a sack of cash. A girl with a slick brown ponytail slammed a serious kick into my shin guard, but it didn't even phase me. I knocked the ball toward Elena, and took off toward Saint Agnes's goal.

Elena was all over it. With a quick pass, Jack had the ball, then Sally, and soon it was all the way at the other end of the field. Suddenly, the ball was headed right for me.

Don't miss, don't miss! I thought as I dribbled toward the goal. I had the shot, but suddenly, I didn't dare take it. What if I missed again in front of Chris? I'd die. I'd die, and I wouldn't be able to ask him to the sports banquet because I'd be dead. Before I even realized I'd made a decision, I'd given the ball a sideways slam to Jack, who thundered it into the goal. But it wasn't enough.

Five minutes later, the game was over. We'd lost.

I trudged over to our bench and stood there like a lump as everyone gathered around to give the old, "Who do we appreciate?" cheer. I hate that stupid cheer. They should just make it "We like fruits and we like nuts—thanks for kicking all our butts!" or something. Oh, yeah—I really *appreciated* getting creamed.

Anyway, so we gave our cheer, and Saint Agnes gave their cheer, and that was the end. I started shoving stuff into my bag. I was antsy— I wanted to find Chris and ask him to the banquet as soon as possible. All of a sudden, I felt this shadow fall across my face. I looked up, and saw Coach standing over me, the setting sun fading red behind her head. With the ball in her hand, she looked like the living incarnation of Agnes, Soccer Saint.

"That shot you took was a tough one," Coach Connors said. "Good effort."

"Not good enough," I said, yanking at my shoelace.

"No." Coach's voice was so sharp that I looked up into her serious face. "It *was* good enough. You tried. That takes courage. That's all

I'm asking for." She looked at me for a moment more, and then she walked away.

I blinked as I watched her retreating into the swirl of soccer players. What is she saying? I wondered. That she doesn't care about winning? I didn't believe it for a minute.

"Rough game, huh?" Jack flopped onto the bench beside me and started untying her cleats.

I shook my head. "The girl defending me didn't even smudge her lip gloss. I mean, I can't even put lip gloss *on* without smudging it!"

"What's the deal with those girls?" Elena griped as she trudged over and flopped on the grass near us. She was still breathing hard, and the back of her jersey was soaked. "They weren't even sweating! They all walked off the field smelling like springtime!"

"So," Jack said, "who's coming out to celebrate?"

I snorted. "We lost!"

Jack shrugged. "So what?"

"You need a celebration *more* after you've lost," Elena pointed out.

I had to admit, this was a good point.

"Everyone goes," Jack agreed, giving me a little nudge. "The M&M's take us, then drop us off at home afterward."

I smiled. The M&M's is an expression I had come up with. It stands for Moms and Minivans. For some reason, it made me really happy that Jack had just used it.

"I'll have to call my mom," I hedged.

"You can call from the restaurant," Jack said. "All the moms have cell phones."

I nodded, but I was hardly paying attention—I was too busy scanning the crowd. Where is Chris? I wondered. I couldn't see him.

Suddenly, I felt a hand on my shoulder. I'd been so focused on looking for Chris that I nearly jumped out of my skin.

"Oh, Orren!" My lab partner was smiling down at me, but my heart sank. I didn't have time to chat—I needed to find Chris.

"Great game," Orren said warmly. "Saw your steal."

"Oh . . . thanks. Too bad we lost." I shouldered my bag and stood up, hoping that was all he

wanted to say. Could I just walk off? I wondered, but that seemed kind of rude.

"Allie, can I talk to you for a minute?" Orren asked.

I scanned the crowd again, but there was still no sign of Chris. Had he left already? That would be just my luck—for Chris to have only seen the part of the game in which I totally stank. "What's up?" I asked Orren absently.

Orren cleared his throat. "Well, I ran into Mrs. Larsen after school. She regraded our lab, and we're getting an eighty on it, so that's good."

"Oh!" I said brightly. "Oh, great. Thanks for letting me know." I started to walk off, but Orren didn't move, so I sort of stumbled and took another awkward step back toward him. "Is there something else?"

"Uh . . . yeah," Orren said slowly.

I waited.

"I . . . uh . . . was wondering if you were going to the sports banquet," he said.

A cold fist squeezed my heart. "Yeah," I said faintly. Please don't do what I think you're going to do, I thought desperately. Please don't—

"Oh. Great. Because I'm going, too. And I thought that we could go together. . . ."

Like invisible arrows, the words flew through the air and shot through my chest. It was almost as though they had pinned me against something. I couldn't move. I couldn't breathe.

Orren was staring at me in that intense way he has. I felt almost as though his green eyes were peeling back the layers of skin, probing into my brain.

I didn't know what to say. Yes? No? I didn't want to go with Orren. I wanted to go with Chris. But if I said no, would Orren think it was because I thought he was a nerd? If I said yes, would I just be doing it because I felt sorry for him? *Did* I feel sorry for Orren? Was I one of those jerks who judge people on superficial stuff? I wondered. Or was I just the kind of idiot who does the nice things because they're too dumb to say no?

And now Renee was going to see me with Orren instead of with Chris. I could just imagine what she would have to say about it.

The thoughts flashed by like cars at the Indy 500. *Zip! Zip! Zip!* Then they were gone, and I was

left in the moment, standing there, facing Orren.

"Sure!" I heard myself say in this freakishly chipper voice. "Sounds great!"

"Okay," Orren said, and this huge smile washed over his face. He looked so relieved that I felt like I'd been stabbed with another arrow. "Okay, great. Well, have fun getting ice cream. I'll see you tomorrow."

I nodded and gave him a smile. I couldn't speak. My throat had completely closed, and I wondered whether "Sounds great!" would be the last thing that I'd ever be able to say for the rest of my life.

Orren trotted off, and I took a huge breath and turned to face the empty soccer field, tears streaming down my face. I just stood there, crying. I wasn't even sure why.

"Hey, Allie, wake up! Ice cream time!" Elena skipped over to me and wrapped an arm around my shoulder. But her smile evaporated when she saw my face. "Oh my god," she said quickly, her eyes growing wide, "what's wrong?"

Jack was with her, and her eyebrows drew together as she looked at me.

"It's nothing," I said, wiping my face quickly. I pivoted slightly, so that I wasn't facing the team. "It's stupid."

Jack and Elena continued to stand there, looking so worried that I had to laugh. I knew that I was just making a big deal out of nothing; but that thought just made another stream of tears pour down my face. "No, *really*, it's stupid," I told them. "You won't believe how stupid it is."

"Try us," Jack urged.

"Did Orren say something to you?" Elena demanded. She looked like she was ready to rip his head off and kick it into the soccer net.

"No, no," I told her quickly. "Well, yes, but nothing bad." I took a deep breath. "It's just, he asked me to go with him to the sports banquet." And then the waterworks started again.

"Well, that isn't so bad, is it?" Elena asked gently.

"No." I shook my head and took a shaky breath. "It's just that . . . I kind of wanted to go with someone else." I pressed my lips together and swallowed hard. "I was kind of planning on asking that person today."

"That's hard," Jack said sympathetically. "But look, Allie, Orren is probably just asking as a friend. I'm sure he isn't thinking of this as some big romance."

Ohmygosh, it hadn't even occurred to me that Orren might think that this was some big romance! What if he thinks I said yes because I like him? I thought desperately. What if he has a crush on me? Groaning, I rubbed my temples.

"Why don't you just back out?" Jack suggested.

"But I really do want to go to the banquet," I said.

"Then tell him that you just don't want to go with him," Elena said.

I shook my head. "I could never do that."

"Yeah," Jack said with a sigh, "me neither."

"Unless I totally hated the guy," Elena volunteered.

And I don't hate Orren, I thought. I took a deep breath. "Okay," I said finally. "I'm okay. This is no big deal."

"Right." Elena nodded. "Nothing that a little ice cream can't solve."

"Besides, we'll all be there," Jack added. "No big."

"Yeah, no big." I smiled, and it was a real smile, not one of those shaky, propped-up fake smiles. "Thanks, guys."

Jack and Elena were right. This was no big deal. Okay, so I wasn't going to the banquet with Chris. But at least it wasn't because he'd said no. That would really be something to cry about.

"Okay, now it's *really* ice cream time," Elena said. She wrapped her arm around my shoulder, and Jack wrapped her arm around my other shoulder, and we walked toward the waiting minivans just like that—locked in a three-way hug.

road chick•en \'rode 'chi-ken\ *n* : someone who can't
decide which side to be on, and ends up standing in the
middle of the road . . . which is, of course, where
the cars are

When I got home, there was this low buzzing
sound coming from the bathroom. The door
was slightly open, so I peeked inside. Lionel had
spread newspapers all over the sink. The newspaper was covered with clumps of reddish hair.
Lionel was using the ancient hair clipper that
Mom had used to give Lionel buzz cuts before he
announced he never wanted a haircut again.

"What are you doing?" I asked.

Lionel looked up at me and rolled his eyes.
"What does it look like I'm doing?" he asked. He
surveyed his head in the mirror, then jabbed the
clipper at the right side of his head. There was a
loud hum and a crackle as another clump of hair
fell softly onto the paper, like an auburn
snowflake. He nodded, apparently satisfied, and

pulled the long guide off the end of the hair clipper.

"I mean, I *see* what you're doing," I explained, "but I don't see why. I thought you liked having long hair."

"It was okay, but I got kind of sick of it," Lionel said. "Besides, we're going out to dinner with Dad tonight, remember?"

"Oh." Right. Dad *hates* Lionel's shaggy hair. When we saw Dad at the beginning of the summer, he wouldn't shut up about it. He kept saying that Lionel looked like a girl. Finally, Lionel gave in and let Dad take him for a haircut. But he'd been growing it out since then. "Well, it looks good."

"Yeah?" Lionel looked surprised.

I shrugged. "Yeah." Lionel's hair didn't look that bad—he'd done a pretty good job. I'd gotten so used to seeing him with long, shaggy hair that I'd kind of forgotten what his face looked like. It was thinner than I remembered. Actually, Lionel looked kind of grown up.

Lionel looked at himself in the mirror, and then smiled at me. "Thanks," he said. "I was a little

worried about it. I should have asked Mom to take me for a haircut, but I didn't make up my mind until just now, and then there wasn't time, so . . ."

Wow, I thought. Here we are, having a normal conversation. I'd kind of forgotten that it was possible to talk to Lionel.

"Anyway, it'll make Dad happy. And *she* won't be at dinner," Lionel went on, meaning Marci. We feel pretty much the same about her. "So I won't have to hear about how I should have had a professional do it."

"Yeah, and we won't have to get a lecture on table manners," I agreed.

Lionel laughed. Marci always acted like Lionel and I were total slobs. Which was really funny, considering that she had a three-year-old who was usually covered in mysterious goo, and was nearly always pitching fits, demanding more cookies and/or large amounts of ice cream. Don't get me wrong. I love Daniel. I just don't love the way Marci pretends that she's the perfect mom, while our mom is raising wild beasts.

Lionel shook his head and started to pack up the clipper. It was weird—suddenly, I was kind of

grateful for my brother. It was a relief to know that someone else felt the same way about our stepmother—that it wasn't just all my imagination. You know, I never felt that I could talk to Mom about Marci, because she clearly makes Mom uncomfortable. And nobody else really knows what Marci is like. But Lionel does.

"You know, you missed a spot," I told Lionel.

Lionel frowned at the mirror. "Where?"

"The back." I tugged at a long tuft that was sticking out behind his left ear. "Want me to get it?"

"Sure." Lionel handed me the clipper, and I flipped it on. It buzzed in my hand as I focused on the spot.

Buzz.

"Oh my God," I said, jumping away from Lionel's head as a huge chunk of hair fell onto the newspaper.

His eyes were huge. "What did you do?"

"I'm sorry—" I said, staring at the stripe of white scalp behind Lionel's ear.

Lionel gaped down at the clipper. We had forgotten to put the guide back on.

"What did you do?" Lionel's voice was a shriek.

"Sorry! Sorry! Lionel, I'm so sorry!" I really meant it, too . . . but as I stared at that bald chunk on his head . . . I just couldn't help it. I started giggling.

"I'm going to kill you!" Lionel grabbed the clipper from my hand and lunged at my head. I screamed.

"What's going on in—oh my God, Lionel, what happened?" The look on Mom's face when she saw Lionel's hair was so funny that I started to giggle again.

"Allie did it." He glared at me.

"I didn't mean to," I pleaded. "I didn't know the guide was off. . . ." My voice faltered and my laughter dried up as Lionel's eyes filled with tears.

"We have to go out with Dad tonight," Lionel said.

"I know, sweetheart," Mom said, giving him a hug. "It's okay. We can fix it. It's not a big deal."

"It *is* a big deal." Lionel's eyes sliced through me like laser beams. "Don't fall asleep," he warned.

"Okay, that's enough," Mom said. "Allie, I

think you'd better let me handle this, okay?" She gave me a *Please get out of here* look, so I just nodded and stepped out of the bathroom, closing the door behind me.

My phone rang the minute I walked into my room.

"Allie?"

"Tam," I said warmly, thrilled that I could tell her the Lionel hair story. "You'll never guess what just—"

"Did Sir Dorksalot ask you to the banquet?"

The receiver turned to ice in my hand. I pressed my lips together, silently cursing myself. For a moment, I'd actually forgotten that Tam and I weren't really friends right now. It took me a minute to switch gears. "What?"

"I heard that Orren asked you to be his date to the sports banquet. And that you said yes. Is that true?"

"How did you hear about that?"

"Who *cares*? Is it true?"

"Well . . . we're just going as friends. . . ."

Silence.

"You can't go."

She said it just like that—like she was a judge, and that was my sentence.

"What?"

"Allie, you can't go to the banquet with him. I mean, you don't want to, do you?"

I couldn't lie. "Well, no . . ."

"Thank God. I thought you were losing your mind for a minute."

"But I can't just cancel—"

Tam blew an exasperated sigh into the receiver. "Allie, you're too nice. Believe me— you're going to regret it. The whole school is going to think that Orren is your boyfriend!"

"But I don't want to hurt his feelings."

"Why do you even care about his feelings? You don't even like him! You'll give him the wrong impression if you go with him."

I heard what she was saying. By telling Orren yes, but not really meaning it, I was definitely being a road chicken. I didn't want Orren to think that we were dating, or anything. And I didn't want anyone else to think that, either. But I also heard what she *wasn't* saying. She didn't want me to go with Orren because it would make her look

bad. She didn't want to deal with him. She didn't want to be seen hanging out with him.

"Look, I've got to go," Tam said. "Either way, you're going to ruin someone's night. Ruin Orren's by canceling, or ruin your own, by going with him."

"Okay, Tam," I said finally. "I'll think about it."

"Good. Look, I'll see you tomorrow morning, and we'll figure out something you can say to him that won't hurt his feelings too badly."

I sighed, wondering what that could possibly be. Clicking the OFF button, I went and sat in my window seat. Two doors down, I could see Justin kicking around a soccer ball in his backyard. He dribbled it back and forth, back and forth, cutting away from imaginary opponents, scoring imaginary goals. He was scowling at the ball, like it had insulted his mom or something, and I got the sense that he was enjoying kicking it around. Actually, that looked like a pretty good idea.

Almost without thinking, I found myself heading down the stairs and out the back door and shouting, "Justin!"

Looking up in surprise, Justin gave me a grin

and kicked the ball clear into my yard. Then he jumped our chain-link fence, scaling it with a metallic clatter.

"Hey," he said, dropping lightly into my backyard.

"You're Justin Thyme," I told him. "I'm really in the mood to kick something."

"I hope you're talking about the ball, and not about me," Justin joked.

I grinned. "Either one."

Justin kicked the ball to me, and we knocked it back and forth a little, not seriously. "So what's wrong?" Justin asked.

"Ahh . . ." I shrugged. "This guy asked me to go the sports banquet with him, and I said yes, even though I kind of don't want to go with him."

"Orren?" Justin asked. "I thought you guys were friends."

"How do you know about it?" I demanded. I wasn't used to being talked about. "God, does everybody know?"

"Tam told me," Justin admitted. "I ran into her after soccer. But she thought you'd back out."

"She did?" At this point, I don't know why that news shocked me.

"Will you?" Justin asked.

"I have no idea," I told him honestly.

Justin shrugged. "Orren's a cool guy."

I laughed. "You're the only one who thinks so."

"Well, he's a *nerd*," Justin admitted. "But he's cool. He's a cool nerd."

"He's a pecooliar dude," I said, half to myself.

Justin laughed. "Pecooliar," he repeated. "I like that. And I think you're cool for not automatically turning him down. Most girls would have."

I sighed. "Tam really thinks I shouldn't go with him."

"It's not a big deal, Allie." Justin knocked the ball my way. "You're friends. Right?"

"Yeah, you know that. And I know it. . . ."

"I'm sure Orren knows it, too."

I didn't feel like explaining that it wasn't Orren I was worried about.

It was everyone else.

- 11 -

flie \\'fly\ *n* : a little, tiny lie, one that really hardly counts

I stared into my closet, frowning at my options. This is the problem with going out to dinner with Dad—he always wants me to wear a skirt. But the last time I'd worn a skirt I felt like a Dweebosaurus and had the worst day ever. Besides, it was a Tuesday night. I had on jeans, and I didn't particularly feel like changing. I'd already had to get dressed for school, then dressed for soccer, then redressed after soccer, and I didn't want to get undressed and dressed again.

Then again, I really didn't want to hear a lecture on how I should dress more "femininely." It's funny, my dad is proud of the fact that I play soccer, but he basically wants me to be this very girly athlete. You know, like those Saint Agnes girls. That's how Marci is. She likes to jog. But she gets more dressed up for her daily run than I do when I'm going to church. She even wears *makeup*.

Sighing, I hauled my red plaid pants from the closet, figuring on a compromise. They were sort of funky, but dressier than jeans. I paired them with this cool black long-sleeved shirt with red Chinese characters on it, and my chunky black boots, then looked in the mirror. Not bad. But my hair was doing this annoying frizz thing, so I twisted the front backward into little snakes on either side of my face and clipped them with small sparkly minibarrettes. Then I dug this ancient lip gloss out of my drawer and smeared some over my lips. Unbelievably, it actually ended up looking pretty good. Wow, I thought as I smiled at myself in the mirror. Maybe I'm getting the hang of this. I mean, I was still no Tam or Renee—I was just a really good version of me.

I heard gravel crunch in our driveway, and I was halfway down the stairs by the time the doorbell rang.

"Dad!" I shouted as I flung open the door.

"Allison!" Dad grinned and gave me a hug. "How's middle-school life treating my prettiest girl?"

I shut the door as Dad stepped into the hall. "Eh," I said.

"That good, huh?" His green eyes were laughing.

I smiled up at him. I don't know why, but I'm always surprised whenever I see my dad. He always looks younger than I remember him. He used to be in the marines, and he's still in really good shape. He almost always wears a suit, except on the weekends, when he wears khaki pants or khaki shorts (ironed) and a polo shirt (also ironed). I don't know if I've ever seen him in jeans, except for this one time that we went horseback riding— and the jeans he wore had creases down the front. He always wears his hair in a crew cut. When I looked at him now, I noticed that it was starting to go gray on the left side—the silver hairs sparkled like stars nestled among the black.

Dad looked me up and down. "Is that a new outfit?"

"Yeah," I said brightly, pleased that he'd noticed. Glad I changed, I thought, giving myself a mental pat on the back.

Dad gave a little shrug. "Well, I guess that's what they're wearing these days," he said, almost to himself.

Suddenly, my mental pat felt more like a slap. What is that supposed to mean? I wondered. Dad made it sound like I looked horrible. And worse, like I just threw on whatever all the other kids did, like some kind of mindless amoeba. Not that amoebas wear clothes. But you know what I mean. "This is what *I'm* wearing," I said.

"Hey, Dad." Lionel trudged down the stairs with Mom right behind him.

I had to swallow a little giggle. Lionel was wearing a baseball cap.

"Hey, sport," Dad said, holding out his arms to Lionel.

Okay, here is another thing that drives me insane about Dad. Lionel is totally not a sport. *I'm* a sport. Lionel is lousy at games and looks like a Slinky in an earthquake when he runs. But, whatever. He's a guy, so he gets "sport."

"Hello, Howard," Mom said to Dad, who nodded at her and said, "Jane." Mom and Dad always act like people who work in the same office. It's really strange to think that they were ever married. I guess the only two things they really have in common are Lionel and me.

Dad hugged Lionel, then stepped back to look at him. "What's with the hat?" he asked, tugging on the bill of the Red Sox cap Lionel had on.

Lionel grinned. "What can I say? I love the Sox."

I was impressed with Lionel's cover story. Unfortunately, I knew it wasn't really going to fly with Dad.

"Well, you're not wearing it to dinner," Dad said in this kind-of-playing-but-really-not voice.

Lionel put his palm on top of his cap. "I wear it all the time. I like it."

"Not tonight," Dad said. His mouth was smiling, but his eyes were frowning as he yanked the cap off Lionel's head. "We're going to a restau—"

There was this horrible moment of silence as my father stared at Lionel's bald head. So that was the solution Mom had come up with—she'd just cut all of Lionel's hair as short as the chunk I'd taken out. There was still hair on Lionel's head, but it was very, very short, and so light it was almost invisible. Kind of like a peach.

In this weird way, I thought it looked kind of cool.

"Oh my . . ." Dad's eyes flashed to Mom. "You let him do this?" he demanded.

"It's just hair," Mom said. Her face was like stone. This is how she gets when Dad gets mad. She turns icy.

"It's *more* than hair, Jane," Dad snapped. "It's how the world sees him. He looks like one of those skinheads."

I opened my mouth to confess that Lionel's haircut was the result of my spazzitude, not a premeditated fashion statement, but my brother flashed me a *Don't say a word* look, then said, "Dad, I did it. Mom didn't even know about it."

Suddenly, I felt awful for Lionel. I knew how excited he'd been to see Dad, and now it was ruined. Thanks to me. And he'd just totally covered for me. Lionel hates lying, but I guess he figured that this was only a little flie. Besides, my brother must have known that if he told the real story, Dad would freak out at me for using the clippers, then at Lionel for letting me use them, then at Mom for letting us run wild.

Dad narrowed his eyes at Lionel, then looked at Mom again. "Don't you supervise them?"

I saw Mom inhale, and I knew that she was doing this yoga breath thing that she claims is very calming. Then she said, "This conversation is over, Howard. If you want to discuss Lionel's haircut, I suggest we talk another time." She gave Lionel a kiss on the cheek. "Have fun." Mom ran her hand playfully over his fuzzy scalp and smiled reassuringly. Then she looked over at me and winked.

I saw the muscles in Dad's jaw clench, but finally he let out this big whoosh of air, and turned to open the door. "I'll have them back before nine-thirty," Dad said in his professional office-worker voice.

"Bye, Mom," Lionel said. He sounded kind of sad.

"Bye." I glanced back at Mom as I followed Dad and Lionel out the door. Suddenly, I wasn't looking forward to this dinner very much. I love my dad, but he isn't any fun when he's angry.

I was in for a horrible night. And it was all my fault.

I looked out at our house from the backseat of Dad's rental car as we pulled up to the curb in

front. For a minute, I felt as though I was seeing it through my dad's eyes—the shutter with the slat missing outside my window on the second floor, the grass that had grown over the edge of the sidewalk, the scraggly miniature azalea bushes that never really bloomed. It wasn't a horrible house, but it was far from perfect. Still, I couldn't wait to get inside and curl up under my covers.

We had gone to our favorite restaurant, Tía Alma, where they have excellent Mexican food, and Dad tried to make up with Lionel by joking about his hair, but Lionel just sulked until Dad turned to me and asked about my science grade. I told him I'd brought it up, but I still got a lecture about how I'd never get into a good college if I didn't start working hard now. Then Dad told us all about the "family vacation" he'd planned with Marci and Daniel. Lionel hadn't said anything, but I could tell his feelings were hurt. I knew mine were. I mean, weren't Lionel and I family? Why weren't we invited? Anyway, I was feeling so stressed around Dad that I ate about five million chips dipped in Alma's special green sauce, and by the time my chile relleno showed up I thought I

was going to barf. But Dad hates it when we "waste" food, so I forced myself to eat half of it and then took the rest home in a doggie bag. *Ugh.*

Now we were all sitting in the dark car without moving. No one spoke.

"So," Dad said brightly, then stopped. I guess he didn't know where to go from there.

"Thanks for taking us out, Dad," I told him.

"Yeah," Lionel added.

"I've missed you guys," Dad said. He looked from Lionel to me, then back again. "But I'll be back in town soon."

"I wish you could stay to see my soccer game tomorrow," I said.

"Me, too, sweetie. But I have to get back to work. You understand."

I nodded, but I didn't really understand. Lots of parents worked, but they managed to come to a soccer game now and then. Mom had come to four. Still, I knew there was no point in arguing. He wasn't coming. End of story.

Lionel leaned over, and Dad gave him a hug. I pecked Dad on the cheek, and Lionel and I stepped out of the car.

"I'll see you soon!" Dad promised. "And I'll talk to you even sooner."

"Love you," I said.

"Good. Me, too," Dad said, grinning, and I shut the door. Then Lionel and I stood there in silence as Dad drove away, the red taillights of his white rental fading into the darkness like embers from a fire.

I don't know why, but I always feel sadder when I see my dad than I do when I don't see him for a long time. I guess it reminds me that he isn't around, or something. I snuck a look at Lionel. By the expression on his face, I was pretty sure he was feeling the same way I was.

"Come on," Lionel said. He jerked his head toward our house and started up the front walk.

"Wait," I said.

Lionel turned to face me. "What?"

I heaved a deep breath. "I just wanted to say . . . thanks."

"What for?"

Lionel's face was only half visible in the light from the streetlamp halfway down our block. The shadows struck his cheekbones, and for a

moment, I was shocked at how much he looked like Dad. "Just . . . for not telling Dad that I accidentally shaved your head."

Lionel rubbed his scalp for a minute, and then actually let out a chuckle. "Oh man," he said, half laughing. "I am so going to get it at school tomorrow."

"Can I . . . can I feel it?" I asked.

Lionel rolled his eyes, but he leaned forward, and I rubbed his scalp. The short, bristly hairs tickled my fingers. "Cool," I said warmly.

Lionel smiled.

"And it looks good, too," I added. "Don't worry about what anyone says."

"Yeah?" Lionel looked dubious.

"Really, I mean it," I said. "You look like a marine."

Lionel laughed, and we both turned toward the house. "Just don't go telling everyone that you're the reason my head is shaved. Then I'll really look like a nork."

That's what he said—*nork*. He used my word. Suddenly, I was really glad that I hadn't told Tam about Lionel's hair. It would have been all over

the school by now. "I'll never tell," I promised. "Gigantic mutant blood-sucking trolls couldn't get it out of me."

Lionel paused at the front door and stared at me. "You're such a weirdo," he said, then pushed open the door.

Mom was sitting on the couch watching when we walked inside. She put the movie she'd been watching on mute, looked at her watch, and grinned. "Nine twenty-seven," she said, shaking her head. "Your dad sure is punctual. Did you have fun?"

Lionel shrugged. "It was okay, I guess. I've got some homework to do. I'll see you in the morning." He tramped up the stairs.

Mom looked at me, and I walked over and snuggled next to her. "Everything okay?"

"Yeah," I told her. "It's just kind of hard."

"I know." Mom wrapped her arm around me and gave me a squeeze. We just sat there like that for a few minutes, and after a while, I felt my breathing fall into the rhythm of Mom's. For some reason, it made me feel better.

"Let's talk about something fun," Mom said

after a minute. "Are you excited about the sports banquet this weekend?"

"Define *excited*."

Mom scooched backward to look at me. "You're not excited? I thought that you and Tam had been talking about it for weeks."

I sighed. "Yeah. But this guy kind of asked me to go with him."

"Really?" Mom was giving me this thrilled smile.

"It's not good."

"No? Why not? Is he a jerk?"

"No . . . he's . . ." How could I explain this? "He's just kind of a nerd."

"Oh," Mom said, nodding. "A cool nerd?"

I rolled my eyes. "I guess."

"Hmm. And you don't want to go with him."

"Well . . ." I hesitated. "He's okay, but . . ."

"You had someone else in mind?" Mom finished for me.

Freaky. Sometimes, I swear, Mom can read my thoughts. "Yeah," I admitted. "So what do I do?"

"Oh, gosh," Mom said with a laugh. "Don't ask me. I'm terrible at this stuff."

"Yeah, look at who *you* married." The words hung in the air for a moment before I clapped a hand over my mouth. I hadn't meant to say that! I'd never said anything *like* that before.

Mom looked surprised for a moment, then smiled at me sympathetically. "Your dad and I loved each other," Mom said, as she stroked my hair. "I know you don't remember, but we were happy for a long time."

I swallowed hard. It was just so hard to imagine that Mom and Dad had ever gotten along. "What happened?" I asked.

"I don't know, sweetheart." Mom continued to stroke my hair, but she had this faraway look on her face. "Sometimes people just grow apart. And it's really hard when that happens. You don't want to believe that someone you've been so close to could seem almost like a stranger."

An image of Tam flashed into my mind. "Yeah," I said quietly. "I guess I know what you mean."

Mom looked down at me and smiled. "But in the end, it all worked out. I got to do things I never would have been able to do if I'd stayed with

your father. I built a business all by myself, and I learned how to be independent, and I made new friends. And those are good things."

I tried to imagine what I would get to do without Tam, but it wasn't easy. My life without her seemed kind of . . . blank.

Mom leaned over and kissed me on the forehead and whispered, "It gets easier."

I looked up at her and tried to smile, but it came out kind of weak. I hoped she was right.

"And as for your date," Mom added, "I can't tell you what to do."

Why not? I wanted to ask. Everyone else does. The TV glowed blue, casting eerie shadows on her face.

"Do you want a cookie?" Mom asked after a while. "I made chocolate-chip."

"No, thanks," I said. "I think I'll just head upstairs."

Mom touched my hair, tucked it behind my ear. "Okay. I'm here if you need me."

I gave her a hug, then headed up to my room.

<hr />

squash \'skwash\ **1:** a feeling that your heart has been squeezed and leaves you all gooey inside **2:** the subject of extreme like

"Hey, Peebles. Hey, lazy cat." Peebles was curled up on my window seat. I went and sat beside her without turning on the light. I was surprised by how many stars I could see. The tree outside my window had lost a lot of leaves, and the little lights twinkled through bare branches. "Pretty," I said, stroking Peebles's fur. Peebles didn't bother waking up, just started purring in her sleep.

Sighing, I walked over to my desk and switched on the lamp. I was about to turn on the computer when I noticed the old LFC notebook sitting there. I had homework to do, but I just couldn't help myself. I flipped it open to the first page.

First meeting of the LFC.
President: Tamara
Vice President: Renee
Secretary: Allie
Tamara's squashes: Bobby F.,
    David S., David D., Franklin L.,
    and Chris G.

Renee's squashes: Bill T., James R., George W., and David D.
Allie's squashes: Chris G. and Franklin L.

That's weird, I thought, looking over the page. I hadn't remembered that Tam had liked Chris in the beginning. Or that I had liked Franklin Linning. That was kind of funny, actually. Franklin had a big head—I mean, literally a big head in comparison to his tiny body—and he was super quiet. I guess he had nice eyes, though. I was pretty sure that I had never really liked him, but I felt like I had to have more than one crush in order to be in the club.

Sitting down, I thought back to the third grade, remembering when Tam had told me about her idea for the crush club. She had been all hot on the idea. But I wasn't. I didn't have any crushes.

"Don't be stupid," Tam had said. "Of course you do! What about Chris?"

"Who?" I asked.

"What do you mean, who? The cutest guy in school!" Tam cried.

I smiled at the memory. The next day, Tam had pointed out Chris during lunch, and I had to admit that he was cute. Way cute. So he was the first guy on my crush list.

I flipped through the notebook, scanning the "Squash Lists." Tam and Renee changed their crushes like they changed their underwear—there were new names added and old ones crossed off at every meeting. But mine stayed the same, except that after three weeks Franklin fell off the list, thanks to the famous incident in which he stuck his finger in the pencil sharpener. After that I thought he was kind of dumb. But Chris stayed—and he remained the only name on my list.

Tossing the notebook aside, I lay back on my bed and stared at the ceiling. It was bizarre to think that my major crush on Chris had basically started because I was looking for a name to put on my list. And then, I guess it just became a habit. But when I stopped to think about it, I couldn't really put my finger on just what it was that I liked about him. I mean, he was cute, sure. But so what?

I racked my brain, but I couldn't really think

of anything we'd ever said to each other—I mean, aside from that time he asked me for a pen. And all those times he hadn't gotten my jokes.

The thought actually made me laugh. Peebles let out a *browr* and looked up at me.

"Oh, go back to sleep," I told her. "Nothing important." Suddenly, I spotted my soccer notebook on my shelf. I pulled it down, and flipped it open to the first page, settling back down on my bed. "'One day till sixth grade, and Tam is afraid of looking like a nork,'" I read.

Well, she solved that problem, I thought. She just found Renee, and became a glommer.

It was funny to think about—I'd never thought of Tam as someone who worried about being a nerd. She had never thought about that stuff in elementary school. But now, she seemed to think about it all the time.

Peebles settled back down and I hauled myself off the bed and started to peel off my clothes. Forget homework, I decided. I was too tired for it, anyway. It was all I could do to change into my nightshirt and go through my usual toothbrushing, face-washing thing. I skipped the floss.

Climbing into bed, I clicked off the lamp and stared out the window at the glimmering dark. I pulled my dark blue plaid sheets over my lips and breathed through my nose, thinking about the notebooks, and Tam. She was definitely changing . . . and I wasn't. I guess we were starting to grow apart, like Mom had said. I only had one question.

How in the world do you divorce your best friend?

- 12 -

friend \ 'freend \ *n* : a fiend in friend's clothing

"So what's the plan?" Tam asked as she walked up to my locker. That was the first thing she said to me. Not *Hello*. Not *What's up?* No, it was all, "You've got to do this Orren thing *today*. People are starting to ask me if he's your boyfriend." Leaning back, she knocked her head against the lockers, like she was faced with some kind of enormous calamity.

Wondering who in the world besides Renee could have asked Tam if Orren was my boyfriend, I hauled my English book out of my locker and slipped it into my backpack. "Tam, did you tell Justin that I didn't want to go to the banquet with Orren?"

Embarrassment skittered across Tam's face, then disappeared. "Well, you don't."

"But I don't want Orren to know that." I slammed shut my locker and faced her. "Besides,

I hadn't even told you whether I wanted to go when you talked to Justin."

Tam rolled her eyes. "I knew that it wasn't even *possible* that you wanted to go with him."

"Look," I said, hitching my backpack higher on my shoulder, "I don't want to be Orren's date. But Orren is a nice guy, and I don't want to hurt his feelings, either."

"Which is why we need to come up with a plan," Tam shot back. "So that you can get this over with."

I was starting to feel like Tam was more of a frieend than a friend. She didn't care about Orren. And she didn't care about whether I liked Orren or not. She just wanted to get rid of him because he was embarrassing her in some way. I mean, it was kind of funny to think that Tam would be worried because some guy had asked me out. It didn't really have anything to do with her. But on the other hand, Tam lived in the real middle-school world, where people judged you by your friends. If she was friends with me and I was friends with Orren, Tam would be lower down on the middle-school food chain—closer to

the Dweebosaurus. And once you're low on that chain, it's pretty easy to become extinct.

"What am I going to say to him?" I demanded. "I can't tell him that I'm going, just not with him."

"Why not?"

I gaped at her. "Because he's a *human being*!"

"Tell him you already have a date," Tam suggested.

"But that's a lie! And it'll be totally obvious when I show up without a date."

"Well . . . maybe you could ask someone else," Tam suggested.

"Like Chris," I whispered. Actually, this wasn't a bad idea. Orren already knew about my crush. He'd probably even understand. . . .

"Chris already has a date."

Momentarily lost in my fantasy about going to the banquet with Chris, sitting next to Chris, talking to Chris, it took almost a full minute for Tam's words to register. *"What?"*

"Renee asked him yesterday." Tam's face had turned pink, and she looked kind of guilty. "I thought you knew."

"But she knows I like him—"

"Allie, *everybody* likes him," Tam shot back. "He's the hottest guy in the entire school. It's not like you can just call dibs on him, or something."

I stared at her. I couldn't believe she had just said that. She knew that I'd liked Chris for *years*. Renee knew it, too. And, even if Renee wasn't my friend, Tam was. Or she was supposed to be. Why hadn't she warned me that Renee was into him?

"Look, just tell Orren that you're going to the banquet with the girls' soccer team," Tam suggested. "He won't want to be the only guy at the table."

Actually, I wasn't so sure that Orren would really care, but I just nodded. I didn't trust myself to speak. I could feel hot tears pooling in my eyes, and I knew that a single word would send them spilling down my face. I couldn't believe that Renee had asked Chris to the banquet after she made me feel like an idiot for liking him. I couldn't believe that Renee would stab me in the back like that. Or that Tam would act like it was no big deal. Like this thing with Orren was a problem that

needed to be solved right away, but my feelings . . . well, who cared?

"So wait a minute, Tam," I said slowly, as things began to click together in my brain. "You're so eager for me to ditch Orren, but who are you going with? Do you even have a date to the banquet?"

Tam's face turned pale, and the muscles in her jaw tensed. "I'm going with Tom."

"Tom Fine?" I repeated. Chris's best friend. So she and Renee had planned it together. . . .

"Allie, are you listening to me?" Tam asked. "You have to do this today. It doesn't matter what you tell him. Just get rid of him."

I nodded again. *So, Orren, the girls on the soccer team are all planning to sit together*, I rehearsed mentally. But this speech was all wrong. For one thing, it wasn't true. But beyond that, I'd sort of thought I'd be sitting with Tam at the sports banquet. I mean, that had been our plan since the first week of school. Come to think of it, though, Tam hadn't really mentioned it lately. But if she wasn't planning on sitting with me, why would she care whether Orren was my date or not? Then again,

Tam would probably want to sit with Renee, and I wasn't sure that I really wanted to sit with her and Chris when they were on a kind of date-type thing.

"Tam . . ." My voice was thick, but I forced out the words. "Are we sitting together at the banquet?"

Tam let out her breath in this big whoosh. "Look, Renee absolutely will not sit with Orren. So if you want to sit with us . . ."

Her unfinished sentence hung in the air, a silent threat.

So she had made her choice. If I wanted to be her friend, I had to follow the rules.

The bell rang, and Tam touched me on the shoulder. "Good luck. Let me know how it goes." Like I was taking an algebra quiz.

Kids started to stream toward their homerooms, like ants pouring from a crushed anthill, as Tam turned away. I saw Justin at his locker at the end of the hall and I thought about what he'd said the day before. That most girls would have said no to Orren without thinking about it. But it was too late—I'd already thought about it. And once you

thought about things, you had to do what was right. "No," I whispered.

Tam froze in her steps, then turned back toward me slowly. "What?"

I shook my head. "No," I whispered. I cleared my throat.

"What do you mean, no?"

"I mean"—I took a deep breath—"I think I'll just go to the banquet with Orren. Thanks," I added, because I felt like I needed to say something.

"What—what do you mean?" Tam's eyes reminded me of closed doors. "You're choosing Orren over me?"

I shook my head. You're the one who's made the choice, I thought, but that wasn't what I said. "No. I just don't want to ditch him. He's a nice guy, Tam. I can't do it."

"Fine. Have it your way," Tam snapped. Then she stormed away.

"This isn't my way," I said, but it was too late. She was too far away. She couldn't hear a word I said.

———◦———

streep•er \\'streep-er \ *n* : someone who plays both offense and defense on a soccer team

"This is it," Jack said as she slung her arm around my shoulders, "last game of the year."

"I can't believe the season is over," Elena said as she yanked on her cleats. "I feel like we just got into the swing of things."

"Not yet," Sarah pointed out in her shy voice, her dark eyes serious. "We've still got an hour and a half left."

"I can't believe we have to play Saint Agnes again," Sally said as she gathered her long corn-rows into a scrunchie.

"Those girls had better be ready to get their little buttery yellow uniforms dirty," Jack said.

I shifted uncomfortably on the splintery bench. Most of the ancient green paint was worn away, and the old wood dug through the seat of my uniform—but mostly I was antsy because I was eager to play. It was a crisp fall day—only a few cottonball clouds floating overhead in a sea of blinding blue.

A perfect day for kicking butt.

186

"Go, team, go!" Justin's voice shouted behind me. Turning, I saw Justin and Chris headed toward our bench. I glanced at Chris, then looked away. Seeing him was kind of strange. It left me feeling sort of hollow, and sad. But not sad because I felt like my heart was broken. Sad because I felt like something had shifted. His blue eyes didn't fill me with familiar fluttery excitement. I didn't feel his presence like a warm blanket wrapped around me.

After three years, I had discovered that I didn't really care about him anymore. Just like that. Not that it made what Renee had done any less heinous.

"So, is everybody going to the banquet tomorrow?" Jack asked, holding up a packet of tickets. "Anyone need to buy a ticket?"

"I bought mine two weeks ago," Elena said. "I've already got my dress."

"Me, too," Justin joked. "How do the tickets work? Can we all sit together?"

"First come, first seated," Jack explained.

"Allie, if we get there first, we'll save you and Orren seats," Jack said. She, Elena, Sally, Justin,

and two other guys from the soccer team were all going together. "And you should do the same, just in case Justin takes forever to get ready."

"Oh, please," Chris said with a groan, "you're always late."

"That is such a lie!" Jack screeched.

I smiled, but my head was spinning. Jack was going to save seats for me and Orren. Like it was no big deal. And no one had protested.

"Okay, well, we've got to get to our game," Justin said. "See you after. Good luck!"

"Right back at you," I told him.

Justin gave me a huge smile, revealing a crooked tooth—the one right between his canine and the big one in the front. His smile was really cute, I thought as he trotted off with Chris.

Funny how I had never noticed that before.

An hour later, I was in the game, and there was nothing but the ball. It was as though the world had ceased to exist, as though I had ceased to exist. There was no team. There was no Cleveland Middle School. No Saint Agnes. No Tam. No Orren. No Renee or Chris. Only a ball and a goal. . . .

Slam!

With a sliding kick, I knocked the ball away from the Saint Agnes right wing, shooting beneath her leg. Like lightning, Sally leaped in and slapped the ball toward their goal. I didn't even realize that I had gotten up, that I was chasing her, until I was closer to the goal than she was.

The whole game had been this way—back and forth with Saint Agnes. We were down by one, but those parolies were starting to get tired. I could feel it. And I was just getting warmed up.

A quick pass to Jack, who slammed it toward me. In an instant, I headed the ball toward their goal. Score!

We were tied. Two minutes later, Elena stole the ball and darted back toward Saint Agnes's territory. She was about to take a shot when one of the Saint Agnes girls dug her in the shin wth her cleat. Elena fell to her knees, and the ref called the foul. I looked to the sidelines . . . just as I'd feared, Coach was motioning to me to kick. This was my shot. My chance to win the game.

For a moment, I was struck with the strangeness of it—it was my chance to prove Coach

Connors right—or wrong. She said I had the talent. She believed in my scoring. But I knew how to defend, that was my thing.

Then again, I thought, maybe my thing isn't my only thing anymore. Maybe I wasn't just a striker or a sweeper. Maybe I was a streeper: both at once.

One step. Two steps. I ran toward the ball. It was like I had super vision. I could see every crack, every stain, every pore in the surface of the ball. Like it was as big as the earth . . . Don't miss, I thought as my leg swung toward the ball.

And I didn't.

A moment later, the whistle blew—game over.

I just stood there, breathing hard until Jack ran up behind me and pounced.

"We did it!" Elena screamed.

For a moment, I felt like I was floating . . . and then I realized that I really was floating, that my teammates had picked me up and were carrying me off the field.

"Put me down!" I shouted. I was worried that they might drop me. "Put me down!" But no one

heard me. They were singing and laughing too loudly to hear.

I could see out over all of the green practice fields from up there. The golden and orange leaves were racing across the grass. I felt the sun beat down on my face, and the wind blow my damp hair back.

I remembered how Tam had wanted me to join the cheer squad. And maybe, I thought, if I had, she and Renee and I would still be friends. But this wouldn't have happened. I never would have had this moment.

Suddenly, my life without Tam was starting to seem a lot less blank.

sulk•a•bra•tion \'sulk-a-bray-shen\ *n* : the worst party in the history of partydom, one that promises nothing but humiliation, bad dancing, and rubbery grilled chicken

"What are you all dressed up for?" Lionel asked as I walked down the stairs in my never-before-worn-in-public long black skirt and hot-pink blouse, along with my chunky shoes. It was Saturday evening. D-Day. Dork Day.

"I'm going to the sports banquet," I told him. "Some of us actually get off the couch and run around once in a while." So what if I was going to a major sulkabration? I wasn't about to admit that to Lionel.

Lionel flipped the channel to MTV. "You got all dressed up for your date with Bore-en? It'll probably be the thrill of his life."

God, I was still not used to being the grist of the gossip mill. "How do you know about Orren? You don't even know who he is!"

Lionel rolled his eyeballs back into his head. "He rides our bus, moron."

"Oh, right." I'd actually kind of forgotten that Orren rode our bus. He still always sat in the front, and he got on at the last stop. I was usually too busy chatting with Justin or finishing homework to pay much attention to him. Wow, I thought. It's actually kind of odd that I had never asked him to join us.

"I can't believe you're going out with that guy. He's the biggest nerd at Cleveland."

"Counting you?" I snapped.

"Counting Shaffer Spence, winner of the regional science fair, counting Victoria Lakes, whose glasses are so thick they could be used to start a fire, counting Jeffrey Jackson, whose face looks like it's about to erupt," Lionel said, ticking off every major nerd in our school on his fingers, "counting *everyone*."

"Look, it's not like Orren is my boyfriend. We're just—" I hesitated. What were we? Orren was just my lab partner and a nice person whose feelings I didn't want to hurt—but that didn't sound very good, so I went with,

"We're just friends. And I'm not going to treat him like dirt just because everyone thinks he's a dweeb. I mean, so what if he's nerdy? At least he's different."

"'Different' is an understatement." Lionel snorted. He looked at me for a minute, and I thought I saw his expression soften. "You're just like Mom."

I was just about to ask Lionel what in the world he meant by that, when Mom breezed in, jingling her car keys. "Ready, Allie?" She smiled at me. "You look beautiful."

I blushed. *Beautiful* isn't a word I get a lot. I guess I tend to think of myself as borderline pretty at best. But it felt good to hear.

"Do you want to come along, Lionel?" Mom asked. "I have to drop Allie at the banquet."

Lionel shook his head and turned back to the TV. "Jed is coming over later. We're going to network his laptop and my computer and play some online video games."

I rolled my eyes. And my brother was calling Orren a nerd? "Have fun," I chirped as I followed Mom out the door.

"You, too," Lionel called sarcastically. "Tell Orren I said hi."

Even the norks were mocking me now.

I couldn't wait to get this evening over with.

"Is that him?" Mom whispered a few moments later as we pulled up to the rear entrance to the cafetorium. Orren was standing alone outside the double doors. He was wearing a new-looking green shirt and a funky blue-and-maroon tie with a pair of black pants.

"Yeah."

"He's cute," Mom said brightly. "When you said 'nerd,' I was thinking of Lionel's friends."

I laughed, wishing that I had a tape recorder. "Well, he doesn't usually look this good," I admitted. Actually, with the funky tie, Orren's frizzed-out hair actually looked borderline cool. And the green of his shirt brought out the color of his eyes.

"Have fun," Mom said. Leaning over, she gave me a peck on the cheek. "Knock 'em dead."

I gave her a wavery smile and took a deep breath. "I'll see you at ten."

"Hey!" Orren said as I stepped out of the car. "You're three minutes late." He grinned, though, so I knew he was kidding.

"You look great," I told him.

Orren looked like I'd just handed him a check for a million dollars. "Yeah?"

I laughed. "Yeah."

He stood there awkwardly for a moment, so I cleared my throat and gestured toward myself. "Oh! You look great, too," Orren said quickly.

"Nice job," I told him.

"You want to go inside?"

Not really, I said mentally, but what I said out loud was, "Sure."

There was a burst of music as we walked into the banquet. I was surprised to see that the center had been cleared to make a dance floor, and there was a DJ playing music. I hadn't expected that.

"Allie! Orren! Over here!" Jack was going Muppet at us like crazy. Elena was next to her, and she waved, too.

I took a step toward my friends and froze in my tracks. Tam and Renee were at a table ten feet away. I was going to have to walk right past Tam.

Renee was leaning toward Chris, whispering something in his ear. Tam glanced at them, then looked down at the table, obviously bored. Tom wasn't saying anything. I took the opportunity to walk past her, staring in the opposite direction, as if the blank wall at the end of the cafetorium was the most fascinating thing in the world. I made it past her without making eye contact, and breathed a sigh of relief as I reached Jack's table.

"Isn't this great?" Elena asked as we sat down. "I love the glitter on the tables."

I looked around. Actually, considering that we were sitting in the cafetorium, the place did look pretty elegant. The tables had been spread with white tablecloths and covered in colorful glitter. The centerpieces were gerber daisies in Crayola shades, and the ceiling was filled with helium balloons in blue and red, our school colors.

"I love the DJ," Jack said as she bopped along to the beat.

"Is this where all of the cool cats are sitting?" Justin asked as he appeared behind Elena's chair.

"Yeah, but we'll let you sit with us, anyway," Jack told him.

"Hey, man, what's up?" Justin asked as he slid into the chair next to Orren and gave him a high five. "Lookin' sharp."

"Yeah, I love that tie," Jack said warmly.

Orren touched his tie self-consciously and said, "Thanks."

I tried to keep my mind on the conversation around me, but I was too distracted by the fact that we were sitting so close to Tam. I wondered whether she was having a good time. It hadn't really looked like it when I walked in. Good, I thought meanly. It serves her right. But there was still a part of me that felt bad. I didn't want Tam to be miserable—I wanted both of us to be happy.

The DJ put on a bouncy dance beat, and Elena grinned. "I feel like dancing," she said. "Who's with me?"

"I'm in," Jack said.

"Me, too," Sally said, standing up.

"Me, three," Justin agreed.

"Let's go," Sally said, pulling Evan and Sam—Justin's soccer friends—out of their chairs

by the hands. "I can't wait to shake my booty."

"Anyone else?" Evan asked. "Orren—you can't leave me alone out there, man."

I glanced at Orren. He had this look on his face—I don't know, like Evan was an ax-wielding maniac, or something. "I'm guessing you're not a big dancer," I said to Orren.

"Not really," he admitted. "But you go."

"You're going to sit here by yourself?" I asked him.

"I don't mind." I knew it was probably true, but still. I minded.

"You guys go ahead," I told my friends, secretly relieved. I really didn't want the whole school to see me dancing with Orren.

"You sure?" Jack asked. "Come on, Orren. It'll be fun."

"Just this one song," Elena begged.

"No, no really—" I started, but Orren cut me off.

"Okay," he said, sliding back his chair. He must have seen the horror on my face, because his eyebrows drew together in confusion. "You want to, right?"

Elena clapped eagerly, so I nodded. She grabbed our hands and dragged us to the dance floor. Jack and Justin let out a whoop as we formed a circle. Justin launched into some weird version of the funky chicken, and Jack was managing to dance without actually moving her feet. She was a total arm dancer. Elena bopped around all over the place, like some kind of Mexican jumping bean.

We were the only ones dancing, and I felt pretty conspicuous as I tried to dance and appear invisible at the same time. But that only lasted a minute. It was almost as though everyone had just been waiting for someone to start the dancing, because after about two minutes, Sarah bopped out to join us. Then half of the field hockey team headed toward the dance floor, followed by a couple of cheer squadders. Everyone was dancing in big circles of friends—except the footballers, who mostly lurked in the corner trying to look cool. The DJ turned up the volume.

Orren did the step-together-step-back that most guys do, but he wasn't bad. He actually smiled at me and leaned over to whisper in my

ear. "I've been practicing," he admitted, which made me laugh. Orren laughed, too. I looked out at the other dancers, expecting to see Tam. She's an excellent dancer, and loves music. But she wasn't there. A moment later, I spotted her still sitting at her table. Her eyes flicked to me for a moment.

Without even realizing what I was doing, I gestured to her to come over. "Come dance," I whispered, even though I knew she couldn't hear me.

Tam looked surprised . . . but a moment later, her eyes flicked to Renee. And even though Renee had her back turned toward Tam, Tam still didn't get up. She looked at me and shook her head slightly, then looked down at the table.

Orren caught the look. "What's wrong?" he asked, leaning toward me. "Tam doesn't want to dance?"

"Tam doesn't know what she wants," I told him. Suddenly, I didn't feel much like dancing anymore. "Do you want to get out of here?" I asked, pointing to the exit sign.

Orren nodded. "Yeah." He looked relieved.

Elena grabbed my hand as we started to walk off. "Back in a minute," I told her. I waved to Jack and Justin, who frowned slightly.

The night was surprisingly quiet as the cafetorium door closed behind us. The air was mild—it was Indian Summer—with only a slight chill as we walked away from the school, toward the soccer fields.

Looking up at the sky, I spotted a brilliant star. "Star light, star bright," I said, half to myself. "Make a wish." I closed my eyes. The ache in my heart told me to wish that Tamara and I could be best friends again, but I wasn't even sure that was what I wanted anymore. Then I thought about Chris. My reflex wish for three years had been to wish that he would like me. But I didn't really care about that, either. In the end, I decided that I didn't know what to wish for. So I just gave up and wished for world peace. That's always a safe one.

When I opened my eyes, Orren was looking at me. "What did you wish for?" he asked.

"If I tell you, it won't come true."

A corner of Orren's mouth drifted up. "It

won't come true, anyway. You just wished on Venus."

"What?" I stared at the sky, where my wishing star glittered. "How do you know?"

"Venus is the brightest thing in the sky," Orrcn said, staring at the darkness above us. "It's practically all you can see when you live in the city. The light from all of the buildings hides most of the stars. But look, you can still see a few. That's Cygnus, the swan. It has a star with a planet in orbit around it."

I looked to where he was pointing, suddenly feeling very small beneath the enormous universe. It made me feel as though there was nothing I could do that would matter very much. In a way, it was frightening. But it was comforting, too. Because I knew that there wasn't a mistake I could make that would disturb the universe. It was funny how I only ever thought about stuff like that when I was with Orren. "How do you know so much about the stars?"

He shrugged. "I don't know. Books. TV. Stars are interesting." He turned his face back to the sky, and his expression held a mixture of wonder and

happiness . . . and some of that feeling rubbed off on me. Orren was right—the stars *were* interesting. And beautiful.

I looked at him, watching him watch the sky, and my heart gave a sudden lurch. No, no—don't get me wrong. It wasn't love, or even extreme like, or any of that romantic junk. Ew—*no way*. No, the feeling was more like . . . like affection, or something. Like the way I felt about Peebles. And, for the first time, I realized I was having fun.

For some reason, I thought about what Lionel had said to me earlier. That I was just like Mom. Actually, I thought that Orren was more like Mom than I was. They both did their own thing and didn't care about what other people thought. I wished I were like that. The truth was, though, I *did* care.

Orren looked at me, blinking, like he was just waking up from a dream. "We're probably missing the dinner. Maybe we should head back."

I wasn't hungry, and I didn't really want to go back inside. I felt like everyone was looking at

me there, forming opinions and judgments. It made it hard to think. Out here, alone with Orren, I could breathe. "Do you want to?"

"Not yet."

"Me, neither." Orren turned back to face the stars.

We stood out there for a few more minutes, until I started to feel cold. Orren gave me his jacket, and then we headed back to the banquet.

The loud music washed over me as I stepped into the cafetorium. It took a moment for my eyes to adjust to the flashing lights, and I blinked as I felt someone squeeze me on the shoulder. I looked over into the warm dark eyes of Coach Connors.

"Allie," Coach said, "I'm glad you're here. I was worried when I didn't see you."

"I couldn't miss the banquet, Coach," I said with a smile.

Coach nodded, smiling. "You played well today." She was wearing a pink slip dress that skimmed lightly over her muscles. I was sort of surprised by her dress—I had never suspected

Coach Connors could own anything so girly. But then I remembered my own pink shirt. I guess we're all more complicated than we seem. "You did what I've been expecting you to do all year," she added.

I looked over at Orren, who grinned. "I guess maybe I am a striker after all," I said to the coach. Maybe I was better at taking risks than I thought.

"I always knew you could do it," Coach said. "You were the one who needed to learn that you could." She patted me on the arm. "Will I see you on the indoor soccer team next semester?"

"I hadn't really thought about it—"

"I'll take that as a yes," Coach said. "We need you." She nodded to Orren, then gave me a smile—a huge smile. I smiled back. Then she walked away.

"She's kind of scary," Orren whispered once Coach Connors was out of earshot.

"Nah," I told him as I watched the coach stride across the room. "She's just fearless. And she expects everyone else to be, too." As I watched her glide across the room, her posture perfect, I

realized that Coach's confidence gave her a certain kind of freedom. Coach was almost like a bird—a hawk, or an eagle, maybe—who doesn't have to worry too much about what the world thinks, because she flies above it.

"Coach Condor," I whispered, smiling.

"What?" Orren asked.

I flushed a little, shaking my head. "Oh, nothing. I was just thinking that Coach Connors is like a condor."

Orren nodded, his face thoughtful. "You know," he said as we moved toward our table, "condors are interesting birds. They feed on dead animals. But they can attack live ones, too—they've been known to bring down deer."

I stopped in my tracks and blinked at him. Leave it to Orren to mess up my metaphor.

"Okay," I said finally, "she's not like a condor."

"They're huge," Orren went on, as though he hadn't heard me. "They have a nine- or ten-foot wingspan. They're pretty amazing in the air. And they're very rare."

I lifted my eyebrows at him. Ten-foot

wingspan? They must really soar. "So—she's kind of like a condor."

Orren snorted at me, like I was really hopeless. "It's a simile, Allie," he huffed. "You don't have to be so literal all the time."

- 14 -

non•shock•er \ non-'shok-er \: *n* : a surprise that, when you think about it, isn't really such a surprise, after all

I squeezed my history book between my belly and the edge of the lockers, flipping through the pages. I always do my homework on a piece of three-ring paper, then fold the page into my textbook. It's a horrible habit. First of all, it virtually guarantees that my locker will be a mess, because half the time the papers slip out of the books and fall to the bottom, like a pile of wet leaves beneath the bleachers. And for another thing, it always takes me forever to find my homework.

It's a strange addiction.

Finally, *finally*, after flipping through chapter seven about twelve times, my homework appeared on page 97. I picked it out and shoved it into the flap of my binder, then slammed my locker closed and turned toward class.

And there they were. Tam and Renee.

My feet did this bizarre kind of jerky robot dance as the sight of them stopped me in my tracks. For a moment, I considered turning around, heading the other way. I'd be late to class, my mind flashed, but it would be worth it.

But in the next moment, my body decided to move forward. Renee gave me this evil grin, but Tam gave me this look like, *Please don't*. I can't explain it, but those were the words stamped across her face: PLEASE DON'T.

I don't know what she thought I was going to do.

"Hi, Allie!" Renee said brightly as she walked up to me. She was wearing this matchy-matchy little blue sweater-and-miniskirt combo. How does she sit down in that thing? I wondered, eyeing the skirt.

"Hi, Renee." I didn't bother giving my face muscles a smile workout. I knew that Renee wouldn't be giving me the big hello unless she wanted to say something nasty, but I walked right into it.

"So—did you have fun at the banquet on

Saturday?" Renee asked. "You and your boyfriend looked like you were having a good time!"

I gritted my teeth. God, Renee was annoying. I looked at Tam, but she looked away. So she still wasn't going to stand up to Renee. I don't know why I was surprised. "We had a great time, thanks," I said, not even bothering to deny that Orren was my boyfriend. I knew she'd just said that to irk me. "Too bad your date looked miserable."

Tam gaped and Renee glared, but there wasn't really much that either one of them could say. Renee turned quickly on her heel and stalked off.

But Tam's dark eyes were locked on me. She didn't move.

It took Renee a minute to realize that Tam wasn't trotting after her. A worry line formed between her eyebrows. "Tam," she called. "Come on!"

Tam's eyes flicked to Renee, then back to me.

"I'm really glad you had a good time, Allie," Tam said quietly.

Don't follow her, I thought. You don't have to. But Tam was already in motion, hurrying after Renee.

Renee flashed me a triumphant smile, and a moment later, their retreating figures disappeared into the swirl of students racing to their second-period classes.

A cold hand of fear gripped my stomach and squeezed. This wasn't supposed to happen.

"Hey, are you okay?" asked a voice next to my ear. I looked up to see Justin standing there, peering at me. "You look kind of . . ." He shook his head. "I don't know."

"You're Justin Thyme," I said, sighing. "As usual."

Justin nodded, but he didn't ask questions. "You going my way?" he asked giving his chin a little jut toward the end of the hall.

"Sure am." We fell into step.

"So—Saturday was pretty fun," Justin said, giving me this sideways look.

"Oh, yeah," I agreed, trying to sound cheerful. "You were right—I'm really glad I went with Orren."

Justin cleared his throat. "So, uh, are you and Orren, like—boyfriend and girlfriend now?"

My eyes locked onto his face, trying to read his expression. Was Justin going to give me a hard time, now? I couldn't believe this. "We're *friends*."

"Oh." Justin nodded, looking relieved. "That's good."

"What's *that* supposed to mean?" I snapped. "Look, Orren is a really nice guy, and any girl would be lucky to go out with him. I am so sick of people putting him down because he's slightly strange. All right! So he's weird! So he's interested in typhoons, and algae, and looking at the stars. Is that such a crime? No! And I swear, if one more person tells me that he's a dork, I think I'm going to *lose it*! He's my friend! Okay? My *friend*!"

Justin's eyes were wide. "Uh . . . okay," he said uncertainly. "I just meant that it was, you know, good for *me*."

I stared at Justin for a moment as my heart did this slowing-down, speeding-up thing. But I didn't have time to wonder whether I was having

a heart attack, because I was too busy trying to figure out what Justin meant. Good for *him*? Did he mean . . . ?

"So, uh, I'll see you at lunch?" Justin asked.

I nodded, unable to speak. Are you saying that you like me? I thought. My lips trembled, and I was about to ask, but I was too slow. Justin had already walked through Mrs. Pearson's classroom door, and the moment had passed.

Oh my God, I thought. The sudden realization stopped me in my tracks. It was like I had stuck my finger into a wall socket, or something—like my body was filled with electricity. Oh my God, I like Justin!

All this time, I'd been too busy paying attention to my crush on Chris to even notice Justin! But we had tons in common. We had a great time together. And he is funny, and sweet, and cute. . . . Of course I was crushing on him. He was more than a squash. He was real. When I thought about it, it was a complete nonshocker.

"Hey, Allie, hurry up!" Jack called as she jogged up to me. "We're going to be late to class!"

She poked me in the arm and we fell into a trot together.

"Lunch patio or cafetorium?" Jack asked. Translation: where should I find you at lunch?

"Lunch patio," I told her.

Jack nodded. "Save for a save." Translation: If you get there first, reserve my seat, and I'll do the same for you.

"And save a seat for Justin."

Jack rolled her eyes. "Thanks, Captain Obvious. Whoever gets there first saves five more."

"Don't you mean four more?"

Jack ticked off the names on her fingers. "You, me, Sally, Justin, Elena, and Orren," Jack explained. Like we ate lunch with Orren every day.

I spotted Orren at the end of the hall. He was reading a book and walking at the same time, headed toward our English class. I shook my head and smiled. The book was a biography of Benjamin Franklin. Where does he find these things? I wondered. "Cool," I told Jack. "See you then."

"See you!" Jack waved and trotted on as Orren disappeared into our classroom.

I hitched my backpack higher onto my back and took a step toward English.

Well, I thought as I headed to class, no matter how bad this day gets, at least I get to have lunch with my friends. Maybe we aren't the coolest kids at Cleveland. But what's the point of being cool when you never get to do what you want?

Suddenly, I realized something. I wasn't a Dweebosaurus, after all. I wasn't about to become extinct, and neither were my friends. If anyone was becoming extinct, it was Tam— the new glommer. She was disappearing, clinging onto Renee while I was learning how to do what I wanted. Like Mom. And Coach Connors. And Jack. And Orren.

Orren once told me that the dinosaurs eventually evolved into birds. Can you imagine that— a freaky giant lizard turning into a tiny chirping creature with feathers and the power to fly? But it just goes to show how much things can change when they have to adapt to a new environment.

That's kind of what happened to me, I guess. I went from feeling like a Dweebosaurus to becoming my own, new creature. Maybe one day, like Coach Condor, I'd learn to fly.

But, for now, I was happy just to be Allie Kimball. My own me. Unique, but not alone.

No. Not alone at all.

First Edition
Printed in the United States of America

Reinforced binding

Library of Congress Cataloging-in-Publication Data on file.
ISBN 0-7868-5169-4

Visit www.hyperionbooksforchildren.com

SIXTH-GRADE
glommers, norks, and me

Lisa Papademetriou

Hyperion Books for Children
New York

SIXTH-GRADE
glommers, **norks,** and me

Then she asked, "What do you think old Nate'll do if he can't find him there?"

"Go back homesteadin'. And you and me, we'll go back home."

"What's beyond Lovelock? You talked with Graber last night. I didn't. Your bedroll was right by his."

"Deadahead, more'n seventy miles away."

"And what's on the other side of there?"

"Texas stops after Deadahead, and New Mexico Territory begins."

Beeler was thoughtful. "Leo, we never traveled out of Texas, did we, except to the mule market in Missouri? Far as I know, no Quiney ever did."

Leo agreed. "I never heard tell of a Quiney who did, but there's some of the boys we lost track of. No Quiney we know anything about has ever been much of a wanderer. And if anyone ever did leave Texas, it would have to be a man from our kinfolks. New Mexico Territory surely ain't for females."

Beeler snorted. "Just how come it ain't, Leo?"

"Graber told me somewhat about it last night. It's supposed to be full of desperate characters from all over, some of 'em even from Texas. It ain't no place for puny, weakly womenfolks."

For the second time Beulah Land snorted.

3 TURNIPS AND CARROTS!

One thing pleased Beeler about the land near Lovelock—there were some little lakes around. A person could take off her boots and soak her feet while she took her leisure in the shade of a willow tree. The horses could drink up. Travis could wander around in the shallow water, bellowing and snorting, or just stand chest deep, looking off into the distance thinking whatever longhorns thought.

But they couldn't dillydally too long by the water, because Nate's pa could be moving on ahead of them, too, going to this Sundown or Sunset, that nobody had ever heard of in either Over-the-River or Comanche Springs.

Lovelock turned out to be a surprise. It was bone-dry. There wasn't a single saloon in the whole town. Nate, who'd traveled more than either of the Quineys, said he could hardly believe it. The three of them stood in front of the Nicodemus Hotel with Travis tied between Two Cents and Jinglebob, staring at the

people of the town. They were mighty rough lookers
—long-haired and dirty and dressed, more often than
not, in buckskin instead of cloth.

Nate told Beeler and Leo quietly, "There are some
buffalo hunters here, and I think some buffalo-bone
gatherers, too."

"How do you know for sure?" asked Beeler.

Nate sniffed. "You can smell a buffalo hunter half a
mile away."

Beeler snuffled too. There *was* a stink in the air. It
smelled the way it did when pigs were slaughtered
back home. That was a time of year she didn't like
one bit. She asked Nate, "With there bein' no saloons
here, where'll we ask about your pa and them men?"

"Cafés and the hotel and stores, I guess."

She nodded. "This time I'm lookin' too. Leo," she
ordered, "you ride herd on my critter and the horses.
Graber'll take one side of the street and I'll take the
other."

Leo burst out, "I can ask, too!"

"No, I'm a faster talker than you are. The next
place we go, you can mebbe ask Graber to let you help
him hunt in saloons."

"Beeler, I sure wish you'd stayed to home. I'd sure
like to get rid of ya."

She laughed up at him. "You didn't think I ever felt
welcome with you, did ya?"

She tethered Jinglebob to the hitching post, then

put Travis next to him. Nate secured Stupid, leaving
Leo still mounted, watching over everything, but
scowling.

Beeler took the right side of the one-street town,
Nate the left. She went first of all into the hotel. No,
five men answering the travelers' descriptions weren't
staying there and never had been.

Next she tried the Fair Deal Chop House between
a livery stable and a ladies' dry-goods store—not that
she'd seen any women in Lovelock yet. But there was
one at the café, an oldish one, wiping off the oilcloth
on the tables. Nobody else was in sight because it
was eleven o'clock. What the old lady wiped off—
crumbs, steak bones, and all—went down onto the
sawdust floor. It wasn't much of a hash house, Beeler
decided.

"What can I do for you, young man?" she asked
Beeler.

"I ain't," said Beeler.

"You ain't what?" The woman straightened up.

"A he."

"No, on second look you prob'ly ain't. You got
braids, though, and lotsa boys around here got them.
Is your pa or ma here? It's too early for grub to be
served up. What're you doin' here? You ain't alone,
are you, girlie?"

"No, I ain't alone. Have you seen five men travelin'
all in a bunch?"

The old lady smiled. "Lotsa times, dear. Them buffalo hunters and wild-horse catchers that come here for eats, they go around together. They surely shovel in the grub—prob'ly because this year they can't spend their money in saloons. Mebbe next year the mayor'll say there can be whiskey again."

Beeler sighed. This was taking too much time. She described the five men as Nate had described them. The old lady looked at the ceiling, thinking and humming. Then she nodded. "Yes, sir, I did. But it was more'n a month ago—more like two months. My memory ain't so clear no more. But I think it was when my son and me just opened for bus'ness. They was like that—tall and short and fat and skinny, but the number five man was bald. He didn' have no yeller curls. His forehead went all the way over and ended at the back of his neck."

Beeler frowned. "Did he have blue eyes?" Nate's were blue, like the color of bluebonnet flowers.

"Oh, dearie, mosta the time I'm too busy to take notice of things like that."

"Ain't there anything else you can remember, Missus?"

The woman tapped her foot and hummed some more. Then she smiled, showing teeth that were mighty fine, too fine to be hers, Beeler decided. "Yep, there surely was. The bald man was mighty polite to me. That made him stand out."

"His kid's polite, too. That'd be him," Beeler cried out. "Where were they headed?"

"Lordy, I don't know, honey. They didn't settle around these parts. I never saw 'em agin in Lovelock."

"Didn't they say at all where they were going?"

Once more the old woman pondered. She sighed, then told Beeler, "Deep down in my gizzard I seem to recall that the bald-headed one said somethin' about restin' from a long ride when he got to where the sun sets." She wiped her hands on her hips. "That's right. And the big one told him to quit jawin' about it with me because they had to hit the trail right away to get the most miles they could outa daylight."

Beeler wanted to know, "Have you ever heard of a town called Sunset or Sundown?"

"No, girlie, but I can tell you somebody who might know."

"Who'd that be?"

"The postmaster of Lovelock, that's who. He come here last week. You'll find him in Barger's Store, where the buffalo hunters get their supplies."

"Much obliged." The girl gave the old lady a swift grin and ran out of the café down along the rutty street to where a glum Leo waited. "I found the galoots," she shouted at him. "They came through here!"

"Where are they now?"

"On their way to Sundown or Sunset—if they ain't already there. We're gonna find out where that is right away." Beeler untied Jinglebob and Travis and mounted. She whistled her Travis whistle. It made the steer jump and start moving, but it did something else, too. It brought Nate bursting out of a store from across the way. He came pounding over, raising up more dust in the street.

"I thought your steer had got loose, Beulah Land."

"Nope, I was callin' you, Nate." Quickly she told him her news and saw hopefulness spread over his face. He mounted Stupid as quickly as he could, though the horse tried to lie down in the street the minute he got his boot into the stirrup.

Barger's Store was a big place, plumb full of men buying this and that and smelling all the way up to heaven—buffalo hunters for danged sure. They made way for Beeler, more out of surprise at seeing a girl in pants than anything else, she decided later. She marched right up to the iron bars that had *Post Office* painted on a sign above them. In a place like Lovelock it was pretty clear to her why the postmaster might want to stay in a cage. It could be safer than out in the store. Buffalo hunters appeared to be mean-eyed as well as stinking of buffalo blood and buffalo fat.

Because it was Nate's pa they were hunting, Beeler let him do the asking. But she stood right behind him

with her hand on the butt of the six-shooter in her
belt. Men were crowded up all around them both,
curious to know what they'd have to say to the postmaster. Would he have a letter for them? She guessed
there weren't many folks in Lovelock who'd get letters
—let alone be able to write them.

Graber said to the postmaster, "Please, sir, is there a
town anywhere at all around here called Sunset or Sundown?"

The postmaster shook his head. "No Sunset or Sundown that I know of right offhand, my boy, but let me
look in my book for one."

"Have you got a whole book of just towns?" Beeler
asked, very impressed.

"I sure have, young man."

This time Beeler didn't correct him. The way the
buffalo hunters were laughing, the postmaster could be
told about it later on. Instead she called out, "Thank
ya."

She watched while the man turned the pages of a
largish book. He soon closed it and looked up through
his ugly little steel-rimmed spectacles. "I take it by
'around here' you refer to the State of Texas?"

"Yes sir, or hereabouts," said Nate.

"Texas? Or *hereabouts*?" The postmaster took off
his spectacles. "Well, Uncle Sam's book of U.S. towns
with post offices in them says there's a Sunman in
Indiana, a Sunflower in Missouri, a Sunbury in Ohio

and in Pennsylvania, and a Sun Prairie in Wisconsin. Nothing at all in Texas—at least not at the moment."

"What about the territories west of here?" Beeler cried out over Graber's shoulder.

The man chuckled. "I looked under the territories also. Nothing. But that doesn't mean much, given them."

"How come?"

"Because the communities west of here are often like mushrooms. They pop up overnight and disappear a month later. Uncle Sam's post-office system can't catch up with them. Many of them are mining towns. You know, here today and gone tomorrow."

Nate asked, "You think if there is a Sundown or Sunset, it's west of here?"

The postmaster brought his lips together, put on his spectacles again, and nodded. "Probably, if there is such a place."

"Is that your cow sense opinion for sure?" asked Beeler.

"Young man, there is no 'for sure' when it concerns anything about New Mexico Territory—or for that matter, Arizona Territory. I'm going on common sense. I am not a cow. The sun sets in the west. You've noted that the states east of here don't have such a town. I should think logic would tell you that this town lies in the far West."

Beeler jabbed Nate in the ribs with her elbow and

hissed into his ear, "Who's this here logic? Mebbe he'd know."

"It isn't a he," Nate whispered back. He said to the postmaster, "Thank you very much."

Outside, away from the throng of buffalo hunters, Beeler drew in a noseful of clear air. Nate was looking at his boots, mighty down in the mouth. "Buck up," she told him, feeling sorry for him. "They rode through here, them men, on their way to the same place you heard of in Old Mexico, didn't they?" She'd decided not to ask about logic.

Graber turned up the toes of his boots sadly. "But *where* is it?"

Being friendly, she hit him on the shoulder with her fist. "West of here, that's what logic says. We'll find it."

He shook his head. "No, it isn't right. All I ever asked was for somebody to go to Lovelock with me. I'll go back to the homestead now."

"You're gonna quit huntin'?" Beeler put all of her scorn into her voice and words.

He looked properly stung. "You mean you and Leo will go on with me? We'll need more supplies."

"Sure we will, Nate. You buy what we have to have here." She hauled her egg money out of her pants pocket and held it out to him.

Suspiciously Nate looked first at Leo, guarding Travis and the horses, then at Beeler. His eyes narrowed. "You're hoping to get out of school by going with me, aren't you, Beulah Land?"

She scoffed, "Not me. Leo is for sure. I don't mind school so much. But it can wait. This way I might be seein' somethin' of the world I'd otherwise never get to see. I been ponderin' while we rode along. It ain't so easy for girls to traipse all over as it is for boys. Girls get stuck at home all the time."

He chewed this over and finally nodded. "All right then." He looked more cheerful around the jowls, Beeler decided. And he took the money. "After all, this town we're looking for might be just over the very next hill."

Beeler looked over the flat prairie. There weren't any hills in sight at all. "Well, mebbe at the bottom of the next big dry gulch and not on the map yet. Ya know," she added, "it's a Quiney duty to help you out all the way to wherever you're goin'."

Graber shivered a bit, even though it was plenty hot in the sunshine of June. "Please don't tell me ever again that you Quineys are hogs for duty."

"A hog, or a pig for that matter, ain't a stupid animal, no matter what folks say. Me and Leo, we took to ya. We like you. Get more grub, and we'll get on our way west to Deadahead. We can do some askin' there, too."

Two Cents tried to kick Beeler as she came up to

Leo, but she dodged his hind hooves the way she always did. "Leo," she said, "we're goin' on with Graber."

He gave her a fish-eyed look. "You and me, Beeler? Both of us?"

"Sure. Graber's buyin' more supplies for us right now." She patted Travis on the muzzle. He'd been mighty well-mannered in Lovelock among so many bad-smelling people.

"Where are we headed, Beeler?"

She swung her arm in a wide gesture toward the west. "Over there. That's where this here place has got to be. The postmaster told us so."

She waited until Nate returned with a sack of supplies and mounted up, too. Then Leo put in, "While you two was in town bein' so all-fired important, I was askin' some questions of my own out here."

"What did you find out?" asked Nate.

"There's a Army trail through here. It runs from Camp Concho, down by Over-the-River, to Fort Sumner in New Mexico Territory. If your pa and them others went into the Territory, they most likely traveled on it, too."

Beeler said happily, "I bet that's so, Leo. It's a good thing them five look so peculiar, ain't it—bald-headed, too! You can't miss spottin' him, that pa of Nate's. More'n likely them five dropped their names in the river if they headed into the Territory."

Graber knew what she meant all right. "There you go again, Beulah Land! Listen here, you don't know one thing for sure about them. You've got it all set up in your head that my father's changed his name because he's in trouble with the law. Next thing you'll say is that you expect to find them hanging from a tree somewhere."

"One thing you can say about old Beeler, she likes to be right, no matter what she says," Leo told Nate, as he gave Travis's neck rope to his sister.

At the same time Beeler noticed that he gave her a funny little smile. She thought it was the kind of grin he'd given her once when he put a burr under Jinglebob's saddle back home just before she mounted. Elnora had seen him do it and tattled on him, so Beeler had scratched his wishbone up plenty that time. It was the same grin all right. Sort of mean and tight. Seeing it didn't give a body a lot of comfort.

Leo looked to have something up his sleeve. Beeler held onto Travis's rope until they'd gone a mile or so from Lovelock. Then she took it off him and dug her heels into Jinglebob's flanks. The horse spurted ahead of the other two, with the longhorn moving smartly alongside him.

She told Jinglebob and Travis as soon as they were out of earshot of her brother and Nate, "Leo is up to devilment. We got to watch out for him. But whatever he's got in mind, it ain't gonna work!"

They trotted into Deadahead in the late afternoon. It was a dugout town, made of houses with their innards dug out underground and with their roofs covered with grassy sod. Several of the houses had flowers growing on the rooftops. Travis paid them some heed as they went through town and hitched their horses to a rail set out in front of one of the only two wooden buildings in sight, a general store. The other one next door was a saloon.

Nate decided they'd try the store before they tried the saloon. Once more they left Leo on guard while they started to ask around. The store man was short, with billygoat whiskers. His wife was taller than he was and some younger, with sharp little blue eyes, yellow curls, and a very fancy gray dress, with a bustle, trimmed in white curlicue braid. Beeler guessed she wore paint. Her cheeks were a wicked-looking color.

Mr. Billygoat Whiskers nodded when Nate asked about the five men. "Yes, sir, me and Elfie, we sold 'em supplies last month, didn' we, honey gal? Or was it month before last?"

Elfie smiled at him as if she truly favored him. "We surely did, a whole fifty dollars' worth." She gave Beeler an odd, questioning look, which Beeler knew by now meant, "Are you a boy or a girl?"

"I ain't a he," said Beeler. Suddenly she asked be-

fore Graber could get in his question about Sundown
or Sunset. "What'd they pay you folks in? American
gold pieces or Mexican silver pesos?"

The whiskery man blinked. "Mexican money. Anything that's hard money is good in these parts."

"Ah hah!" Beeler told Nate.

"Ah hah, what?" He turned his back on her, letting
her know she wasn't going to get a rise out of him,
though it ought to be clear as sin to him. If the men
used Mexican money, they sure could be bandits.

"Where were they headed, ma'am?" he asked the
woman storekeeper.

"I don't know. We were very busy that day trying to
outfit some men bound for the mines in New Mexico
Territory." She gestured toward a stack of pickaxes
and shovels against a wall.

Nate asked, "Did they buy mining supplies?"

"No, sonny," came from the man. "I'd have remembered that. Only grub and ammunition."

Nate looked a bit worried now, Beeler thought. He
asked, "Were *all* of them carrying guns?"

"To the best of my memory they were, sonny."

"Even the bald-headed galoot?" asked Beeler.

The woman chuckled. "I think he must have been,
or else I'd have taken note that he wasn't. Most menfolks do hereabouts. It's fit and proper for *men*." She
cast a very disapproving look at the six-shooter in

Beeler's belt. "He had such fine manners. He even took off his hat to me when I measured out pints of speckled beans for him. That's when I saw he had no hair to speak of."

"Bald as a boiled egg is how I heard it in Lovelock," volunteered Beeler.

"Are you looking for those men?" Mr. Billywhiskers wanted to know.

"We sure are," said Nate. "I think I'm the bald one's son."

"Don't you know?" Elfie sounded surprised.

"I haven't seen him in a long time," Nate explained. "He had curly hair last time I saw him."

"Well," remarked the woman, "it could be that he has lost it all by now. Time has a way of making tracks on a lady's face and on a man's scalp." She asked, "Will you be wanting supplies too?"

"A pounda coffee beans—if you got 'em already roasted," said Beeler.

As the woman picked up a scoop to take the beans from a big jar on the counter, Nate asked her husband, "Do you think they traveled west?"

"It would appear so. There's nothing north of here or east of here. If you've traveled the military road from Lovelock, you'd have met them going south. Flat as this country is, it'd be hard to miss five riders."

"Thank you for your information," said Nate, paying for the bag of coffee beans.

"How many of you are there?" Elfie asked Nate.

"Three of us and something that belongs to her." Nate jerked his head toward Beeler.

"Something?" The man looked puzzled.

Beeler explained. "My critter. Come on out and see him."

The couple followed her and Nate out to the edge of the porch where Leo, the horses, and Travis waited. "There's my animal." Beeler pointed to the steer. It seemed to her he wasn't getting much thinner for all the trotting around he'd been doing. Traveling was mighty becoming to him. His hide was as slippery and shiny-looking as black satin.

"He's our watchdog," said Graber.

"Always on the job," boasted Beeler, "and never barking at the moon like some fool hound."

"No, he only unnerves my horse and me by prowling around half the night stepping on dry sticks in the mesquite," complained Nate.

To Beeler's surprise, Leo took off his hat to the woman. The sun shone on the redness of his hair. "Howdy," he told the couple.

The woman nodded and nudged her husband. "Just look at him. Such a darling little boy!"

Beeler was stunned. Leo, that runt, darling?

"Do you suppose he'd like a big piece of pound cake and raspberry shrub cooler? He looks spindly," said Elfie Billywhiskers.

"He probably would," agreed Nate.

"I surely would." Leo was already off Two Cents, tethering him.

Beeler stood waiting beside Travis, expecting to be included in the grub invitation. She noticed that Nate was waiting, too, jiggling the sack of coffee beans.

But only Leo got "invited." He sashayed past Beeler, smirking, holding his hat over his breast. When he was beyond her, he turned and said, "You ride herd on things for a spell, ya hear?"

Mr. Billygoat Whiskers ignored her, too. He turned to Nate. "Do you want to have a look at the new map I've got of New Mexico Territory?"

Nate grinned now. He shoved the sack of coffee beans off onto Beeler and trotted beside the man into the store again. Beeler plunked herself down on the porch, opened the sack, and took out a coffee bean. She started to chew on it. It was bitter as gall. No, she didn't like Deadahead. Nate would probably go from map looking to cake eating. Her eye fell on a sod house across the way. The grass beside it was green and high. The flowers on its roof were yellowish-white, the very color of pound cake. She got up and untied the steer, leaving his neck rope dangling. Maybe he could get some pleasure out of grazing, and she could get some out of watching him.

For a long time she sat on the porch in the fading

sunlight, now and then yelling at Two Cents when he put back his ears to take a hunk out of Jinglebob. When he stuck his neck way out, that Two Cents looked just like a snake. He was a trial to everybody. Nobody came near Beeler while she watched the horses. Nobody seemed to be at home in Deadahead—or maybe the houses had been deserted because folks moved on. Maybe they'd all lit out for New Mexico Territory too!

Finally Beeler heard footsteps from behind her on the porch. Elfie Billywhiskers was there smiling, a piece of cake in her hand in a napkin. "The sweet boy said you might like some, too."

Beeler shrugged. "I ain't partial to pound cake." She turned her back.

But that didn't stop the woman. "How about that handsome animal of yours? Wouldn't he like a carrot or a turnip?"

For a fact, Travis doted on root vegetables. Beeler got up again. Why make things hard for him? "Sure, he favors 'em just fine."

Elfie smiled again. "Go behind the store, dear, to the root cellar. I opened the door already. The turnip bin's in the far right corner. Take some turnips and a carrot too."

"Much obliged." Beeler walked around the side of the house, found the open door in the ground and the flight of steps under it. She went down them into the dark coolness of the cellar where these folks stored their root vegetables. Because it was underground, it had an underground smell. She could just make out the turnip bin. She took two turnips and started back when all at once the door came slamming shut over her head.

A big turnip in each hand, Beeler stood in the dark listening to Elfie Billywhiskers calling to her from outside the door.

"Don't you try to shoot your way out. You can't. I've bolted the door already. Our root cellar will hold even a dangerous lunatic like you. It's where you'll be until the doctor comes from Lovelock. Your little cousin has told me all about you, Bertha Mae Muller!"

4 MR. McCARTY

Beeler threw both turnips hard as she could at the closed door of the root cellar. She ducked one boomeranging back but got hit on the knee by the other so hard that it made her fall down. She pulled herself up, went up to the door as near as she could, and pushed on it. Elfie had shut it tight—just as she said. It wouldn't budge one bit.

Beeler turned her back on it and sat down on the bottom step. "Hang and rattle, Beulah Land. How're you gonna get outa here?" She repeated fiercely, "Hang and rattle! Quit fightin' your head."

She put her head in her hands, muttering furiously. But slowly the muttering stopped, and she scrooched around to look at the door again. Cracks of light showed only at the edges. The door appeared solid enough for coffinwood. Beeler went up to it and pushed some more, not that she was very hopeful. For sure it was locked from the outside—bolted and with

71

a padlock on it by now too. Shooting at it wouldn't be worth a hoot, though it would surely attract some attention.

She sat down again. Attracting attention by hollering, shooting, and shouting wouldn't do a mite of good. Deadahead wasn't a Quiney town. Nobody would stand up for her here. That's what the Elfie female expected, for her to kick up a big fuss that would make people believe she was loco.

"What was the name she called me?" Beeler suddenly asked herself. "Bertha Mae Muller!" That was the name of the yellow-headed girl in Cottonwood Leo was half stuck on. Leo! *Cousin!* Sure as shooting, it was coming clear now to Beeler. Leo was behind this whole thing. Only she and Leo would know who Bertha Mae Muller was. Nate wouldn't.

"Why would Leo say he was my cousin and tell that big lie about me?" Beeler wondered. The answer came even more quickly than the name Muller had. To get hold of Jinglebob and to keep her from traveling with him and Nate. The look she'd seen on his face back in Lovelock ought to have made her wary of him. She'd guessed he was up to something, but she just hadn't been wary enough.

Her thoughts went to Graber. She pondered for a while, then decided that he wouldn't be party to her being clapped into a root cellar. But he'd go on travel-

ing with Leo and leave her behind all right. Leo was
smarter than she'd given him credit for. He would
cook up a story that'd convince Graber fast. Graber
hadn't wanted her along in the first place. They'd
surely plan to leave her here in Texas. Probably until
they came through Deadahead on the way back and
picked her up. Or maybe they figured the doctor from
Lovelock would send her back to Nerissa with some
travelers going that way.

"Cuss that Leo!" Beeler suddenly exploded, bang-
ing her hand on her knee. It hurt, making her think
of Jinglebob, which hurt too. Leo would take him, of
course. He might just leave Two Cents behind for
her but probably not. For certain Leo would take her
supplies.

She laughed suddenly in the dark brown gloom. At
least, Leo wouldn't be taking Travis. Travis had never
cottoned to him. The critter was loose, even if he had
a rope around his neck. Anybody but her who tried
to mess with him would learn fast what he was dealing
with. Travis! Beeler started to worry about him.
Would he get into trouble? Maybe Deadahead folks
didn't fancy having their roofs chewed on by longhorns. Maybe somebody would shoot him as a public
pest. Nate wouldn't let that happen, if he could stop
it, but what if he'd already lit out with Leo? After the
dirty deed Leo had done, he wouldn't be likely to stay

around in Deadahead. He'd want to put some distance between him and her.

Her mind went back to her critter. He wouldn't be getting his turnips. All at once she got up to examine the door once again. The light coming through the cracks was fading. It was getting on to dusk. That was good. There wouldn't be a moon until later on. A black critter in a dark night. That was just fine!

She'd wait. Because she was hungry she felt around in the root cellar until she found the potatoes and carrots. She helped herself to a raw potato and, after she'd finished it, stuffed two big long carrots into her back pocket because they were skinnier than turnips and more comfortable. When she guessed it was dark enough, Beeler got as close as she could to the side of the door where the daylight had shown widest. She put her fingers into her mouth and whistled loud as she could—so loud that it hurt her ears. She waited a bit and whistled some more.

She didn't have to whistle more than six times. While she was getting ready to pucker and blow for the seventh time, she heard a whuffling sound from the other side of the door. He'd hung around the way she guessed he would. Travis was there outside, being curious. When he made that kind of sound it proved that he was.

"I'm down in here," she called out.

A thud answered her. The steer had pawed the

door. Beeler laughed as the thudding got louder. Travis hated doors. Doors kept him out of the Quiney house where he always wanted to go. He hated front porches almost as much because Nerissa wouldn't permit him to sleep on hers. Because the root-cellar door was nearly flat with the ground, Travis would be bound to think it was a front porch, too.

Beeler called out again, "Travis, I have to get out of here. I've got some carrots for you."

The thumping got wilder now. The door shook while dirt rolled down from the sides into the cellar. Beeler knew an instant later from the rattling and crashing that the longhorn was standing on the door trying to hook the crossbar with a horn. She surely hoped he wouldn't fall through and get stuck.

She moved farther back into the root cellar out of the way. The strong door held. It was the ground on the left side of it that gave way, tumbling down the steps in a rush of clods of earth. Beeler didn't delay a blessed minute. She pushed up through the dust and squeezed out beside the door, though she had to shove the curious steer's muzzle away because he was blocking her escape.

Beeler was out and on her feet just in time to grab his neck rope before Mr. Billywhiskers came out onto his back porch with a lantern. Behind him came his wife with a shotgun.

"Where'd they go?" yelled Beeler. "Where'd that

runty cuss of a brother, who calls hisself a cousin, and that fat curly-headed kid ride off to?"

"You get back down in that cellar," cried the woman.

Beeler stuck out her tongue. "You can't make me do it. My animal'll kick down your entire emporium if I tell him to."

"I can shoot him," said the woman.

Beeler leaped in front of Travis. "Then you got to shoot me, too."

"Elfie," pleaded the man, "you mustn't shoot the child—even if she is a dangerous lunatic. What would folks think about us if you did?"

Mrs. Billywhiskers lowered the shotgun. "Are you going back down there, Bertha Mae?"

"No, I ain't. And I ain't no Bertha Mae Muller neither. Did Leo Quiney travel west? He's my brother."

The man looked at his wife. "He did, some time past."

"And you, you old mossback, you saw him take all the horses with him. The bay horse belongs to me."

Elfie had a cackling laugh. "They got all the horses with them. That'll hold you here, whoever you are. You can go back down there in the cellar or be locked up in the store until the doctor's come. You must be a lunatic, travelin' with two boys. It isn't fit and proper. Well, you can't trail after them pestering them anymore, can you?"

Beeler glanced at Travis, who was snorting because he didn't like lanterns and hollering folks. She sighed, then told him, "Just remember, Travis, it won't be for very long." She led him to a nail keg beside the house, got up on it, and flung a leg over his back. The longhorn snorted some more and pawed around a bit, then let Beeler neck rein him away from the back porch.

"Much obliged for the cake and carrots and all your hospitality," she called back over her shoulder, as they headed past the root cellar for the street.

Travis swayed along in the ruts past the store. By the time they were abreast of the one saloon, curious folks were coming up out of their sod houses across from it. If Travis hadn't made noise enough at the root cellar, Mr. Billywhiskers and his rouged-up wife surely had. There'd been some uproar!

Beeler waved to the folks of Deadahead. It was going to be nice saying *adiós* to them. To one galoot standing on the steps of the saloon she even took off her hat and said "Good evenin', Mister." She paused to ask him, "Which trail's the soldiers' road to New Mexico Territory?"

He pointed north by west. Even if his mouth was wide open, he didn't say a single word. Beeler watched him shiver once. Then he turned in a circle and went right back through the swinging doors fast as he could.

"Thank you kindly," she called after him, as she

and Travis left Deadahead. Under her breath she told
the steer, "I never could stand the looks of a old whiskey soak. He sure hightailed it back into that saloon
fast as he could. He was hardly polite at all."

Several miles outside of Deadahead Beeler slowed
Travis to a stop by jerking on his rope and saying
"whoa." She'd ridden him often enough when he was
a calf for him to know that when she pulled up on the
rope she had it in mind for him to stop so she could
slide off. He wasn't any Jinglebob. Riding Jinglebob,
even bareback, was the next thing to sitting in a rocking chair back home. Bareback on Travis resembled
trying to get comfortable on a sawhorse more than anything else. Longhorns were pretty much what folks in
Texas called them: "A pair of horns with a steer
hitched underneath them." Travis's spread wasn't
quite four feet wide yet, but he'd have a respectable
five feet pretty soon. And from then on there was no
guessing how long those handsome blue horns would
be.

Proud of him and of herself, too, Beeler pulled the
carrots out of her pocket by moonlight and gave them
to him, one by one. She talked to him. "You did real
fine back there, critter. I'm sure glad them folks didn't
take after you with Winchesters for eatin' the flowers
off their roofs. Mebbe they wanted somethin' to come

along to keep the green growth down. Mebbe you did
'em a service." She patted him on the muzzle, then
leaned against him to look northwest while he
chomped carrots.

She'd already seen the point of fire way off in the
distance. A campfire for sure. That was where Leo
and Nate most likely were—out of Texas and into New
Mexico Territory. They were danged certain she
wouldn't be following them. Well, let them count
their chickens before they hatched. With a half moon
to help her keep Travis on the trail, even though
there were some clouds out at times to drift over it,
she ought to be on top of them by midnight. And
aboard the big longhorn she didn't have to be afraid
of coyotes or wolves. They'd shy off from him.

Flinging her arm around the steer's neck, Beeler
told him, "And then, Travis, all hell's gonna bust
loose." A minute later she hauled herself up onto him
once more and said, "Rattle your hocks outa here."

Because it was hard to tell just how far away a campfire was, it took Beeler longer to get to it than she'd expected. She came up as quietly as she could and stood
staring at the fire, still a goodly piece away. Her eyes
were mighty sharp. She could pick out Graber in his
Mexican hat and that runty Leo real good, but there
was somebody else with them.

He was wearing a black hat. His horse was there,

too, hobbled not far from the camp. It was a big gray.
But the stranger wasn't fussing over it. He'd brought
Jinglebob up near the blaze and was petting him.

Beeler put wrinkles between her eyebrows pondering. She'd planned to come crashing right up onto
Leo, threaten him with a chasing from Travis, then
jump off and beat the stuffing out of the no-good son
of a goat backstabber. Then she'd give old Graber a
good piece of her mind. But with somebody else there,
it might not be the best thing to do. She might get
shot, and more than likely her critter would.

"You stay out here, Travis," she told him softly, as
she got down. "When I whistle, you come on in."

Beeler had been told more than once by Nerissa
that she had a voice like a rusty gate hinge. But it was
a girl's voice all the same. As loud as she could, she
started to sing as she walked forward, "Jesus Loves
Me." That would do double duty—to let them know
she was loose again and on her way up to them and
calm the longhorn, being left alone for a while. He
loved that tune. When Nerissa played it on the cot-
tage organ, he'd sneak up and stand under the big
pecan, enjoying it.

It satisfied Beeler's thirst for revenge to watch Leo
jump up and Graber too. It wasn't quite so pleasurable
to see the stranger drop Jinglebob's halter and draw
out a pistol. He carried a hogleg on his hip. Beeler

buttoned her jacket over the six-shooter in her belt and went on singing as Nate called out something to the stranger. She guessed Graber must be telling him they knew who it was, but the stranger didn't put down the pistol.

"It's me, Leo. It's me," Beeler called out. Then she went on with the hymn again and sang it until she almost reached the campfire.

By this time she was glad to see that the stranger had put the hogleg back. Taking off her hat, Beeler stepped into the firelight. She said howdy to the stranger while she gave him a quick look. He wasn't too old yet, probably around twenty or so, but he was getting on. He was so thin he wouldn't make a meal for a yearling tomcat. He wore old pants and boots and a black handkerchief at his neck. His hair under the black hat was shoulder-length and yellow colored. He wasn't a buffalo hunter. There wasn't any smell to him at all.

Beeler gave her real attention to her brother. "Yep, it's me, old Bertha Mae Muller, you runt. You got snake's blood, havin' that Elfie Billywhiskers lock me in the root cellar. Well, it didn't work. I'm back, and I'm ready to scrap with ya."

"How'd you get outa there?" Leo demanded. "She said that cellar'd hold you."

"Root cellars won't hold me when my temper's fiery

and my feelings tindery, you son of a goat horse thief, Leo Quiney. You're the worst brother a girl ever got saddled with."

"Muller? Quiney?" Beeler heard the stranger's soft voice as he turned his head toward Leo.

Leo sank down beside the fire. "We're both Quineys, her and me. She's my sister."

"Your sister was out on the prairie all by her lonesome, *walkin'*?" asked the stranger.

Beeler felt she might warm to him for saying such kind words. She told him, "I wasn't plumb afoot but the next thing to it. I've got my critter with me. I'm gonna whistle him in now, Mister . . . ?"

"Henry McCarty, ma'am."

Beeler had a smile for him and for his politeness. "I'm Beulah Land Quiney. We're from Santa Rosa County, Texas. You know my runt of a brother and Jonathan Graber here. They talked a woman in Deadahead into lockin' me in a root cellar as a dangerous lunatic." She gave Nate a toothy grin of triumph. He was looking mighty red in the face, the way he ought to look. "Ain't that the truth of it, you fat scrub?"

Graber suddenly blazed up. "No, it isn't! Leo told me you had the chickenpox and the woman had put you to bed until the doctor came from Lovelock. Leo and I planned to pick you up again when we came back."

"Sure, sure. And you waited for me to get unsick like a real gent, didn't you? And you took my horse. Well now you know what Leo really did to get rid of me because he wanted Jinglebob." She turned away from Leo and Nate to point to her horse. "Mr. Mc-Carty, that is my animal. The coyotes belong to them two. Keep your hogleg where it belongs, and you'll meet my other animal."

She whistled. Seconds later Travis, red-eyed in the firelight, hove into view, his horns glistening.

McCarty laughed. "Well, look at the brush splitter. Did you ride him here from Deadahead?"

"I surely did. He goes where I go. He lets me ride him when I want to. Where are you from?" Beeler had decided that she wouldn't hit Leo right now. She'd be polite, too. She'd wait until the stranger had gone.

"Just about anywhere in New Mexico Territory. I been all over."

"Where are your folks?"

He didn't say anything for a minute, then he replied, "My pa and ma are dead. I got a brother in Silverado. That's all."

Beeler said, "It's the same with us Quineys. We're leppies, too. But I got plenty of brothers. Most of 'em, I'm glad to say, are better'n him." She nodded toward Leo. "Mr. McCarty, did Graber tell you about his pa bein' missin'?"

"He sure did. He asked me about Sundown or Sunset, but I never heard of it—though there's a Puerto del Luna just north of here."

"That means 'port of the moon,'" said Nate unhappily. "It has to be the wrong place."

After she'd watched Travis mosey off to graze, Beeler went up next to the fire, took Leo's cup, and poured herself some coffee. "Are you gonna hunt for Sundown with us, Mr. McCarty?"

"No, I'm stayin' in this part of the country."

Beeler watched McCarty squat down beside the blaze. He surely had little feet and hands, not much bigger than hers. He pulled two little white rocks from his pocket and nervously began to toss them from one hand to another. His eyes never kept on any one thing for more than a couple of blinks. They were light eyes, bluish, set off more by the sunburned brown of his face. Beeler looked over the rim of the tin cup at McCarty's belt. He wore his hogleg low, even if it was a common .41 six-shooter. It surely had a tiny little handle. Cowboys mostly had pistols, but McCarty, she had the feeling, wasn't any more a cowboy than he was a buffalo hunter.

She spoke to Leo. "I ain't gonna forgive you. I'm gonna keep a eye on you from now on all the way to Sundown. The first trouble you give me you'll be missin' your best bridle teeth." Next she spoke to Nate.

"Mebbe I'll forgive you, but you was mighty quick to believe a cock-and-bull story you coulda checked out pretty easy."

Leo muttered, "I ain't gonna fight with ya, Beeler. It'd be useless as barkin' at a knot."

"That it would, runt. I'd win—like always." Beeler turned to McCarty and asked sweetly, "Have you seen much of Texas, Mister?"

"I been to El Paso a couple times, ma'am. Mexican gals there smoke *cigarillos*. Have you ever tried one?" He pulled out a long black thing from his vest pocket and offered it to her.

Beeler looked at the *cigarillo*. She'd always hankered to try a cigar but hadn't. She'd had a chew of tobacco, though, turned green, and been sick for two days on it. Maybe *cigarillos* did that, too.

"Thank ya, no. I ain't a Mexican." She didn't feel so warm toward him now. Tempting her with tobacco!

He laughed. "That's too bad. They taste mighty fine." He struck a match on the sole of his boot and lit the *cigarillo*. "Let me gave you a piece of advice. You ain't in Texas now. There are lotsa Mexicans here, and they ain't got no love for *Tejanos*. Step polite-like here."

"We don't have it in mind to pester any Mexicans," Beeler protested. "Nate talks Spanish real good."

McCarty looked solemnly at Nate. "That's good. You better do the talkin' around Mexicans then."

"I will. Thank you for the warning, sir."

" 'Sir,' " McCarty laughed again. Now he threw away the rocks, took the pistol from its holster, and began to turn it easily on one finger of his right hand, cocking it as it went over. Beeler sat down across the fire from him and watched, fascinated by the skill of his hand. Leo watched too. McCarty saw their interest, smiled, transferred the six-shooter to his left hand, and did the same thing. It wasn't as if he had it in mind to fire it. He was playing with it, thought Beeler, the way somebody would play with a pretty-colored lizard.

Finally Leo exploded admiringly, "Holy snakes, you can do that just as good with one hand as the other one! What else can you do with it?"

"Well, I can put all six bullets in a tree while my horse gallops past it. I can put two pistols on the ground, and when you toss up two empty tin cans, I can grab the hoglegs and bust open both cans while they're still up in the air."

Beeler spoke up hastily. "We ain't got nothin' but Winchesters with us, Graber's and Leo's."

"But, Beeler," started Leo. "You got a . . ."

"Sure," the girl interrupted him. "I *had* a six-shooter, but old Mrs. Billywhiskers took it away from me in Deadahead."

Leo sounded amazed. "How'd she do that?"

"By holdin' a shotgun on me. How else?" Beeler told a second lie. She gave McCarty a sidelong glance. He wasn't an ordinary cowboy. The easy way he played with the pistol made her feel chilly all over. It was a "play-pretty" to him, the way a doll was to a weaner gal. She'd keep her jacket buttoned no matter how hot it got as long as they were with him. Henry McCarty made her jumpy.

It didn't ease matters one bit later to have him start to talk in his soft voice about the haunted waterhole he'd visited in south Texas. The ghost of a pale woman with a baby in her arms walked around it at midnight. He'd seen her. Beeler hoped Mr. McCarty would keep his promise and not travel with them.

Suddenly she became aware that he was talking to her, "How come a little gal like you is on this here errand, too, ma'am?"

Beeler chose her words carefully. "More'n likely Leo didn't tell you he stole my horse. He did it twice, so he's a two-time horse thief. I'm only followin' the horse and seein' that he's took care of. I used to care about Graber's locatin' his pa until he did me that dirty trick back in Deadahead along with Leo."

McCarty sounded melancholy. "You know, that's just about all I ever did care about myself, ma'am. Horses and my only brother and a little Mexican gal in Fort Sumner—and a Englishman once who was mighty good to me."

"I never laid eyes on a Englishman," said Beeler. "But I'd surely like to see what one looks like. I'd like to go to England where they all come from before I get bogged down in carpets the way most girls do back home."

"Mebbe you'll be that lucky. I never been to England. I don't think I'm gonna get there either." McCarty put the six-shooter into its holster, got up, and stretched. He said to Nate, "Thanks for the good grub. I'll ride with ya a ways tomorrow and see that you're on the right trail."

"We'd all appreciate that, sir," Nate said politely.

Beeler watched McCarty go over to his bedroll. What she'd appreciate would be his leaving right now. He hadn't even twitched when she'd told him Leo was a horse stealer twice over. That more than likely meant McCarty was too. She'd spied her bedroll lying beside Jinglebob's saddle on the ground a few feet away. She wouldn't have to sleep on a Tucson bed, the bare ground, tonight. But it wouldn't be restful having a six-shooter poking her in the ribs all night.

Henry McCarty left them at noon the next day. At breakfast she'd spied the pink scars on both of his skinny wrists. He'd had sheriff's irons on him, and not long past either. She had whispered to Nate as they saddled up Stupid—who generally needed two people, one to hold his head, the other to get his saddle on his back—"Be careful, Graber. I think mebbe McCarty's a wanted man."

Out of the corner of his mouth Nate had told her, "You better stop whispering to me. He's looking at us."

Beeler had watched their night visitor ride north and, when he was out of sight beyond a swell in the land, had breathed easier. After that they followed the soldiers' trail he'd marked out for them, and no one said a single word about him, which was odd.

The country had changed since they'd crossed over into New Mexico Territory. It wasn't green prairie anymore. It was higher and rolling. The land was green-gray and tan, and there were bluish mountains ahead, the first real mountains the Quineys had ever seen.

Sometime after they'd parted company with McCarty, they saw two horsebackers coming from the west. Beeler opened her jacket while Leo got one Winchester ready and Nate the other. The riders, both men, were old roosters this time. One was gray-headed and had a face shriveled by the sun. The other one was wide-faced with a dark mustache that drooped over his mouth, covering it up.

He was the one who asked, "What the devil are you sprouts doin' out here in the wilds?"

"Looking for Sundown," answered Nate. Then he explained about his father.

"I never heard tell of such a place," said the man with the mustache, "but I wish you good luck lookin' for it. My name's John Poe. I'm huntin' somethin' too—a boy not much older'n you." He stuck out a finger at Nate. "He's got yellow hair and blue eyes . . . name of William Bonney."

Nate answered, "We were with a Henry McCarty last night, sir, no one named Bonney, though he did have yellow hair."

Poe had a very sharp laugh to him. "McCarty will do. So will the Antrim Kid. Most folks call him Billy. He's wanted for murder as well as horse theft. He's killed a lot of men hereabouts. He's mighty nervous. You're lucky you're all right. Where was he headed?"

Beeler shivered, thinking how, bold as brass, she'd come to the fire last night and whistled Travis in too. McCarty might have turned his hogleg on all of them. That would have given him Jinglebob, the other horses, and their supplies. But he hadn't taken anything more than a plate of beans and bacon.

"What direction was he headed?" asked Poe.

Leo spoke up right off. He'd surely admired McCarty. "South!"

Nate didn't say until Poe looked at him. Then he stared at the ground and said, "East—sort of."

Beeler glared at the two boys. What liars! No wonder Nerissa got mad at men for sticking together. "No sir, Mr. Poe. McCarty, or whoever he is, rode north!"

The gray-haired man started to chuckle, then said, "We know that he didn't ride west or we'd 'a seen him, Poe. Somebody here's a Texas flannelmouth. I bet it's the fat kid and the redheaded filly. Sprouts like that little bitty one over there ain't got the horse sense yet to tell lies. We'll ride south the way he says to."

After the two men had ridden past them going south, Beeler spoke scornfully. "Texas flannelmouth liars! That's the pair of you. How'd you ever tie up with a wanted man in the first place? I thought it wouldn't be smart to ask you last night in front of McCarty—or whoever it was."

The answer came from Nate. "He came up to us out of the dark and asked if he could share our fire. He was polite as could be. I felt sorry for him. He looked hungry and ragged."

Beeler nodded. "I took note of that too."

"Like his pockets were plumb empty of jingle," volunteered Leo.

Nate went on. "He told us that he could read and write."

This made Beeler sigh and glare at her brother

again. Outlaws could read and write! Leo couldn't yet.

Leo ignored her, saying, "Ya know, I think he was plain lonesome, and we wasn't anybody who'd be bothersome to him."

Beeler looked north where McCarty had ridden alone. She nodded. That was her opinion too. She said, "High lonesome, more'n likely. I guess that's what happens to men the law wants. Let it be a lesson to ya, Leo."

5 MARVELOUS MELINDA

The three Texans didn't talk again about Henry McCarty. Beeler knew why. Thinking about him made her mournful. But that wasn't all that did. The country up ahead didn't comfort her. She grew more and more awed by the mountains stabbing to the western sky. Santa Rosa County had hills, but nothing that could be called mountains. These must be as big as those mountains in Switzerland that the schoolmarm had shown stereopticon slides of once. Just looking at them had made Beeler feel like a wart on a big pickle. These mountains did the same thing to her. She guessed Leo felt sort of the same way. He kept glancing behind him to see the familiar flatness of the prairie, then ahead of him with a queer, doubtful look on his face.

Nate didn't seem so disturbed. He'd seen mountains before in Old Mexico. Mountains meant mines to him, he told Beeler and Leo once when they halted the horses. Mining was something his father knew a lot about, and he might be prospecting for gold or silver. People in the next town they came to might know if there was a mining town named Sunset or Sundown in these mountains.

While Beeler listened to him, she kept her eyes on his face. She was pondering Graber all right. He had some sand in him and seemed to know what he was about, but she still wondered about what had gone on back in Deadahead. He or Leo had better never try any more dirty tricks on her. But she had to admit that she didn't feel exactly easy about things without them either. They were out of Texas now. Down in her gizzard she knew that she'd made a big step. By leaving Texas she'd thrown in her lot with them— Jinglebob's and Travis's, too. The fact didn't sit well on her mind, but she wasn't about to let the boys know. Those two were thicker than feathers in a goose-hair pillow.

It seemed to her that they rode quite a ways before they came to a place they never even learned the name of. It wasn't anything more than a trading post for antelope hides. One thing this country was full of was antelope. Antelope liver cooked up just fine for supper.

The long-bearded man at the trading post wasn't any help at all when it came to knowing about Sundown. He'd never heard of it and had no idea where it could be. Sociableness was in his character, though—either that or he was lonesome. He told them that they'd gotten off the trail to Fort Sumner and were southwest of it. He thought now that they'd done that, they might be smart to travel along in that direction toward Silverado, where he'd heard lots of folks traveling out of Texas were headed. That was the big mining town in the Territory. He added that fifty miles west of his trading post they'd get their feet wet crossing a river named the Pecos, and it would be wise of them to join up with some other travelers going the same way just as soon they could.

"It's Indian country down there. You got to keep a eye peeled for Apaches," were his last words to them. "It's hard to figure Apache Indians. Sometimes they let you go by without your ever seein' 'em. Sometimes not. Watch your horses good. Apaches like mule and horsemeat better'n they like beef."

Beeler patted Jinglebob's flank. No Apache would get him! "How about grass for the horses and my critter up ahead?"

"You'll find some, even if the grazin' ain't as good as it was in Texas."

As Beeler started southwest, away from the mountains on Jinglebob with Travis by her side, she found herself almost wishing McCarty was riding with them.

He'd said he had a brother in Silverado. That meant he knew the way there, and she was more than sure he knew how to get on with Apaches.

The Pecos wasn't much more than a brook and easy to ford. A couple of miles farther west Beeler and the boys were pleased to see three riders coming. Winchesters and six-shooter ready, the Texans waited. The horsebackers were men once more, but this time they didn't ask about McCarty. The biggest, fattest one, almost redheaded enough to be a Quiney, called out, "Who'd ya be? And what're ya doin' out here?"

After she whistled Travis next to her, Beeler called out, "Come on in, and we'll talk." She kept her hand on her belt.

One of the riders laughed. "Ah, they ain't nothin' but kid colts!"

The horsebackers came in closer, riding around the Texans, giving them the once-over. But it was Travis they mostly stared at. Travis accommodated them by snorting and turning around so they could admire him from every side. Beeler was proud of his handsomeness. Finally the redheaded man said, "Is this here animal you folks' steer?"

"He ain't theirs. He belongs to *me*," said Beeler. "He's got our brand on him, a letter *Q* with a barbed tail on it. That means Quiney down in Santa Rosa County, Texas."

"It don't mean nothin' here," came from the third cowboy. "We're from the Chisum Ranch. All this country's Chisum land from Fort Sumner to the Texas line."

"And there ain't no welcome mat out for settlers or squatters," said the redhead.

"We aren't settlers. We're only passing through, sir." Nate told his story and asked his question.

The redhead pushed back his hat. "I never heard of any Sundown, kid, but that don't mean much. You better go to Ross and ask there. It's a tradin' post." He laughed and pointed at Travis, who was facing him, being curious. "How come you got that big cactus boomer with ya? You figure he'll come in handy for ready beef on the trail?"

Beeler sizzled. "I'd eat you first—hooves, horns, and tail!"

She couldn't miss Nate's sigh, it was so loud. "Put it this way, sir. The steer is a child's pet."

This made all three Chisum cowboys laugh. The redhead called out before they rode off, "You colts are holdin' too loose a rein on that carrottop heifer. You watch out or she'll be wearin' the bell in your outfit."

"She already is," Beeler heard Leo muttering, as he tried to manage Two Cents, who had it in his cranium to follow the riders.

A mile or so farther on, Beeler told both boys in

her most scornful manner, "In any outfit the one person who ain't a horse thief ought to be wearin' the bell and be the boss!"

The traders at Ross weren't any help either, though they invited the Quineys and Nate to "set and eat a bean" with them. The traders, all members of the same family, warned them that Apache country lay due southwest. The Indians hadn't given any trouble for a while, but a place to be careful of them was thirty miles ahead on Ramada Hill. Six miles beyond the hill was the town of Ramada where they ought to be safe. They'd be smart all the same to hook up with some other travelers. Maybe if they were lucky they might be able to find the circus that had been in Ross just the week before.

Beeler saw Nate's jaw drop and watched him stare around at the tiny trading post and deserted country as if he didn't believe his ears. He didn't look much different when he heard that the circus had got lost on its way from a silver town up north to another mining camp.

"A whole circus got *lost?*" Nate asked.

The head trader laughed. "Well, stranded's more like it. They didn't make no money here. Somebody up north said we was a town of five hundred folks— not just fifteen of us. We headed 'em toward Silverado. There's a heap of folks there now, if you can believe anythin' anybody says about this Territory."

"And they went west to Apache country?" Beeler wanted to know.

The traders all grinned at the same time. Because they were related they grinned the same way, with a gap between their two front teeth. "Oh, we didn't guess the Apaches would bother them much," said the head trader again.

"Are they a big outfit?" asked Leo.

"No, they ain't. But they got them animals with 'em. It ain't them common ordinary camels of theirs. The Apaches seen camels by now because there've been camels runnin' loose ever since the U.S. Army brought 'em out here during the War. It's them other beasts."

"What're they?" Leo got the words out before Beeler could.

"Them other critters they got. Them things that look like oversize panthers. One of 'em's got hair growin' all over his shoulders. It's a awful sight. They cough a lot at night."

Beeler heard Graber's quick intake of breath. Even Stupid heard it and shifted from one forefoot to the other. "You mean they have honest-to-goodness lions? African lions?"

The head trader replied, "I dunno where they hail from, but they don't come out of any hills around here."

Nate turned to the Quineys. "They're the sort of

animals that ate the Christian martyrs back in the days of ancient Rome."

"That's it," came from one of the trader's sons. "The man who corrals them brutes calls hisself Daniel. He told me the Bible talks about lions and a Daniel."

"Lions ate Christians later on. Daniel's too early in the Bible, but all the same he certainly does have a lot to do with lions. They refused to eat him," Nate corrected the boy. He spoke next to Beeler, "I've always had an ambition to look at a real lion."

Beeler thought a minute, then replied softly, "Sure, you would, you scrub. You want to see the animals that chewed up the Christian saints all right. You ain't the only one who knows about them. I heard about 'em in Sunday School once. You're plenty wicked, aren't ya, Graber? I'd rather see the poor Christians than the lions that ate 'em. Chew that over."

Nate spoke severely. "It's educational to look at lions, Beulah Land. The Lord knows if there's anything a Quiney needs, it's education. Besides it's not as if these lions are the same animals that ate the Christians."

"They're outa the same tribe, ain't they?" Beeler gave Travis a worried glance. Every mile he went he looked handsomer. Running all over Texas had taken a bit of tallow off him but only enough to put him in prime condition. She asked Nate, "What else do lions eat except folks?"

She'd never noticed what an ornery grin he could put on. "Meat. Just about any kind, I suppose—I think they prefer beef."

That night, because of Apaches, they didn't light a fire and ate a cold supper. They were climbing by now. There were more mountains ahead to the west. And it was getting colder at night because of the increasing altitude. Beeler shivered in her blankets, wishing she could curl up with Travis the way a person could with a warm dog or cat. You couldn't do that with a long-horn, no matter how friendly. But Travis was a good watcher, always on the job. When he heard noises he started bellowing like a lost calf in high grass. But mostly he bellowed at coyotes that yapped all night long anyway.

Beeler was still mighty uneasy. It wasn't so much that this strange country was unfriendly. It was just nobody's country. It made her feel even friendly toward Leo at times. Not that she could see that it made him feel that way toward her, but he didn't give her that mean smile anymore so she guessed he wasn't planning anything. Bad as he was, he wouldn't leave her afoot out here where there was nobody for miles around.

Ramada Hill was a steep one. They led the horses up it and down it, Winchesters ready, glancing from side to side. But there didn't seem to be anything to be scared of in the ocotillo bushes and cactus on top. The bottom of the hill was even bushier, full of mesquite and hackberry trees. Beyond them was a line of cottonwoods and more mesquite, which meant only one thing—water. By the way the trees grew, it was most likely a river.

"Be careful of Indians now," Beeler whispered to Nate, as she mounted Jinglebob again, being sure to hang tight to Travis's neck rope.

"Beulah Land, I'm being careful. If we run into any Apaches, please keep quiet. I'll try to talk to them in Spanish."

"Why that lingo?"

"Because the Spanish and the Mexicans were here a long time before Americans came. Apaches ought to speak Spanish if they speak anything except Apache."

Beeler grunted, "Mebbe so. I'll oblige ya to keep the peace."

Leo led the way now on Two Cents with the Winchester in one hand. They'd learned along the trail that Leo was the better shot of the two boys. Nate followed behind, and Beeler brought up the rear with Travis's neck rope fastened to the saddlehorn so she could get to her pistol if she had to.

They heard the queer sound the minute they got out of the brush beyond the hill. It was a sort of grumbling rumbling. For a minute Beeler thought it must be the river up ahead or maybe even a waterfall. But the noise of a river over rocks wasn't a thing that stopped and started.

"Is that Apaches?" she asked Nate.

"Indians don't make that kind of noise. I don't think anything I ever heard did." He smiled all at once. "I think it just has to be lions!"

"From where?" demanded Leo.

"Over there by the river, I'll bet." Nate stood up in his stirrups and shouted, "Hey, is there anybody there down by the river?"

There wasn't any answer, but a very unusual thing happened. Out from under some sagging cottonwoods a contraption suddenly appeared. It glittered in the sunshine. Only the front half of a wagon, it had just two wheels. Two black horses wearing a red harness pulled it over the ground toward them. Most astonishing of all, a lady in a purple dress and purple bonnet with white plumes on its top was driving the queer rig. And it was coming fast.

Jinglebob, who'd never seen such a sight, reared up while Travis tried to jerk away. Two Cents had one look at the wild contraption, turned around on his hind legs, and galloped back toward the hill taking

Leo with him. Stupid held his ground, probably because he was so winded from going up the hill.

"Yoo-hoo," cried the woman driver.

"What is it?" Beeler yelled at Nate.

"It's only a chariot," he called back.

Beeler managed to calm Jinglebob down and to whistle once to Travis, who was plenty wild-eyed and jumpy by the time the lady in the chariot was up to them. Now Beeler saw that each black horse had a white silk banner over his back with printing on it. She read it out loud, even if some of the words were mighty big.

CLAYTON'S CIRCUS
Dauntless Daniel, Tamer of Wild Beasts
and
Marvelous Melinda, Bicyclienne
Camels   Performing Jugglers   Charlie and Blossom

The lady in the chariot pulled up next to Nate. Beeler got a good look at her. She was handsome as a heifer knee-deep in red clover, with dark hair and dark eyes, all purple velvet, white feathers, and white lace—and wearing white gloves. Her voice was velvety, too. "I'm Miss Melinda Holcomb, Bicyclienne, dear," she told Nate.

"I'm Jonathan Graber, ma'am." He lifted his hat.

"This is Beulah Land Quiney, and that's Leo Quiney back there on the runaway horse."

Miss Holcomb giggled. "I hope I didn't scare you just now. I was practicing driving the team. I always go first into a town, you know, ahead of the circus wagon. It's good advertising. So few people in the Territory have seen chariots."

Nate was gallant. "You didn't scare us, ma'am. It's just that our horses haven't ever seen a chariot either."

Because it didn't appear that Nate was going to get around to it, Beeler asked, "Can we ride to Ramada with you, ma'am?"

"If Mr. Clayton says so, and I'm quite sure he will, you may." Miss Holcomb drove up beside Beeler now to look at Jinglebob and Travis. She smiled and said, "A commendable bit of horseflesh and cowflesh you have there, young man."

"I'm a she. Beulah Land's a she-name."

Miss Holcomb's black eyebrows arched higher up. "A girl traveling with menfolks?"

"My brother and Graber and me—we're on a errand, all of us. A errand of duty. All us Quineys are hogs for duty. And a girl ought to help out, too, shouldn't she, when it comes to duty? Howdy!" Satisfied with her noble speech, Beeler stuck out her hand and shook the white kidskin glove up and down. The lady smelled up to the skies of lilacs in bloom.

"Duty is ever commendable. Come along, my dears." She touched the blacks lightly with a long, gilded whip, making them move forward, then turning them about. They were mighty well-trained, thought Beeler. The woman led the way toward the riverbank with her chariot bouncing around over the bumps in the ground. It didn't strike Beeler as the best way to travel.

"What's a bicyclienne?" the girl asked Nate, coming abreast of him and Stupid as they followed.

"A lady bicycle rider, I suppose."

"I never set eyes on a bicycle, but I saw a picture of one in a *McGuffey Reader*, Nate."

Nate laughed. "I had one when I was little. I fell off it and cut my lip, and I've kept away from them ever since." He glanced over his shoulder at the same time Beeler glanced over hers. Leo had Two Cents turned in the right direction by now and was coming back. Beeler wondered if Two Cents, Jinglebob, and Travis were so emotional about chariots how they would act around bicycles and lions, something else they'd never seen.

The circus wagons were camped beside the river called the Hondo. But it wasn't the river that took Beeler's eye. It was the lions. There they were, two of them, bigger than any cat she'd ever heard of, each in his separate cage. One had brown-yellow hair all over its shoulders—not a bad-looking color, thought Beeler, contrasting it in her mind with her own hair. It was a sort of hairy blond critter. The other one, the one without a mane, resembled a great big yellow female cat. She was licking a paw while the first one was staring straight ahead with eyes like yellow marbles. Both lions turned their heads lazily to stare at the horses, the steer, and the newcomers who were people. For a fact, lions weren't bothered by horses. They yawned, both of them.

Beyond the caged lions were three camels tethered to a red-wheeled wagon. They gave the lady in the chariot and the Texans and their animals a bored look, too.

Beeler spotted some ordinary brown horses tied to cottonwoods and two other wagons. The back of one wagon was open. As Beeler rode by it, muttering to both Travis and Jinglebob to keep them from acting up some more, she took a quick look inside. This wagon was full of shiny metal things, mostly wheels, big and little. Miss Melinda's bicycles, she guessed.

And now a very tall man came walking up from the river, carrying a bucket in each hand, going toward one of the two tents under the trees. He only glanced at the chariot, but when he saw Beeler and the others, he put the buckets down and came forward. He was handsome, too, with blue eyes and whitening hair. He had on red pants with a blue stripe down each side and a blue coat with gold braid and fringe on the shoulders. Duded up that way, Beeler figured he might be Dauntless Daniel, who tamed wild beasts.

Miss Holcomb waved at him. "Oh, Mr. Clayton, the children want to go to Ramada with us."

The circus man walked up, looked over Nate, Beeler, the horses, and Travis, then shook his head. "There isn't any attraction here, Melinda. Longhorn steers don't draw crowds—maybe back in Boston, Mass., but not out here."

Nate put in fast, "We don't have it in mind to be part of your circus, Mister. All we want to do is go through the mountains and Apache country with you. We've got our own supplies. It won't cost you anything. We're worried about Indians."

Clayton laughed. "Apaches haven't even bothered us." He motioned toward the lions' cages. "It's my guess Indians don't know what to make of Blossom and Charlie, so they only peek at us as we go by."

"Would you sic your lions on Apaches, Mister?" asked Beeler.

Beeler saw a look of pain cross Clayton's face. "Those valuable animals chasing Apache Indians! Lord forbid. They're my finest attraction."

Beeler heard someone sniffing and looked over her shoulder. It was Miss Melinda. But Clayton didn't

pay her any heed. He didn't even seem to hear her
when she said, "Lions. Lions! Your finest attraction!
That's all I hear all day—you bragging about those
lions. The lions make unpleasant noises all night long,
and they smell. It's enough to drive a lady to. . . ."
Suddenly she turned to Beeler and said, "It's enough
to drive a lady to the company of other ladies." She
smiled. "You'll live with me in my tent while we go
to Silverado. *I* say you can travel *all the way* with us.
That's my tent over there, the biggest one. The smallest one belongs to him. When it rains, he lets the
lions sleep in there with him." She sniffed once more,
swung the chariot around and bounced away.

Nate asked, "Mr. Clayton, have you ever heard of
a town called Sunset or Sundown?"

Clayton shook his head, "No, boy. I never played
it in my life. I remember every town I ever played.
I pride myself on my memory."

By now Leo was in the circus camp, even if Two
Cents was snorting and dancing. Jinglebob was trembling. Beeler couldn't decide if it was the chariot or
camels or lions bothering the horses. Miss Melinda had
been right about the lions. Lions had a powerful smell
to them all right.

"We'll help you work however we can," Nate told
Clayton.

"Maybe you can drive a wagon. I'm shorthanded

just now. Two of my workers left when we were up north. The other three went on into Ramada to get things ready for tonight's show."

Just then the lion with all the hair on him let out a cough, and all four of Two Cents' hooves left the ground at the same time. Travis leaped sideways.

"You'd better dismount," the circus man warned Nate. "You seem to be making Charlie nervous with your noise and jumping around."

Beeler glanced at the cage. The lion with the mane didn't look one bit nervous. He had got up and was stretching and yawning just like a huge pussycat. She tethered Jinglebob and Travis to trees beside the Hondo where there was grass. Then she walked to the biggest tent. Tents were queer things. There weren't any doors to knock on, so she yoo-hooed the way the bicyclienne had. "Yoo-hoo," was an elegant expression, Beeler thought.

"Come right on in," said the lady's voice.

Miss Melinda's tent had half the comforts of home. She had a blue rug and a brass bed. There was a mirror hanging from the tent pole. The only thing missing were pictures and mottoes on the walls. But that would be expecting too much for a tent.

The lady charioteer was on her knees opening a trunk. She said, "Mr. Clayton will unharness the chariot horses for me." She flung something out of the trunk onto the bed. It was lavender colored and sparkly. "That's what I'll wear tonight. When I ride the unicycle with Blossom."

"That's one of the lions, isn't it?"

"Oh, yes."

Beeler felt silly. All the same she asked, "Does the lion ride a bicycle, too?"

Miss Melinda's laugh sounded the way water glasses ring when you hit them with something. "Of course not. Blossom trots along beside me on a leash. She is reasonably civilized, though she did bite a Sunday school teacher up north when the woman got too close to her."

This made Beeler nod. She'd surely tell Nate about that. Still after Christians!

Miss Melinda threw something else out of the trunk, more lavender cloth. "How do you like my costume? Here's the rest of it."

Beeler picked up the two things. One looked like the bottom half of long underwear with feet in it. The other was a sort of corset and corset cover all in one piece. It had black spangles sewed around the neck and purple-and-black cloth flowers, too. There weren't any sleeves at all. It was surely the most naked-looking thing she'd ever seen.

"Holy snakes, ma'am, you don't plan wearin' this in public, do ya? Folks'll see your legs!"

Miss Melinda giggled as she got up. She was looking Beeler up and down. "Well, my dear, aren't you showing your legs in those boy's trousers?"

Beeler dropped the costume onto the bed. "That's diff'runt. I'm travelin' and ridin' a horse astride."

"Well, you could have a sidesaddle, couldn't you, and wear a skirt? I am riding a bicycle. Can I do that in a skirt and bustle? Don't you see my point?"

She flopped down onto the bed and sighed. "Ramada! It will always be the same, I just know it. I'd have all sorts of beaux in Ramada if we'd stay long enough. They'd send me mash notes and five-dollar gold pieces with holes drilled in them for me to wear around my neck. Half of the eligible men in a town always fall in love with circus ladies who wear spangles and tights. Do sit down, dear."

Beeler sat down on the bedspread beside her, hoping her dirty pants wouldn't leave marks on it. She tried hard to be polite. "It must be a trial to have so many beaux in love with you. I never had even one."

Miss Melinda looked glum. "Generally it's very gratifying. But it just breaks a lady's heart when she can't get the one she really is after."

"Who'd that be?"

"Dauntless Daniel Duckworth. That's his real name, you know. But who ever heard of a lion tamer called Duckworth! So he says he's Daniel Clayton."

Beeler nodded. She'd figured Daniel and Clayton were the same man. It didn't seem likely anyone else would sleep with lions in his tent. The lady patted Beeler's hand. "My dear, there is nothing in the world half so painful to the heart as unrequited love."

Beeler took off her hat. "Yes, ma'am. I guess so, but my sister-in-law, Nerissa, back home in Santa Rosa County says having it requited is worse sometimes. She says livin' with all of us and with my oldest brother is like wearin' a mustard plaster both front and back."

Miss Melinda pulled some fancywork out of a tapestry bag under a bed pillow. "Tell me about you, dear. What's this errand you're on?'

Beeler told her. The lady had tears dropping from her eyes when she heard of Nate's pa being missing and stamped her foot, mad as all get out, when she heard about Beeler's being locked in the root cellar. She vowed that Travis must be the finest and most intelligent longhorn in Texas. He ought to be able to learn tricks easy as pie and in no time at all be a circus performer too.

Beeler was tickled to hear Travis praised. "My critter is the smartest one in the whole state—and my cuss of a brother's the most sneaky, ma'am."

The bicyclienne snorted. "He's getting in practice to be a man, isn't he? Look at Mr. Clayton. Saying straight out in front of me that the lions are his biggest attraction. That's ridiculous! *I* am. People pay to see me and my bicycles—not those animals of his."

"Yes'm," said Beeler, although she was thinking along other lines. For a fact, Miss Melinda wouldn't keep the Apaches away, not even if she was driving her chariot. Mr. Clayton was probably right. It took lions to do that.

Suddenly Miss Melinda said, "Men simply don't have tender feelings like us, dear. I'm so glad you came along today. I haven't talked to another female in ages—just to unfeeling brutes and bullies of men."

"You're right," said Beeler. "Menfolks surely don't take things to heart the way we do!" Before they found Sundown, Beeler was afraid she'd have to scratch up Leo's wishbone for some nasty remark, though she was sure he wouldn't desert her anymore. And maybe there'd have to be some knuckle scratching, too, with that scrub, Graber—even if he was bigger and older. "Miss Melinda, you know, I think I might have to beat up on both of them two I'm travelin' with before we get where we're going. I'm watchin' both of 'em good."

The bicyclienne took a lilac-smelling handkerchief out of her bosom, wiped her eyes on it, and very gently blew her nose, all the time nodding, agreeing with Beeler.

6 UNEXPECTED AUDIENCE

Three men in red flannel shirts, Clayton's helpers, came along soon to take down the tents. Miss Melinda had put on her lavender costume and a long black cloak over it. She got into her chariot and led the way to Ramada. Behind her came the camels, then a flat wagon with the two lion cages on it, driven by Mr. Clayton, and behind them the supply wagons. Leo, Nate, and Beeler with Travis brought up the rear.

That night in the adobe town of Ramada the Quineys and Nate saw their first circus. It made them gasp with wonder, just as the Spanish-talking town-folks gasped too. The performances weren't held in a tent but in a big circular corral next to a livery stable. Clayton's helpers had cleaned the corral ahead of time.

Two helpers put on white knee breeches and came out first, acting like harlequins, juggling some wooden balls in the air. After that the camels were led around the circle grunting, kneeling, and getting up again. Beeler could see that they hated bestirring themselves.

Miss Melinda came after the camels. Beeler thought she really was marvelous. She had stored her chariot and horses in the livery stable and didn't bring them out into the corral. Instead she shot out smiling on a tall, high-speed bicycle. Around and around she went, zooming until it made Beeler's head spin to watch her. It wasn't until she stopped to bow that Beeler could see the diamond-studded gold medal around her neck. The San Francisco and Oakland Bicycle Club had given it to her just the year before.

While the people of Ramada clapped, a helper brought out a very funny-looking bicycle with one great big wheel and a little bitty one. Miss Melinda rode that around too for a while. And when that was over the helper brought Blossom out on a leash and with a red collar around her neck. Under his arm he carried one wheel only.

Everybody gasped some more. Blossom wasn't yawning now but showing her fangs. Dauntless Daniel didn't do a single thing to tame her down. He stood watching from the door of the livery stable while Miss Melinda blew kisses to the audience. Then she got up on the one wheel, still smiling, balanced there for a time, and took the leash from the helper. With Blossom traveling by her side, the bicyclienne went slowly around the corral in the opposite direction from the one she had taken on the other wheels. Then she reversed. As she went faster and faster, the lioness trotted or cantered or galloped. And then it was all over. Miss Melinda got off and curtseyed while the people clapped. Blossom let out a cough, then yawned.

Next it was Mr. Clayton's turn. He had barrels for Charlie to jump on to and off of when he yelled "Up" and "Down" at the lion. Charlie snarled and clawed the air a couple of times, but that was all he did except for jumping and swishing his tail when Clayton cracked his whip.

Finally came the pretty-baby contest. It cost the folks of Ramada ten cents to vote once for the handsomest baby in town. Miss Melinda held up each contest baby and walked around the corral with it. Then a helper collected the ten-cent pieces. The prettiest baby raked in ninety cents for the circus—most of which, Beeler noticed, came from the baby's pa. For a prize the bicyclienne kissed the baby on the forehead. It bawled.

The circus was over. The helpers walked around with hats in their hands, collecting whatever folks would throw in. Because it seemed the polite thing to do and she was traveling with the circus, Beeler took off her hat and collected, too. She got one American silver dollar, a Mexican peso, two other Mexican coins she couldn't recognize, a silver button, and a piece of blue-green rock that might be turquoise. She decided Mexicans were generous folks and said *"Gracias"* a lot, a Spanish word she already knew. Nobody here seemed to care she came from Texas. But maybe they didn't know. She didn't tell anyone either.

Miss Melinda was tickled when Beeler gave her what was in her hat. She took the button and the rock and gave the rest to Mr. Clayton, who was sort of pleased too. "We've made enough to get to Silverado," Beeler heard him tell his bicyclienne. "We'll buy some supplies here, and tomorrow morning we'll start on our way."

There were lanterns set on the ground behind the corral railings. Their light blocked out what was beyond them. Beeler knew, though, what was west of Ramada—mountains, great big ones. She hoped Miss Melinda didn't plan to travel through them in her chariot. Horses and four-wheel wagons would probably have a hard enough time. Going up and down steep Ramada Hill had taught her that lesson.

For a fact, they *were* traveling with the circus! Nate, speaking Spanish, had asked everybody he'd met in Ramada if they'd ever heard of Sunset, Sundown, or Puesta del Sol? Nobody had.

The bicyclienne drove a wagon with Nate riding beside her. Packed inside it was her chariot, filled with bicycles. Beeler on Jinglebob, with Travis alongside, rode next to the wagon. Leo rode with one of Clayton's handlers, the man who looked after the camels. Two Cents and Stupid were tied to the back of the bicycle wagon because they just refused to be anywhere near the lions or camels. Mr. Clayton decided they annoyed the animals, too, so he kept them out of the way. Jinglebob, though, got along just fine with everybody, especially Miss Mclinda, who fussed over him. One thing was true about him, Beeler had to admit. He surely appreciated being admired. He was like two-legged folks that way.

The mountains weren't much like the stereopticon slides Beeler had seen once you were into them. They weren't snowy, probably because it was July and hot by now. At least it was hot during the daytime, hot enough to ride in shirtsleeves. As they went up a narrow path into the pine-covered mountains, Beeler did some deep pondering about Miss Melinda and Mr. Clayton. It seemed to her that the bicyclienne had given up a lot to be part of his circus. She'd said she could work in any circus in the whole world! To think he liked lions better than he liked her. Where were his tender feelings?

Sometimes Beeler glanced at Graber up on the wagon seat out of the corner of one eye. For a while she'd suspected he might have some tender feelings some-

where, but after what he'd done in Deadahead, she
doubted it. It appeared to her that sometimes she posi-
tively seemed to be bothersome to him. Or at least he
acted that way.

The mountains were plumb full of deer. One of
Clayton's helpers was a good rifle shot, so there was
always venison when they stopped at night. They went
through canyons and along ridges by day, but at dusk
Clayton called a halt in some flat place beside a stream.
This was so the horses and Travis could graze. The
lions tolerated venison just fine.

Beeler was happy to share Miss Melinda's nice tent
and sleep on her rug, because it got breezy and cold
at night up so high. To enjoy the rug she had to drink
sassafras tea, though, with the bicyclienne to thin
their blood for summer. But she said no to drinking
the canteen water Miss Melinda had dropped a rusty
nail into to put iron into a person. It tasted like water
a rusty nail had been dropped into.

Leo and Nate slept under the wagons with the
helpers, out of the wind, while the lions in their cages
went into Clayton's tent so they wouldn't catch cold.

Beeler talked to Nate and Leo about Mr. Clayton
and the lions the third night in the mountains. This
time they camped in a little meadow ringed around
by big rocks. The Texans were squatting by a fire of
their own, drinking coffee when Beeler spoke up. "Miss
Melinda says she thinks Blossom and Charlie sleep on

Dauntless Daniel's bed with him. He lets them out of their cages."

Leo shook his head, swallowed a mouthful of beans, and said, "No, I got curious and peeked under his tent. I seen his bed. It ain't that big. Blossom was the only lion laying on his bed. That's because she's the littlest. Charlie, he sleeps beside the bed. He's sort of a carpet for Mr. Clayton's bare feet."

Beeler exploded, "Holy snakes, are they that tame?"

Leo nodded. "Mr. Clayton, he told me once that he brought 'em up from kittens, both of 'em. The only reason he keeps 'em in cages is because otherwise they might run off and try to join up with some mountain panthers and get clawed up bad or killed."

Nate took a swallow of coffee. "That probably explains why they're yawning all the time. They must be bored."

Beeler asked Leo, "Why does Charlie let out those growlin' sounds when Mr. Clayton makes him jump up on barrels?"

"Clayton says it's because Charlie just hates to work. Blossom hates to work, too. That's why she shows her teeth when the chariot lady drags her around on a rope."

Beeler was stunned at all Leo knew. "Is it because he worries so much about his lions that Mr. Clayton's goin' gray-headed?"

Leo shook his head. "Nope, he told me about that,

too. It's because of all them women who've tried to catch him over the years. He says womenfolks fuss over him somethin' terrible. That's the way they act around lion tamers. They want to tame the tamers. He's inclined to be bilious, particularly when he loses at poker. That's really what's wrong between him and the chariot lady."

"What?" Beeler wanted to know.

"He thinks she's purty, but she keeps after him to take Morley's Vitalizer and use goose-grease gizzard oil on his chest when he gets a cold—not to mention rust water and sassafras tea."

Beeler nodded. "I know all about them last two. I drew the line at rust water myself. Miss Melinda's mighty set in her ways when it comes to fussin' over folks."

"Rust water would make a bobcat bilious," said Leo disgustedly as he stood up.

Beeler knew that Leo didn't take much to circus life. Looking after camels was lots worse than taking care of horses. He'd already complained that camels could spit in your face. One had got him right between the eyes, and he'd taken it hard.

"I'll take a good look at Travis and Jinglebob while I'm lookin' at Two Cents," he told his sister. "It's awful quiet out there tonight."

"Aw right," she warned, "take a look, but keep out

of my critter's horn range. You know he don't favor
ya, Leo."

She turned to Nate after Leo had left. "I don't know
why he felt called on to do that, Graber. Nights have
been quiet all along up here, haven't you noticed?"

"Yes, Beulah Land, I have. That's because of the
lions and probably the camels too. Wild animals don't
like anything strange around. And you have to admit—
Blossom and Charlie are strange!"

"That's prob'ly so." She changed the subject. "Miss
Melinda's sufferin' from unrequited love. Would you
know anythin' about that?"

"Maybe."

Beeler waited for him to go on while she watched
Miss Melinda at the other fire, stirring venison stew
in a big cook pot. She didn't keep her eyes on Nate's
face because that wouldn't have been very polite, but
she'd had one glimpse that had told her he knew
something about unrequited love all right.

But he never got to explain about it because Leo
came back too soon. He wasn't running. As a matter
of fact, he wasn't even walking fast. But there was
something about the way he was moving that made
both Beeler and Nate look up at him. Leo was whiter
in the face than a wash boiled for three days on the
back of a hot stove. He spoke before they could ask
what ailed him. "There are Indians out in the rocks.

Some of 'em are sittin' on top of the rocks watchin' us. I seen 'em good. Some got white paint on their chests."

Nate reached up and grabbed Leo's arm and pulled him down to kneel beside the fire. "Beulah Land, pour Leo some more coffee. You two sit here and drink it while I go tell Mr. Clayton."

Her hands trembling as badly as Leo's, Beeler poured coffee. Some of it got into her brother's cup. As Nate walked off to the other campfire, she asked softly, "Leo, are you dead sure you ain't seein' things that ain't there?"

"No, they're on the rocks. I figure they're all around us. Apaches for sure. What d'ya know about Apaches?"

"Nothin', except what you heard too. They favor mule and horsemeat. Nate knows somethin' about Comanches. I sure hope he knows what he's doin' now. Apaches ain't Comanches, and one kinda Indian's diff'runt from another kinda Indian. That's somethin' a lot a folks don't know. They think all Indians is the same." Beeler knew she was chattering to keep her courage up. She went right on babbling like a lost turkey until Nate came back.

He didn't say a word to her and Leo. Instead, he got up, just as white as Leo had been, on top of a tree stump, waved his arms in the air and did a queer sort of stomping dance. Then he started to yell—not in English but in Spanish.

Leo whispered to his sister, "He's gone loco. Scared plumb outa his mind. The Apaches'll put a arrow into him." Leo got up, but Beeler hauled him down again.

From flat on the ground, she saw how the circus folks were moving around. They'd heard what Nate had said to the lion tamer. The helpers weren't running—even if they were moving very fast. One was taking Charlie's barrels out of a wagon. Another was dragging the bicycles down. Miss Melinda had trotted into her tent right away.

The third handler came up onto the stump the minute Nate got off it. He'd brought three wooden balls with him and began to juggle them. Nate yelled some more, standing beside him.

And now something happened. Long-haired men with red-flannel bands around their foreheads and high leather moccasins came out to the edge of the wagons. Some of them did have white paint on their bare chests. The rest had what looked like long night-shirts down to the calves of their legs. They had paint on their faces. Three of them had Winchesters, the others, all nine of them, had bows. There wasn't a feather on any one of them.

While the juggler went on, the other handlers set up Charlie's barrels. Clayton let the lion out of his cage the second the juggler had finished and shouted at him to get "Up." Charlie growled but jumped up onto the smallest barrel.

Beeler saw that the Apaches didn't move back one bit when Charlie came out, but they watched every move he made as he went through his downs and ups on the barrels.

When Clayton was through, he called out, "Melinda." She didn't come, though. Beeler guessed why. That costume took so long to get into with all those little bitty hooks and eyes. If a person was nervous, it'd take even longer.

Beeler found the courage to get up to sit beside Leo. She poked him with her finger. "Leo, you get up and do somethin' to keep the Apaches lookin'."

He squeaked at her, "Holy gatlins, what'll I do?"

"Walk on your hands. The way you do at home. Stand on your head. Do anythin', but do it now. Miss Melinda's bogged down in somethin'."

Leo got to his feet shaking all over. But he flung up his hands and did a wobbly cartwheel. Then three more. Finally he stood on his head, waving his legs in the air, and then for a couple of yards walked on his hands. Finally he collapsed, panting, a foot or two from Beeler. The Apaches had watched every single thing he did without moving.

Beeler took a breath all the way down to her boots. It was up to her now. She got up and started to sing.

The first thing that came to her mind was "Nearer My God to Thee."

Nate knew that hymn tune, too. He came beside her to sing it through. And when they were finished, he started in on "Evalina." He put his arms around Beeler's waist and waltzed her around the campfires while the Indians went on looking. When they were through "Evalina" and were about to start the third time on it, which was very hard work in that altitude, Miss Melinda finally showed up.

She came out this time in black and blue spangles and dark-blue tights. She grabbed the bicycle nearest her tent, which turned out to be the unicycle. And once she was on it she started cycling so fast that Clayton couldn't hand Blossom to her, though he ran after her with the lionness on her leash.

Marvelous Melinda was doing the act all alone, meandering in and out in the places that weren't too bumpy. And she was smiling and waving at the Indians. The light from the two campfires made the one turning wheel twinkle red and her dark spangles glow like coals of scarlet fire. When she'd finished, Melinda poised on her unicycle for a minute, blowing kisses to the Apaches just as she had to the people of Ramada.

The Indians didn't clap, but they didn't go away either. They just stood staring. Finally one of the Apaches carrying a Winchester stepped out ahead of the others. Beeler's hand went to her waistline under her jacket. Leo's Winchester was by the fire along with Nate's. They hadn't dared to pick up their guns.

The Indian came straight toward the bicyclienne. She'd got off her unicycle and was standing beside it, holding it up. The Apache walked slowly, but Mr. Clayton moved fast. He ran out and planted himself in front of the lady. "Boy," he called out to Nate. "Tell this Indian he can have anything in this circus except for Miss Holcomb!"

Nate spoke in Spanish to the Apache, who only gazed at him. The Indian kept right on walking, but as he did he put out one hand and gave Clayton a shove out of the way. While Nate went on in Spanish, the Apache circled the bicyclienne, who had a frozen smile on her face. Then all of a sudden he reached out and grabbed the shining unicycle from her. He tucked it under his arm, turned his back on Clayton and Miss Melinda, and walked back to the other Apaches. They moved aside to let him through and, when he was gone, turned around and followed him.

"Ah-h-h!" cried the bicyclienne, flinging herself into the lion tamer's arms.

"My Melinda!" came from him.

Beeler sank down onto her heels. She felt weak as mush in the knees. Leo and Graber came over now too.

Leo's face was sweating. Graber had gone greeny-pale.

"What'd you say just now to the Indians?" Beeler asked Nate.

"That the squaw was Dauntless Daniel's. I said what he wanted me to say—that they could have anything else in the circus but her."

"I don't think the Indian ever did want her," said Leo. "He wanted that wheel."

"You're right, Leo," agreed Beeler. "Apaches must have plenty of squaws of their own. But one thing they haven't got is bicycles."

"They haven't got lions either," came from Leo. "I woulda took a lion."

Beeler glanced at Miss Melinda, who was bawling on the lion tamer's chest, wetting him down plenty. It appeared to her that Mr. Clayton and the bicyclienne had come to a meeting of minds. Clayton looked like he was taking to her like honeysuckle to a front porch.

Beeler let out a sigh while she looked at Nate. He'd surely used his head back there when the Apaches showed up out of nowhere. If he hadn't, they might all be dead by now or all their horses taken away. What if he'd picked up his Winchester and started shooting out into the dark? No, he was plenty smart. She thought back to their talk about unrequited love and wondered what he'd meant by that one word—"maybe."

She wondered, too, the rest of the next day while

she led Jinglebob down a steep place how an Apache
Indian would let folks know he'd like a performance.
She wasn't so scared now that she could think some
about it and see the odd side of giving a show for
Indians.

Leo, up ahead of her on the trail, must have been
pondering the same thing. He called back, "If you and
me had passed the hat to the Indians, what dya suppose
we'd of got?"

"A arrow in our gizzards, more'n likely." Then she
said, "You done real fine back there. You walked good
on your hands."

She heard him laughing. "By gatlins, you said somethin' nice to me, Beeler."

"Hang on to it, Leo. It might be the last time before
we find Sundown."

There was a Mexican town just out of the mountains, but Mr. Clayton and Miss Melinda didn't get
married there. The bicyclienne told Beeler that she
wanted to be able to understand the preacher's words.
Beeler understood. She wasn't sure she'd trust Clayton that much either—or any other man. She thought
it would be smart to wait until they got to Silverado,
too, and found a sin buster who talked English.

The country west of the mountains was a high plain,
swept over by winds all the time. It was hot, and so was

the dust that blew into their faces. All of the circus
people and the Texans wore handkerchiefs over their
noses and mouths, but the poor animals couldn't.
Jinglebob and Travis snorted a lot, and the lions
coughed even more. Mr. Clayton kept the circus away
from the dangerous White Sands. It gave Beeler the
willies just hearing about them. Even the bugs were
white out there, Clayton said. West of the sands was
another Mexican town where they gave a show in front
of the one hotel. That show gave them more money to
get to Silverado, where they expected to do right well.

It was yucca country from now on—high desert that
had waves in it. Beeler wasn't so interested in the tall
plants as she was in the deserted adobe houses that had
once been way stations for the old Butterfield Stage
Line. They made fine camping places for the circus.
She had got over her wariness of mountains, and it was
a good thing too. Just about everywhere she looked,
there they were—purple in the distance. New Mexico
Territory wasn't like any parts of Texas she'd ever set
eyes on. They were carrying water and hay for the
horses and camels now. As Clayton said, the country
ought to be camel country, but not even camels did
well in it. Travis kept swinging his head from side to
side and planting his hooves in the sandy dirt, pawing
until Beeler whistled him on. He didn't think this was
like Texas either.

Before they got to Silverado the circus went through another little Mexican town that had copper mines all around it. Nate had told the Quineys that mines were deep holes with underground tunnels going off them. At least silver mines were like that and gold mines, too. But copper mines were holes right on top of the ground. According to the Mexicans nearby, these were old, old mines. Indian prisoners of the Spanish conquerors of Mexico had dug copper in them a long, long time ago. Beeler thought that was mighty interesting information. A person learned things traveling.

Silverado was different too. It took a bit of a climb to get there, but it was worth it. It was nearly two miles up in the sky. Because there were trees in the mountains not too far away, Silverado's houses were made out of wood. There were a lot of saloons, of course, and a couple of hotels and stores. But there was something else: gold and silver bricks lying on the boardwalk outside the offices of shipping companies.. Everybody in the circus had his eyes sticking out so far you could have knocked them off with a board as they rode by the piles of yellow and white bricks. The ore had been melted down in Silvarado's smelters and shaped into bricks to be carried to San Francisco. Nobody laid a hand on the bricks, not even the drivers of the fourteen-horse teams that went up and down the street all day and all night, going to and coming from mines around Silverado. Beeler longed to heft a brick of gold just to see how heavy it was but decided not to.

Mr. Clayton and Miss Melinda found a preacher in Silverado, and he married them in the parlor of the best hotel in town. A circus helper stood up with the lion tamer. The hotel owner's little bitty wife stood up with the bicyclienne, who had on her purple outfit. Even though she'd never set eyes on Marvelous Melinda before, the hotel lady bawled. Beeler didn't understand why. Getting double harnessed wasn't that bad. Lots of folks got married and lived to a ripe old age.

Afterwards Beeler said to Leo, "I heard every word the preacher said. She roped, throwed, and branded him just fine. Very legallike." She eyed Graber, who was looking out the hotel window past the bride and groom. He and Leo had been moseying around Silverado earlier that day while she'd talked a livery stable man into seeing to it that Jinglebob and Travis got a special feed. It had cost her twenty-five cents to get it done, but the critters were resting easy, side by side, though not in the same stall. The man hadn't cottoned to the thought that longhorns belonged in stables, but he looked at it differently when Beeler told him, using Nate's expression, that the steer was a child's pet. Graber had been pretty smart to say that. Using it worked just fine.

Nate finally turned his head to look at her. He grinned. "A man in the Silverado Emporium told me just before the ceremony that he's heard there's a town called Sunrise Flats or something like that in Arizona Territory."

"Has he been there?" Beeler wanted to know.

"No, but he says a miner coming east talked about it. We'll start for there in the morning. I told Mr. Clayton just before he got married that we were leaving."

Leo asked, "Did you hear about your pa and them four other galoots?"

"No, they don't seem to have been here, but that doesn't prove much. Silverado's a busy place. Nobody knew Mr. McCarty's brother here either."

Beeler laughed. "That ain't no cause to wonder. I bet he's dropped his name in the river and is usin' a new one now."

"I don't know," came from Graber. "The man who told me about Sunrise Flats said Silverado has lots of hangings but no robberies to speak of. I almost hate to leave it. He said, 'Nowhere on God's footstool are women and children safer!' "

Beeler had to smile. She reckoned she knew why. In Silverado a person got hanged before he did anything that was against the law. That's why gold and silver were out on the walks in plain sight.

"Is Arizona Territory like this here one?" Leo asked.

"Are they sort of against us Texans there, too?"

Beeler listened closely. She guessed they'd been lucky so far. Nobody had made anything of their being from Texas.

Nate said, "I don't know how they feel about Texans there, Leo. The man said Arizona Territory was maybe a bit wilder even than it is hereabouts. It's lots hotter—lower down and more lonesome."

Beeler pondered this without joy. Finally she said, "That's what the preacher back home in Cottonwood used to say about hell!"

Nate agreed. "That crossed my mind, too, Beulah Land."

7 "HIS TOWN"

Miss Melinda, or really Mrs. Duckworth or Mrs. Clayton, gave Leo and Nate each a kiss on the cheek the next morning but dragged Beeler aside before the Texans rode out of Silverado. She took a piece of black ribbon out of her reticule. Two little five-dollar gold pieces with holes in them hung from the ribbon, which she tied around Beeler's neck under her shirt collar.

"Holy snakes, I didn't earn these and my neck's not clean, ma'am."

"I know," said the bicyclienne, "but I want you to have them. Mr. Clayton likes my gold and diamond medal, but he doesn't like to see my presents from old beaux. He thought you and the boys did just wonderfully when the Apaches came. He's too shy to tell you. But you were real performers! You went right along with his idea to give a benefit performance for the Indians." She smiled. "My dear, before you go, I want you to buy something for me at the store." Now she gave Beeler a silver dollar, too.

"What do you want?"

"A large bottle of liver regulator and a little one of Thompsan's Hair Dye, brown in color. And a bar of Pears soap for you. The regulator and hair dye are for Mr. Clayton."

Beeler nodded. She'd forget to buy the soap. "Anythin' you want for the lions?"

"No, I'll try to stop their coughing later." She laughed. "Do you suppose a lion has ever had lard and turpentine rubbed onto its chest? It's a wonderful remedy for coughs."

"No, ma'am." Beeler thought with pity of poor Blossom and Charlie. It was her horseback opinion that the lions would get washed pretty soon. Mrs. Clayton was soap-and-water crazy. She'd never believe it was natural for lions to cough. That's what Dauntless Daniel had told Nate once.

It was high time to skedaddle from the circus!

One of the gold pieces bought supplies for the Texans to take them to Sunrise Flats. The other one they'd keep dangling around Beeler's neck until they needed it. And Nate still had some jingle in his pockets. If they found his pa in Sunrise Flats, Nate said, they wouldn't need money. Mr. Graber would take care of all of them and be happy to pay travelers bound east for Texas to let the two Quineys travel home with them.

Beeler didn't say anything to Nate about her suspicions, but the morning they rode out of Silverado she dropped back to ride beside Leo for a while. It took some hard jerking on Travis's neck rope to make him behave because he hadn't taken to livery-stable life one bit, and he wanted to run loose.

"Leo," she said, "my cow sense tells me that we hadn't better count too much on Graber's pa doin' anythin' for us except mebbe sayin' 'thank you kindly.' Him and those men with him! Don't it seem queer to you that nobody we talked to has ever set eyes on 'em except that woman in Lovelock and then old Billy-whiskers and that wife of his who fed you cake in Deadahead. No one else seein' hide or hair of 'em means somethin' to me if it don't to you."

"What?" Leo was being scornful again.

"They don't want to be seen. They're keepin' away from towns and tradin' posts. There's only one reason why they'd do that. They're up to devilment."

He scoffed, "Nate's pa used to be a wisdom bringer, remember? Do you think a teacher'd be up to devilment?"

Beeler nodded her head and looked wise. "If they set their minds to it, they could do it better'n most folks could, I bet. They're plenty smart. And, too, they can get ideas out of books that are wicked. I heard tell there are lots of wicked books."

Leo hooted. "Next thing you'll be sayin' is that preachers can hatch up devilment, too."

Again Beeler nodded. "A sin buster who goes bad— he's the worst kind of all. Nerissa claimed she knew one once who ran away with the Christmas collection plate and the only singer in the choir who could carry a tune in a 'tater sack. Everybody missed the singer real bad."

Satisfied with the expression of shock on her brother's face, she whistled to Travis and went up to ride behind Nate. Her eyes on his widish back, she murmured to herself, "Poor cuss. Down in my gizzard I have the feelin' he mebbe ain't gonna have much good news comin' whenever he does find this here Sundown. But I'm gonna try to make it up to him. After all there's only one of him and eleven of us Quineys left as far as I know. If he hitches up someday with me, that'd make him half a Quiney and never lonesome again."

She glanced around her as they left Silverado. That town had smelled pleasantly of fresh-cut lumber. It had been interesting, too, with all the gold and silver lying around loose. She liked traveling, even with Leo along to cramp her a bit. She thought pityingly of

Nerissa and the other Texas womenfolks she knew. They were surely bogged down in carpets. All the traveling most of the women in Cottonwood did was walking around their coffeepot on the stove looking for the handle!

The road to Sunrise Flats led southwest, according to Nate. It was only a trail that wandered between more mountains, mostly through forests. The country was plenty wild. Beeler knew it was grizzly bear territory, though they never saw one the nights they camped. But they heard catamounts wailing in the timber and coyotes too. Leo shot a buck deer that ran over the trail in front of them, so they saved on supplies. The venison lasted them two days. Although Apaches were supposed to live in this part of New Mexico Territory too, they didn't catch sight of one Indian. Anyway folks in Silverado had said that they weren't the same kind of Apaches as around Ramada. Maybe these Indians didn't take any interest in three folks traveling together, or they were too poor looking to bother with.

Travis looked to be thinning down some more now that the grazing hadn't been so fine. He couldn't hang behind here and graze because once you rode beyond a bend in the trail you lost sight of anything behind you. He hated pine cones. Beeler wouldn't lose him to Indians or catamounts or grizzlies. Sometimes she felt guilty over him. Poor little critter. She hadn't planned to fetch him so far from Santa Rosa County. What he was doing now wasn't natural for a steer. But Travis had surely earned his keep. There wasn't a finer watch animal anywhere, even if he hadn't given warning about the Indians. What was more, Beeler suspected just seeing Travis, who looked a lot fiercer than he was, kept wild things, four-legged and two-legged, away.

Sunrise Flats, the Texans discovered when they got there, was where the man in Silverado had said it would be. But that wasn't what folks who lived there called it now. The Quineys and Nate learned the new name five minutes after they rode into town. That was because of Travis and because of the town dogs. There must have been twenty of them, Beeler decided later, though in the uproar she didn't have time to make a head count.

The minute the Texans passed the blacksmith's shop at the very end of town, the dogs showed up. They came pouring out of an alley between the blacksmith's and a saloon like dried peas from a split sack, all of them yapping and barking.

Nate shouted over them, "Hark, hark the dogs do bark!" He could do that because Stupid stood quiet and let them snap at him. Two Cents reared, while

Jinglebob let fly with his hooves at a couple of dogs before Beeler pulled up on his reins. Travis was the real troublemaker. Because he hated dogs he let out a bellow and jerked on his neck rope, pulling the saddle horn he'd been tied to clear off. Then he was gone, charging down the street.

Yelling and whistling, Beeler galloped after him. The dogs deserted Stupid and Two Cents and came dashing at Jinglebob's heels. Everybody in town stopped what he was doing to watch as the black steer went rumbling past, bellowing, hooking his head to the left and then to the right. Ladies with market baskets on their arms quivered behind porch posts. People came out of stores to stand on the boardwalk, then leap back as Travis hooked toward them. Windows were opened and heads poked out while Beeler went on whistling, scared that somebody would shoot Travis.

A little Mexican boy in a big straw hat stood in front of one saloon. He yelled out, *"Toro, toro."* He was laughing until Travis all at once switched direction and headed straight for him with the dogs at his heels. The boy lunged to one side only a second before Travis lumbered through the saloon's swinging doors. All the dogs ran under them after him.

Beeler drew Jinglebob up and listened. Lordy, what a hollering and yelling and uproar of barks and bellows! Glass was being broken everywhere, she

reckoned, judging from the tinkly crashing sounds.
She looked over her shoulder. There wasn't going to
be any help from Nate or Leo. No such luck! Nate
couldn't get Stupid started on his way, and Two Cents
was still pawing the sky with his front hooves. Beeler
dropped the reins over Jinglebob's head to make him
stay and slid off. She looked at the saloon and shook
her head. But she went up its steps anyway. Beeler
knew all about saloons. Nerissa always made her and
the weaner gals cross the street from Cottonwood's
saloons, they were so wicked. It made walking down
the street a bunch of zigs and zags because there were
so many places of sin. And it made the Quineys, all of
them, keep quiet about the bottle of whiskey Nerissa's
husband kept out in the barn under the hay.

Saloons were the hatching places of devilment. Wary
of what devilment she might be getting into, Beeler
went through the double doors, too—but nowhere near
as fast as Travis and the dogs had.

What a sight she saw! Travis in the middle of the
floor with broken tables and chairs all around him.
Spilled beer and whiskey made wet spots all over the
sawdust. A whole ring of dogs surrounded Travis,
snarling and barking. Now and then he'd rush one,
and it would move back. A whole ring of people surrounded the dogs. Some of them were up against the
walls, others in corners barricaded behind chairs and

hat racks. Three ladies in short dresses were up on the long wooden bar that ran from one end of the saloon to the other. One of them let out a screech when she caught sight of Beeler.

Beeler called to her, "Don't yell so. The critter belongs to me. I've come to save him." She walked toward the circle of dogs. They were just common ordinary pot hounds as far as she could see. "You get outa my way," she told two of them, lifting her boot. They moved aside, snarling, so she could get to Travis, who was trembling. She spoke loudly to him, so everybody would know he was hers. "They ain't nothin' to be scared of—jest old flea-trap dogs." She took him by one horn and by the neck rope. Then she told the saloon folks, "I got my critter. Now you get your dogs away from him."

A big man wearing a white apron, which was an odd thing on a man, came from behind the bar where the ladies were standing. He had two brooms in his hands. He gave one to another man and together they began to sweep the dogs out onto the street. Most of them went willingly enough, although a couple yelped on the way. Leo and Nate came in during the second wave of dogs going out.

The white-aproned man had a mouth alive with gold teeth. He asked Beeler when the dogs were all gone, "Who's gonna pay for my busted furniture and glasses? And all that spilled liquor?"

Beeler, who was patting Travis to keep him calmed down, asked in turn, "Ask them dogs to pay ya, Mister. They started it the minute we set hoof in this town of yours. What kinda welcome do you folks in Sunrise Flats give strangers anyhow?"

"Texans, ain't ya?" asked the man.

"We're only passing through," Nate added hastily.

While people came away from the walls, and the ladies were helped down off the bar, Nate explained his errand. The saloon man shook his head. "This town used to be Sunrise Flats, but it ain't anymore. I never heard tell of Sunset or Sundown. I never seen five men like you describe 'em. Maybe they went somewheres else in this town and then rode on west."

Beeler noticed that Nate's tale had seemed to soften Mr. Goldtooth the way it seemed to soften other folks. It made them feel sorry. She decided it was time to make tracks out of the saloon with her critter before the man asked again who'd pay for the damage to the busted things. The stink of the liquor wasn't one bit pleasant either.

She'd started to lead Travis out when all at once the man asked, "Who'd you three boys be?"

Nate was gallant, even if he put her last in line.

"This is Leo Quiney and I'm Jonathan Graber. That's Beulah Land Quiney with the steer."

Beeler lifted her hat. "I'm a she, not a he. The critter ain't theirs. He belongs to me. He's named Travis. He's never been in a saloon before."

"*Travis?*" The saloon man looked as if somebody had just hit him over the head with a club.

"Did you say *Travis?*" one of the saloon ladies asked.

"That's what we call him."

Everybody started to laugh. While Beeler and the boys looked on puzzled, all the folks in the saloon bent double, laughing. When the saloon man quit leaning against the bar to support himself and wiped his eyes with his apron, he said, "Forget about the damage your steer's caused, girlie. It was worth it, every busted chair and table and glass."

Now it was really time to get out of there, away from all these lunatics. "Much obliged," said Beeler, as she hauled Travis out of the Gay Lady Saloon, over its porch, and down into the dusty street of the town. Whatever the town was named now, it surely wasn't much to look at. It was on a flat piece of ground with some big rocky hills not far off, so she could see why it had been called Flats once. The town was made of adobe houses and false-fronted wooden stores and saloons. As she and the boys stood in the street, Beeler noticed the red brick building across from them. The

gold-painted sign on its windows read *Travis Bank.*
She looked to its left. There was a store there. Its
black-and-white painted sign was *Travis General Emporium.* Two doors away she spotted the name again:
Travis Undertaking Parlor. Now she turned to look
behind her, and in a row she spied: *Travis Sundries
and Medicines, Travis Saddlery,* and *Travis Hand
Laundry.*

"I guess this town has to be named Travis?" she
said to Nate, who had also been looking around.

"I guess so." He seemed down at the mouth. "Leo
and I'll tackle some of the other saloons and ask
about my father and Sundown or Sunset. As long as
we're here, I suppose we ought to find out everything
we can. Please stay with the horses and your animal."

"You think I shouldn't go inside saloons?" Beeler
was touched at Nate's thoughtfulness. She was smiling
as she watched him and Leo head into the saloon next
door to the Gay Lady. She kept right on smiling as
she watched the boys walk back and forth across the
street from one den of devilment to another. There
wasn't a dog in sight. Travis was king of the street.

"You done just fine in there," she told him. "You
done better bustin' up a saloon than the temperance
ladies in Cottonwood coulda in the same amount of
time." Destroying the town saloons was one of Nerissa's dreams.

Suddenly Travis jerked his head, alerting Beeler. Somebody was coming out of an alley toward them. Whoever it was appeared odd because it wore black floppy pants, a black jacket, and a little round black hat. The person had black hair in one long braid down its back and sort of yellow skin. When whoever it was got within spitting distance, Beeler saw a mustache. It wasn't a lady then, but what else it was she surely didn't know.

The man in black smiled. "Little Master, Big Missy sent me to see you."

Beeler had caught the words "Little Master." She let out a sigh and took off her hat. "I ain't your master, Mister. I'm a she. Who'd you be? Don't come too close to my critter's horns!"

"I Po Wing. Very fine animal with horns, Little Missy's. Big Missy want me ask you come to her house now."

"What's a Po Wing?"

"Me. Chinese man."

"Ah." Now Beeler understood. She'd never laid eyes on anyone from China. But the schoolmarm in Cottonwood had told them about China, over the ocean from California.

Po Wing said again, "You please to come to Big Missy's house."

"Who's Big Missy?"

"Boss lady. Missus Travis. Missus Louie Travis. She very big boss."

"What does she want me for?"

Po Wing stuck out a finger at Travis. "She want to talk about that animal. Boss lady hear that he come to town. I think Big Missy want to give you money for him."

Beeler drew back. For sure, it hadn't been cow country they'd just traveled through, though there'd been some sheep about. Did Mrs. Travis hanker for beef? "I ain't sellin' him, Mr. Po Wing."

Po Wing shook his head. "Boss lady don't want to buy him. She want *see* him and you. She say come now."

Beeler looked around her. There were quite a few people standing on the walks in front of stores. All of them were staring at her and Travis; quite a few of them were grinning. Neither Nate nor Leo was in sight.

Making up her mind because of the mention of money, Beeler hitched Jinglebob to the same rail with Two Cents and Stupid. She'd take Travis with her if that's what Mrs. Travis wanted. "Hey, Mister," Beeler called out to a man sitting on a chair outside the funeral parlor. "Will you tell them boys I'm ridin' with that I went to Mrs. Travis's house with Mr. Po Wing? Do you know him or where the house would be?" Beeler came closer. Would the Chinese want to rob her of the gold piece around her neck? "Mister," she asked softly, "can I trust Mr. Po Wing?"

"You surely can. He's the most honest man in town. As for the house, it's the only brick place except for Mr. Travis's bank building. I'll send the boys there if you ain't back soon. Good luck to ya."

"I'd be obliged to ya." Beeler took the steer's neck rope, told him, "Come along, Travis. Somebody else's prob'ly got it in mind to admire you," and followed Po Wing down the middle of the street.

Boss Lady's house was yellow brick, not red, and it was good sized. It looked more like a courthouse than a place to sleep and eat in. Beeler wondered about the inside of it, but she never got to see it.

Mrs. Travis came outside, slamming the front door behind her, before Beeler, the steer, and Po Wing were even there. She was a sight! She had frizzled red-brown hair, a set of bottom teeth that rose up out of her lower jaw when she tried to look pleasant, and a scrooched-up expression. She looked a lot like one of the flea-trap dogs in town. But what was more she was beef to the hocks—surely a solid woman. Because the sun was out and hot, Mrs. Travis had a parasol up over her head. It was ruffled and pale pink to match her dress. They suited her the way a sidesaddle suited a hog.

"I am Missus Travis, Mrs. Mimi Travis," she said in a highfalutin voice.

Because she was talking woman to woman, Beeler lifted her hat. "Yes, ma'am," she told her.

Mrs. Travis put her handkerchief to her nose. Through it she wanted to know, "What is that black beast with you called?"

"Travis, ma'am. We're from Texas."

"I am told he caused consternation in a saloon here in my husband's absence on business in San Francisco. Your animal is obstreperous."

Beeler didn't know if these big words were good or bad. She said, "Dogs run him into a saloon, if that's what you got in mind. It wasn't my Travis's fault."

The woman snorted through the handkerchief. "You realize, of course, that this town is named for my husband, who founded it last year?"

Being polite, Beeler told her, "It appears to me he owns it. His brand looks to be on jest about everythin' in it. Didn't it used to be called Sunrise Flats?" Beeler saw Po Wing grinning behind the woman where she couldn't see him. Beeler guessed it was the only place he ever dared to grin.

Mrs. Travis took down the handkerchief. Her face was a pure caution. For a fact, she had a mean disposition and right now meant murder. "My husband made this town what it is. Its name has been changed to honor him. He is its most important citizen. He is the mayor. It is *his town*. He *never* goes into saloons. He must not be made a laughingstock of by a cow from Texas."

"Travis ain't a cow. Travis is a steer."

This made Mrs. Travis clap the handkerchief back real fast and talk through it some more. "Whatever he is, he smells strongly of cow. Or you do. I can't tell which. What would you ask of me to get you to leave town with him right now—this very instant?"

It was on the tip of Beeler's tongue to cuss her out, but she thought better of it. Mrs. Travis was offering cash money to get rid of Travis! Now she knew what the Chinese servant had meant about money. "Hang and rattle. Don't fight your head," she told herself, wondering how much to ask for. Then she took a deep breath and said, "Twenty dollars, and we'll light out right away. Cash on the barrelhead, too."

"Give this little road agent from Texas twenty dollars, Po Wing," snapped the woman. She handed her reticule to him, then with her hand on the front doorknob said, "Perhaps you wonder, girl, why civilized people in New Mexico and Arizona Territory don't like Texans. Half of you are desperate characters escaping justice—wanted even in Texas. The rest of you are out to make the territories part of Texas. What is your name? I have every intention of asking the sheriff about you, let me warn you!"

After the Chinese had given Beeler one double eagle and she'd pocketed it, she called out, "Bertha Mae Muller." Mrs. Travis wouldn't check out the name Quiney they'd used in the Gay Lady Saloon. It had come to Beeler's mind that there might be some of the Quineys they hadn't heard of for a long time out here in Arizona Territory, too. The sheriff might have heard of one or two of them. Why get them in hot water? Kin had to stick with kin.

Beeler met Graber and Leo in the middle of the street and showed them the money. Then she told the story of Mrs. Travis and all the insults to her and her critter, ending up with, "I surely feel sorry for that poor galoot who married with her."

Nate nodded. "I suspect he needs the comfort of saloons even if he's rich enough to own half of the businesses here. The postmaster told Leo and me some things about Mr. Travis."

"Uh-huh," came from Leo. "He said poor old man Travis has the look of a dyin' calf in a snowstorm on his face all the time."

Beeler pocketed the gold piece again. It was hers and Travis's. But she'd spend it if the three of them needed it.

"Did you find out where Sundown is, Nate?" she asked.

"Not exactly. But a saloon lady said she thought she recalled five men, 'funny lookers,' she claimed, a couple of months back. She said they were all shapes and sizes. They didn't drink much—though a couple of them gambled. One of them was wearing Mexican type spurs with big rowels. Another one was bald."

"He was truly bald," added Leo. "She said his head was so scalped of hair that when he took off his hat to her it looked like the moon was risin' up out of a line of hills."

Beeler rode over Nate's sound of annoyance. "That musta been them all right! Where'd they go?"

Nate answered, "The saloon lady didn't know, but when I asked at the post office, I turned up a Sunvale in this territory. It just got started as a town."

"Whereabouts in Arizona Territory?" asked Beeler.

"Well, the postmaster didn't know. It isn't in his book of post offices yet. He heard about it from somebody passing through here last week. He encourages travelers to drop in and tell him the names of new places. It keeps him up on things. When we find Sundown, he wants me to write him a letter and tell him where it is."

Beeler leaned against Travis, looking down at her wearing-out pants. She guessed maybe she did smell a bit high. She knew Leo did. Nate was examining his duds too. Even the Mexican leather looked scuffed and shabby. He said, "Let's mount up before Mrs. Travis sends somebody to see that we do leave. But that isn't the only reason I want to get going! There was a sign behind the bar in two saloons."

"What'd it say?" asked Beeler.

"I memorized it. It said, 'Gents will please leave their six-shooters behind the bar while in town. This will lessen the customary collection for burials.' "

"Well, did they leave 'em?" Beeler demanded.

"No, they didn't—not a lot of those I saw. That's the trouble."

Beeler nodded. She looked up at a sky that didn't have one cloud in it. "How many more miles do you suppose it's goin' to be to Sundown?"

8 MISS MUFFET

Riding west into Arizona Territory gave Beeler more of a sinking feeling. They were still pretty high up in canyon country, surrounded by caves that might have bears in them. The pines and scrub oaks didn't help much, even if they were green, because they could hide wild animals and wilder folks. It was closed-in land, scarey for prairie people. Some of the rocks around this part of the country were as black as Travis's hide, lava from old volcanoes, Nate explained. Crossing them on horseback was a slipping and sliding business, and when you looked up from these rocks just as often as not your eye had to look at more, piled up on top of each other as if somebody loco had tried to build something. Beeler reckoned the Almighty must have got weary of work and turned careless when he made this part of the world and thrown it together any which way out of what was left over from better parts.

Worse, there was never one horsebacker in sight to tell them where Sundown might be—nobody at all. It made a person want to pull her bedroll over closer to somebody else's at night when the coyotes yowled—even if the somebody was Leo Quiney.

Beeler reckoned she felt some better about him, though. He'd done fine when the Apaches visited the circus, and he hadn't done anything out of line in the town of Travis. He looked to be improving. Beeler even told him one night while she was bashing up coffee beans for boiling with the butt of her six-shooter, "You ain't the raw product you was when we headed out from home."

He'd turned to Nate with a make-believe scowl on his face. "You hear that, Graber? She's said two kind words to me now. Didn't you think she done good, too, at times?"

Nate had laughed but only said "Yes." Beeler had kept an eye on him when he wasn't looking. He was thinning down now for sure, dropping tallow all the time. And his hair was yellow curls all over his head but not quite to the bottoms of his ears yet. It became him, losing lard and having curls, though she hoped he'd never get to the point Leo was—thin enough to split a hailstone. As for herself, her pants were getting looser every day. She was moving up onto the last notch of her belt.

The chance never came to ask Graber what he'd meant by unrequited love and that "maybe." But she'd keep on bearing it in mind, and someday she and he would ride over that same trail again.

When it came to trails, the one through these mountains wasn't easy to follow because it seemed not enough folks had traveled it to mark it well. In some places, especially over the black rocks, and there were whole acres of them in spots, the trail got lost. That's when the three of them fanned out and looked for sign of a trail leading west.

The afternoon of the second day out from the town of Travis, Beeler was afoot leading Jinglebob over the slick lava. She was hunting northwest, past the mouth of another canyon. Nate was searching due west and Leo southwest.

All at once Travis, who was behind Jinglebob, let out a snort and started to run, streaking by Beeler. Jinglebob reared up nickering. Beeler jerked out her six-shooter, then let go of the reins so Jinglebob could clatter off over the rocks after the longhorn. It must be a bear or a panther for sure! She let out a yell for the others. They'd come riding fast with Winchesters. Her eyes scanned the mouth of the canyon for some big animal watching her, but she couldn't spy any. There wasn't a wild thing in sight at the moment.

But as she stood her ground, her pistol ready, some-

thing did show up from behind some small rocks. It
was walking mighty heavy for its size. The noise it
made was what had spooked Jinglebob and Travis.
The animal was white and black and pretty to look at
—if you didn't know what it was. A skunk!

There wasn't anything more deadly to beast or man.
A skunk was the scariest thing a person could run into.
Not because of its stink, which was plenty bad enough,
but because sometimes it had a disease called hydrophobia. It could be rabid. In Texas rabid skunks had
been known to sneak into a man's bedroll with him
and bite him. And he'd go loco and be a danger to
everybody around him—gone pure brute himself.
There wasn't any saving a person with hydrophobia.
Being bit by a skunk that had it was as sure a death as
being sentenced to hang by order of an Arkansas judge.
Only a lot slower and more painful.

Her hands so shaky that she had to aim the six-
shooter with both of them, Beeler drew a bead on the
skunk. It was coming straight on toward her, waddling
its way, rattling pebbles because it walked so heavily.
That wasn't a natural thing for any wild animal to do,
coming right up to her, so it must be sick. Wishing
she had a shotgun to blow it apart, Beeler cocked the
pistol.

But before she could pull the trigger, she heard a
kid yelling from somewhere. It was too young a voice

to be Nate or Leo. This was a weaner's voice. And now she saw the kid, a raggedy-looking little girl not more than five years old, coming on the run behind the skunk.

"Señorita Mofeta!" she squealed.

"Get back, I'm gonna shoot!" Beeler called out to her.

The child stopped dead still in her tracks. Her stare went from the skunk to the pistol. Suddenly she shrieked, "No, *señor*." To Beeler's horror the dark-haired child ran forward, scooped the skunk up in her arms, and buried her face in the animal's fur.

Beeler hung onto the pistol, trembling by now as if she had Saint Vitus Dance. And then Nate showed up on Stupid. He took in the whole trouble in one look. "My God," was what he said. Then he came out with fast words in Spanish. Beeler guessed he was telling the girl to put the skunk down. But she hung onto it.

Her head jerked up, and she talked back to Nate. After she was done, Beeler heard Nate sighing with relief. "It's all right," he said to her. "Put away the pistol, but let me uncock it for you first." As Beeler handed the pistol over to him, Nate told her, "The girl says she's María Lopez. The skunk is Señorita Mofeta. She doesn't have hydrophobia." He laughed. "She's María's pet. Would you believe it—a child's pet?"

Her hand still trembling so she rammed herself with the six-shooter as she put it back into her belt, Beeler asked, "Where'd them two come from?"

Nate talked some more in Spanish. "Back in the canyon. María lives with her brother, father, and grandmother."

"Why'd they live way out here?"

"Let me ask her."

Nate went on in Spanish again. Then he said, "There's a mine back there. María's worried that the *señor* with the long red hair will shoot Señorita Mofeta. She means you."

Leo was beside them now and heard both Beeler and Nate laughing. "What's goin' on?" he asked. He took a gander at María Lopez and the skunk and reined Two Cents around, ready to get out of there pronto.

"Come back, Leo," Nate called to him. "The skunk's a pet. She's healthy. The little girl says she doesn't do what skunks generally do."

"How come the skunk don't?" Beeler wanted to know.

"María says Señorita Mofeta thinks she's a cat."

Beeler's jaw dropped halfway to her brisket. "How come a skunk'd think that?"

"She's been raised by the Lopez family. I ran into this once before in Old Mexico. A skunk's death on mice and pack rats and all other kinds of vermin. A real cat wouldn't last a week out here among the coyotes and mountain lions."

"I reckon that'd be true," granted Beeler.

"It is true. A skunk hasn't any real enemies."

"It hasn't got any real friends neither," said Beeler. "Nate, please tell that little gal I ain't a señor no more'n she is and I won't shoot her pet." She lifted her hat while Graber talked to María.

María seemed embarrassed. She came forward, still carrying the skunk, and stared into Beeler's face. She said, *"Lo siento mucho, señorita."* Then to Nate she added, *"La gringa salada es simpatica."*

"What'd she say?" asked Beeler.

"That she's very sorry she thought you were a boy and that the frog with freckles of an American girl is nice."

"Frog?" exploded Beeler. "I guess we can be on our way. Leo, go round up Jinglebob and my critter for me."

She turned away, but the little Mexican girl pulled at her arm, dragging her hand down into the skunk's fur. Beeler petted it nervously even if the fur was plenty soft. María said something more.

Whatever she said got Nate off Stupid in a hurry. "She wants us to come see her grandmother. She says she likes company. She wants to feed us."

María Lopez looked over her shoulder past Señorita Mofeta's head, then led the way into the canyon.

Nate told Beeler, "All you have to do is act *simpatica.*"

"For a good feed I reckon I can do it for a while at least. Mebbe Leo can, too, as soon as he gets my animals."

The Lopez family lived in a house that looked to be made of old boards nobody had wanted to throw away. It was close by a square black hole cut in the side of the canyon. A sure-enough mine, Beeler told herself.

A boy, larger than María, came out of the mine pushing a wheelbarrow. María shouted at him, "Matias," and the boy dropped the handles of the barrow to stare. Matias called out something in Spanish. The door of the shack opened, and in it stood a gray-headed woman wih a shotgun. Beeler and Nate stopped still.

María called out to her, holding up Señorita Mofeta. Then, tucking the skunk under her arm, she gestured toward the Texans. The old lady put down the shotgun. "María, put Miss Muffet down now that you've found her," she told the child in English.

The old lady came up to Beeler and Nate. She said, "How do you do?"

"Very well, thank you," came from Nate, who introduced himself and Beeler, and then added that Leo was on his way too.

The old lady's eyes were the light blue of Nerissa's prized forget-me-nots, though her face was as wrinkled as a burned boot. She wasn't any Mexican—not with those blue eyes and talking English so well.

Beeler just had to know. "How come you talk English to us and Spanish to them two kids?"

"Because I speak both languages. I'm Señora Mary Rose Seton de Lopez. I was born and reared in Galveston." She shook Beeler's hand, cracking the girl's knuckles. Then she shook Nate's.

"Light a spell," she told the Texans. "We'll be eatin' pretty soon. I know we look to be so poor we don't even own a name, but we set a pretty good table."

Nate accepted for both of them, then asked, "Do you know where a town named Sunset or Sundown would be—or a place called Sunvale? My father might be there."

"They must be new places. I don't know of them. I've been sitting on top of a silver mine for two years now. I'm a widow woman. My son, Pedro, rode off to town with some ore samples to the assay office three days ago. If you're about to ask about the children's mother, she's dead. She died a year after María was born. That child's a trial to me. I try to teach her and Matias, but all they want to do is chase that skunk and hack away at a vein of silver. I want them to know their ABC's and how to figure numbers so they'll be ready for school when Pedro and I leave here."

A loud sound over the rock floor of the canyon made everybody turn around. There was Leo, leading Jingle-bob and holding Travis's neck rope. Beeler watched him. He put the end of the neck rope between his teeth and Jinglebob's reins in the same hand as Two Cents's and took off his hat to Señora Lopez. Beeler was disgusted, remembering Elfic Billywhiskers. That Leo could butter up womenfolks when he wanted to like nothing she'd ever seen. But he only buttered up stranger ladies. He'd never took the trouble to brighten her life or Nerissa's.

Señora Lopez handed the shotgun to Beeler and went up to Travis. He let her pat him and then she patted Jinglebob. When she came back, she said, "There's some hay and oats here for your animals back of the shack. That steer's getting to be mostly legs and horns. It's a pitiful pass he's come to."

"We rode a long ways from Santa Rosa County, Texas. So has he," Beeler apologized for Travis.

"And you all sure look it," agreed the old lady. "I'll hunt up a needle and thread to patch your britches. Then you can tell me what brings you out here in the wilds. I bet it's a good story."

Beeler whispered to Nate, after Leo had dismounted and gone with Matias to lead the horses away, "Ask the Missus what brought her out here and why she's got herself tied up with Mexicans."

He spoke fiercely to her. "I'll ask her why she's in Arizona Territory—but not about Mexicans. Mexicans have very good manners. They wouldn't ever have asked her husband why he married a woman from Texas!"

Beeler fell in step with Graber. "But I'll bet you some Mexicans wondered."

He gave her a look that said "Wilt," but she wouldn't give him that satisfaction. "I wouldn't be at all surprised that they did wonder," he hissed.

The shack was as miserable inside as on the outside. It had a table and rickety chairs and two bunk beds only. It seemed clear that the Lopez children slept on the floor. The only valuable things in the place were the one glass window in the back wall and a large black cookstove. Something in a pot was on it cooling, and whatever it was smelled just fine to Beeler.

Señora Lopez waved her hand at the Texans to take a seat. Just as Beeler got comfortable, thinking how long it'd been since her backside had felt a chair, there came a scratching at the door.

"Let Miss Muffet in, please," the old lady ordered Leo, who was closest to the door.

He got up and opened it and in came the skunk. She walked straight over to a bowl in a corner. "That's a good puss," said the old lady.

Beeler asked, "Why do you call her Miss Muffet?"

"Because when she was just a baby abandoned by her maw, I used to feed her on curds and whey. Does that answer you, honey?"

"It oughta," came from Leo. "Beeler used to carry many a bucket of milk to that steer of hers when it was little."

"Yes, it answers her question," said Nate, kicking Beeler under the table.

"Why're you kickin' me, Graber? What'd I do that was bad?" Beeler demanded.

"You started in asking questions," he whispered.

Beeler glared at him but kept quiet. There was no stopping Leo, though. "Can Miss Muffet do what other skunks do, Missus Lopez?"

"Far as we know, she can, but she's much too well-trained. And by disposition Miss Muffet's mighty polite."

Later on Señora Lopez gave them and her grandchildren a bowl of chili beans that tasted better than any Beeler had ever had before. The old lady served fresh fried doughnuts with them, first cutting out the holes for the skunk to eat. Miss Muffet wanted out the minute she'd gulped down the raw dough. Afterwards the old woman took up some knitting out of a basket and said, "Of course, you're wondering what brought me out here in the middle of nowhere."

"We surely are, ma'am," came from Beeler, as she jerked her foot away from Nate's boot.

"Well, I came out here as a bride, married to Mr. Terwilliger." She sighed. "We left damp Galveston because of his health. He lived on egg yolks beaten with potatoes and water for a whole year at one time. It was all his stomach would stomach. We had the Hog's Eye Basin Ranch until he died. Then I clerked in a little trading post until I met Mr. Aitken and married up with him. We had a ranch, too. It was a mighty pretty place. I had a flower garden. I took snuff then and saved all them little bottles to make borders for my flower beds. Then Mr. Aitken died, too. He died with a bottle in his hand and a bottle inside. He was never destined to die of thirst." She dropped a stitch, muttered some, then picked it up. "Next time around I married Señor Lopez. He was Mexican. We had some fine times at fandangos in town before he died. We used to take our son to them when he was your age, Leo, and Señor Lopez was still alive. Have you ever been to a fandango?"

"Yes," said Nate.

"No," said Beeler and Leo.

"Well, the floorboards are greased slick with tallow for the dancing. And such music from the accordion and fiddler—not to mention the guitars! Mexican guitars. Señor Lopez was a fine dancer. He died right in the middle of the floor."

Beeler thought this shack was a far place from fandangos. She felt mighty sorry for the lady who'd had three husbands. "But how come you left town?" she asked. "I guess you musta lived near one?"

"Our son wanted to be a miner, not a rancher, so we sold the spread when his wife died. He built this shack so we can live here and guard the mine."

Leo put in, "It must have plenty of silver in it."

"It has some. That's why I met you with a shotgun."

"We ain't thieves," volunteered Beeler. After a stabbing look at Leo, she added, "Leastwise not silver thieves."

"I didn't reckon you were. All the same I do a lot of worrying. That was good ore my son took to town with him, and the word gets around a place fast when samples are good. I'll be glad when he gets back and we leave here. He's thinking of selling the mine. I want to move back to civilization—or what Arizona Territory calls civilization. It surely isn't Galveston. I want to talk English more than I do. Spanish is a mighty pretty language, but all the same I like to talk English at times. Sort of to keep my hand in I write to my sister whenever I can. She lives in Houston. Do you write to your kin, Beulah Land?"

Beeler felt herself turning red in the face. For a fact, she'd been around some post offices since she'd left Cottonwood, but she hadn't thought to write Nerissa. "I didn't ever have no paper or pen, ma'am."

"A poor excuse," grunted the old lady. "To get a letter a body has to write one. I write some, and I get some. Riders coming over the trail from Bartlett fetch me letters. There are two things I'm always glad to see out here—the peddler's wagon and somebody bringing a letter."

"When we find Sundown, I'll try to write from there," promised Beeler.

The rest of that afternoon Beeler spent in the shack. Matias took Nate and Leo into the mine but wouldn't let Beeler come too. Women in a mine made for bad luck, Señora Lopez told her after they'd gone. The old lady laughed. "Dumbest thing I ever heard tell. I went in there once when they were all out of sight. There was nothing to see but rocks. Nothing bad happened, but I never let 'em know I went in. I humor men, not fight 'em."

"That ain't *my* way. I won't jolly 'em along when they're bein' stupid," Beeler spat.

"Suit yourself, honey."

That night the Quineys and Nate spread their bedrolls on the floor next to the Lopez children's blankets. María and Matias chatted in fast Spanish with Nate and in very slow English with the Quineys. Their grandmother was trying to teach them English when she could catch them. Catching María was the hardest.

She preferred chasing Miss Muffet up and down the canyon. When the skunk wanted out that night and scratched at the door, María whimpered. She wanted to sleep with the animal. Beeler was relieved when Matias got up and let the skunk out into the night.

Breakfast at the Lopez's wasn't Mexican style. It was sourdough pancakes and molasses and good coffee. Beeler hated to leave and so did the boys, but they had to. Señora Lopez had sewed up the tears in their clothes and the horses had been fed and had a rest. They were just about to say *gracias* and *adiós*, and Beeler was wishing she had a farewell present to give María, when they heard the sound of hoofbeats on the canyon floor.

"Papa," shouted María and raced ahead and around a boulder. She came running back just as fast, calling out, *"Hombre, hombre!"* this time.

Beeler felt for the pistol while Nate and Leo readied their Winchesters. With all this artillery around, Señora Lopez still went into the shack for the shotgun.

The man who came riding in on a chunky sorrel had a yellow mustache and beard streaked with tobacco stains. When he saw the guns trained on him, he put his hands in the air. He smiled and said, "If you're Missus Lopez, I brung a letter for ya from Bartlett."

"Who's it from?" she asked.

The rider shook his head. "I can't read, so how'd I be able to tell? The postmaster in town, he give it to me because I was ridin' this way and knowed where this canyon is. He said the letter was from someplace in Texas, though."

"All right, get down, and come on in and have some coffee. I'm expecting a letter from Texas." The old woman lowered the shotgun. "You come back, too," she told the Quineys and Nate. "It'll be from my sister, Nora, and I might want to reply to it right off. You can carry it with you and mail it for me in the next town you come to."

"We'd be honored to do that," said Nate, as Matias came up with their horses, Travis trailing them. Nate and Leo put the Winchesters into the saddle scabbards while Beeler stuffed the six-shooter back under her left ribs. They followed the stranger into the shack while Matias took the horses and Travis back of the shack once more. Beeler guessed she knew why. Miss Muffet was loose. She hadn't come in that morning yet at all. Once the horses and longhorn spotted her, there'd be no holding them.

The stranger sat down at the table without taking off his hat. He waited until Señora Lopez had poured him a mug of coffee and more coffee for the Texans. María and Matias, curious about the letter, came inside, too, to stand against the wall. The man reached his hand into his vest pocket.

Out came a derringer, a little bitty one, instead of an envelope. Beeler caught her breath. At short range a derringer could kill a person easy.

"Don't anyone of ya say a word," he warned. "I heard tell in Bartlett that this mine's got lotsa high-grade ore in it. I have it in mind to take a sack of it with me wherever I'm goin'."

Señora Lopez said calmly, "My son isn't here to get it for you."

"I know it. I seen him in town, braggin' in the assay office."

"There isn't anybody to dig out the ore here. It isn't easy work," said the old woman.

"Ain't there? How about them three boys and the biggest Mex kid?" The stranger jerked his head at the Texans and Matias Lopez.

"We won't do it!" said Nate, surprising Beeler.

"Look, sonny boy, I don't want to have to shoot any-body. But if I have to shoot one, I'll do it right where his galluses cross to get the others workin'."

"I ain't a he like them," Beeler put in hastily.

"No matter. You're big enough to swing a pickaxe."

For a while there was dead silence with everybody staring at the robber. Beeler was just about to say that it was bad luck to have womenfolks in a mine, but as she opened her mouth there was a scratching at the door.

The high-grader didn't turn his head to look at the

door. He asked from where he sat, "What's that there?"

Other words came out of Beeler. "It's Miss Muffet. She's been out all night."

Señora Lopez put in real fast before the man could say anything. "Lands sake, Beulah Land, let her in before she sets up that awful yowling. She's probably caught a mouse and wants to show it to us. Let her in, and then you can go to the mine."

Beeler moved to the door. She opened it, held her breath, and called, "Here kitty, kitty, kitty."

In tromped the skunk without looking either to the right or the left. She paraded right over to her bowl in the corner as though she never even saw the high-grader.

He saw Miss Muffet, though. He let out the wildest yell Beeler had ever heard, dropped the derringer, ran for the window, and jumped through it, glass and all. Headfirst, he went.

Leo was standing over him with the shotgun before he could get up. Beeler was behind him with the six-shooter and Nate with the derringer. Nate and Leo hog-tied the man, who was cut up around the face and hands by the glass. Then Nate gave the derringer to Señora Lopez while María and Matias watched, big-eyed beside their smiling grandmother.

"He'll stay tied up that way until my son gets here. Then Pedro'll take him to justice," she told the Texans.

Nate and Leo had their backs turned while they con-
ferred with the old lady on how long it'd be before
she thought Pedro would return, so Beeler snuck into
the mine for a quick look-see. Nobody had eyes now
for her—only for the scowling tied-up high-grader.
The mine disappointed Beeler. Señora Lopez had been
right as rain. There wasn't anything to see but some
wood shoring and some pale gray streaks in the rock
wall.

After the Texans said *adiós* for the second time and
mounted up, Beeler did some pondering. Travel was
really only interesting when there was something
interesting to look at.

Menfolks could keep their old mines from now on.
From the way Nate described them once on the trail,
one tunnel-type mine was pretty much like another.
Once you'd seen one, you'd seen them all.

9 MAJOR GORDON

Señora Lopez had given them good instructions on how to find Bartlett, but as they rode farther west Beeler was uneasy again. Because the town was out on the desert, the woman had even told them how to travel there. By night! By day it would be hot enough to sizzle a horned frog. They'd have to carry enough water for themselves and their animals. In a pinch Travis could get water out of prickly pear cactus, but the horses weren't that talented. Señora Lopez had told them about the special kind of cactus that looked like a green barrel, in case they ran real low on water. It had water inside. Mesquite anywhere meant water not far off. She warned them, too, about all the dangerous biting things on the desert—oversize hairy spiders, rattlesnakes, and poison lizards.

Nate told the Quineys the first night they camped that he'd traveled in the desert before, in Old Mexico. He knew how to get around in sand country, but he had let Señora Lopez talk. She was getting practice in English and that was what she wanted. Still and all, even if Graber knew about dry country, Beeler wasn't boiling over with eagerness to ride through it.

Sleeping for two days in the shade of rocks away from a scorching sun and sky too bright blue for eye comfort and riding two nights under a sky glitter-white with stars brought them finally to Bartlett. At sunrise they came through a gravelly countryside dotted with greasewood and prickly pear, and there it was—Bartlett. It was mostly an adobe town set on a riverbank fairly close to some more mountains, which was to be expected in this country where you weren't ever really out of sight of them. What was surprising, though, was that the railroad was here—so far west.

Once more Travis, Two Cents, and Stupid had to be led over the gleaming new tracks. Critters for the most part just didn't take to unnatural sights. Jingle-bob didn't kick up one bit of fuss this time, though. He stepped carefully over the tracks with Beeler still on his back. She was mighty proud of him, although how he'd act if he ever saw a locomotive was anybody's guess. But there wasn't a train or engine in sight here in Bartlett—only a lonely-looking depot. That wouldn't spook any horse.

They found one man out so early walking up the center of Bartlett's street. He was sober enough to tell

them that he hadn't heard of Sundown or Sunset or
even of Sunvale, but then he'd only been in Bartlett
for six weeks. Bartlett was just a railhead town for a
bigger, older place a distance away, Hard Rock. It
had been set up in 1879, a couple of years back. He said
it had seven thousand folks, elegant cafés where you
could eat lobster brought by fast stagecoach from the
Gulf of Mexico, and a real live theater where world-
famous players came. If anybody had any idea where
Sunvale or those other places were, it would be the
postmaster of Hard Rock! It was one of the most
important towns in Arizona Territory—and close to
gold fields.

"Is Hard Rock a very rough town?" Nate had asked
him.

"Sure is, son," had been the reply. "But there's a
Law and Order Society there, and there's a sheriff
and whole family of brothers workin' with the U.S.
Marshal. And,"—the man laughed—"there's Major
Gordon."

"Is he part of the U.S. Army?" Nate asked.

"No, but Major Gordon's a whole force alone, let
me tell you. You look up the Major the minute you
get in town, and you'll be helped. Lord, will you ever
be taken care of!"

Three hours riding south, in the cool of the morning

through miles of seven-foot-tall yucca plants, brought them to Hard Rock. It was a desert place, like Bartlett, but set on hills covered with cactus and it had more than one street. The Quineys and Nate gawked plenty as they rode up the main street. There were some fancy buildings here. Some of them were saloons and gambling houses; others were cafés. Piano music came spilling out of a swinging-door place that was the most oversized saloon Beeler had ever set eyes on. It was made of wood and even had paint on it, a nice gray shade. Hard Rock had three of the biggest adobe houses she'd ever seen. One was a theater, another a boardinghouse hotel, and the third one a church with a wooden steeple on top. As they read signs looking for the post office, Beeler took note that Hard Rock had a newspaper, *The Nugget*. It had doctors and lawyers and even dentists, which was more than Cottonwood had—dentists.

But judging from the men they saw, it had its hair on all the same. Some of them had rough-looking, mean faces even if they were dolled up in fancy frock coats and more than likely weren't anything more than porch-perching dudes.

They surely stared at Travis as if they'd never seen a Texas longhorn before. One man in a plug hat shouted out, "Hey, look, them kids brought their beef with 'em!"

"He's jerky on the hoof," a velvet-collared galoot across the street called back.

Beeler told her critter beside her, "Never you mind them. You've thinned down some. They haven't come half so far as you and me, Travis. If they did, they wouldn't run so much to lard as they do."

The post office showed up finally along the street. Nate dismounted and tethered Stupid to the hitching rail out front. Neither of the Quineys went inside with him. They were surrounded by a crowd of kids.

A small girl with long, straight, corn-colored hair, a sunburned nose, and round green-brown eyes stood nearest to Travis. Her dress was rose-colored calico, her sunbonnet dangling by its strings. She spoke to Beeler, pointing to the steer, "What's his name, Mister?"

"I ain't a mister. His name's Travis."

"Where'd you come from?"

"From Santa Rosa County, Texas," Beeler told her. Then the two girls howdied and shook. "I'm Beulah Land Quiney. This is my brother, Leo."

The girl grinned. "I'm Lorena." She eyed Travis some more, then went around to shake Leo's hand too. "Why'd you come to Hard Rock?" she asked.

"We're huntin' some folks," said Leo.

Nate came out before Lorena could ask any more questions. Beeler thought he looked to be sagging. She guessed by the expression on his face he hadn't had any luck finding Sundown again. "Well, did ya find out where Sunvale or them others is?"

"No, the postmaster never heard of any one of them."

"Shall we start lookin', and askin' in the saloons again?" Leo was halfway off Two Cents.

Lorena piped up. "Oh, you better not go in saloons. It'll get you in trouble here. I looked under the door of the Glass Palace once to see the pretty mirrors and got thrashed for it. By the saloon owner—not by her."

"Who's her?" asked Nate. "Your mother?"

"Oh, no! Major Gordon. I'm an orphan. I live at her house."

"Is it an orphanage?" Nate wanted to know.

"It's a lot of things. A boardinghouse and hospital and a hotel. Major Gordon runs it."

"A *lady* major?" asked Nate.

Lorena giggled. "It's what folks here in Hard Rock nicknamed her. She's really Ella Gordon. She ain't married. Come on home with me. You'll get tossed out of saloons here. Maybe she can help you out."

Nate shook his head, but Beeler spoke to him. "Remember what the galoot in Bartlett said. Major Gordon's a people helper."

"All right, Beulah Land." Nate hauled himself back onto Stupid. "Lead the way, please," he told Lorena.

Lorena ran ahead of them, her hair flying, until they came to the big adobe hotel they'd already noticed. She ran inside yelling before the Texans came to a halt.

A minute later someone came out onto the wooden porch with a broom in her hand. It was a lady wearing a pair of overalls and man's shirt. Over the overalls was a yellow calico apron. She had thick dark hair piled up in a knot on top of her head, a sunburned face, and spectacles.

Lorena came right behind her, smiling and pointing. "That's them, ma'am, the ones I was telling you about. The cow's name is Travis. He's from Texas."

Major Ella had sort of a deep voice for a lady and had a queer sort of accent, not Mexican, but a bit blurry. "Good Lord," Beeler heard her exclaim. "They look like the work of a Kansas cyclone."

Nate took off his hat and so did Leo. Then Nate introduced them all and explained his errand and asked his usual question.

The woman shook her head. "I don't know of the town, I'm sorry to say. Are you hungry?"

"Hungrier than a woodpecker with a big headache," came from Leo.

"We can pay you," said Nate.

"There'll be no charge," said Major Ella, "on one condition. You must all have a bath before lunch."

A bath! Beeler was horrified. "We haven't any clean duds."

Major Ella came closer and removed her spectacles. "Why, you're a girl!"

"Yes'm. Beulah Land's a girl name in Texas. The pants fool a lot a folks."

This made the woman smile. "Don't pay those folks any heed. There's nothing as practical as trousers. I wear skirts to church and that's the only place. Now take the horses behind the house and give them to Doyle. He'll stable the poor things."

"What about my steer?" asked Beeler.

"Tell Mitchell to tie him somewhere out of the sun where he won't be in anyone's way. Mitchell will see that he has water and hay. He needs some beef on his bones."

Doyle turned out to be a yellow-headed boy, a frying-size kid, and Lorena's brother. Mitchell, no kin to her, was Leo's age, brown haired, brown eyed, and muscular. With Beeler helping him, he tied Travis to the crossbar of a clothesline.

"What's this Major Ella like?" Beeler heard Leo asking him. "She wants us to take a bath."

Mitchell looked mournful as he said, "She comes from Scotland. They must be awful clean over there. The Major's fine in character, but she thinks soap and water will cure anything."

"I ain't gonna grow up and be like that," Beeler exploded.

"Tiger cat, ain't you?" asked Mitchell with a sly smile. "Well, let me tell ya, Major Ella's gettin' the water and towels ready right now."

"She makes us wash all over every week," came from small Doyle. "Sometimes when we get dirty, it's oftener than that." He looked mournful too as he spoke.

Beeler had the first bath. The instant she was into the tub, Lorena knocked on the door, popped in, scooped up all of Beeler's clothes, and started out again. She left the gold pieces behind.

"What're you up to?" yelled Beeler.

"Washing your clothes. The washboard and the Major are ready. She says in this sun by the time you've washed your hair, too, your clothes will be almost dry. I'll fetch you a wrapper of hers."

"Where's my brother and Graber?"

"Waiting in line for the tub. Hurry up."

Beeler scrubbed, noticing how the water got browner and browner as she shed Texas and New Mexico Territory. Finally it looked like a Texas river in the springtime. Once she was out and into the striped flannel wrapper Lorena brought her, she reckoned she was a pound lighter and a ton weaker. She waited in Lorena's little room playing seven-card stud poker with her, with deuces and one-eyed jacks wild, until her clothes were dry.

Lorena listened carefully to what folks said. She thought Beeler had lots of grit to come after Jinglebob the way she did and all the way to Hard Rock too.

"Well, it wasn't exactly that. It's come to be a bit more with me." Beeler looked at the jack of diamonds in her hand, thinking of Nate. Leo had stuck like glue lately. There hadn't been one chance to ask Nate again what he'd meant by that "maybe" or about unrequited love. Those Apaches might have done the bicyclienne and lion tamer some good, but they hadn't done her any. They'd picked the wrong minute to show up for sure.

After a lunch of roast-beef hash the Quineys and Graber had more chance to see how Major Ella came by her nickname. She'd already locked up their Winchesters and six-shooter before she'd made them take baths. Now she even had Leo in a new shirt. He and Nate were a mite paler, Beeler noted.

Major Ella, her orphans, and the Texans sat at a round table in one corner of her dining room. She wouldn't let anyone say a word until they'd eaten everything on their plates, which wasn't hard to do because the grub was good. She told them, "Chatted food is half-digested food. We'll talk later."

After lunch she jumped straight to the point—first about their problem finding Nate's pa and then about Travis. She said, "The editor of *The Nugget,* our newspaper, eats supper here because I consider his stomach. He doesn't like the fancy fluff duffs served at the local cafés. I'll tell Mr. Hays about your quest tonight, and he'll make an appeal in the paper for any information about Sundown or Sunset or Sunvale. Everybody in Hard Rock reads *The Nugget*. It's a weekly, but it comes out day after tomorrow."

"Thank you," said Nate.

Major Ella was brisk. "If nobody comes forward, I'd advise the three of you to abandon the whole enterprise. Stay here for a time and let your animals recuperate and then go back to Texas."

Nate sighed. "I guess you're right, ma'am."

"I am right, young man." The woman turned to Beeler. "Now about that longhorn of yours. My clothesline won't hold him. He's already pulled loose and run under a laundry. He ate your brother's shirt even if it had been washed. You know how grass eaters crave something salty. He took the sheets down into the dust as well, so they had to be rinsed over again. He was so fouled up in clothesline Mitchell had to cut him free. My solution is for the steer to have the run of Hard Rock."

Beeler leaped up. "Somebody'll shoot him!"

"No, they won't. There will be mention of him in the newspaper also. But he must have some sort of easily visible distinguishing mark."

"He has," said Leo. "Big horns for his age."

"No, no!" Major Ella waved her hand, brushing away Leo's comment. "I mean something truly spectacular. I favor a ribbon on one horn and another on his tail. That would mark him out just fine as a child's pet."

Beeler sat down. Travis decked out in ribbons? "How about a sign on him?" she said, thinking of the chariot horses.

"No, he could lean against something and rub that off. The ribbons will do the trick. And they will not hamper his movements."

"How long'll it be before we hear from somebody who might read about us in the newspaper?" asked Beeler.

"We'd best give it a week."

Beeler pulled the gold double eagle out of her pocket and gave it to Major Ella, who gave it right back.

"No money is required. You will work for your room and board. I have found a job for you, Jonathan, in the general store. The owner has supper here too. You will sweep the floors, clean and fill the oil lamps, and dust the counters. I'll collect your wages. Leo, you will help Mitchell and Doyle in the stables and do odd jobs I require. You, Beulah Land, will help in the kitchen and wait on table. And keep out of the sun. All it does for women here is make them shrivel up."

"I don't know how to wait on tables," protested Beeler.

"It's a simple process. Keep your hands clean, your mouth shut. Serve plates from the left and take away from the right. That is all there is to it. Everyone eats the same victuals."

Beeler felt defeat. She'd met her match—someone more set in her ways than Nerissa was. She hoped there'd be some results from the newspaper piece fast.

Major Gordon was finished with them now and was dictating a grocery list to Lorena, who always wore a pencil on a string around her neck when she was in the house. "Tell that clerk at the general store that I need a tub of lard, a crock of apple butter, and two loaves of sugar."

Quick as a flash, she turned back to the Texans. "Tonight we'll take in an early candlelight revivalist service. It's in a tent. You can go there, Beulah Land, in trousers." She clapped her hands. "Now off with you—every one of you. Beulah Land, clear the table, then ask the cook what you can do to help him. Jonathan, you go to the general store now with Lorena. She will introduce you. Leo, you go out with the boys and curry comb the horses that will permit you to work on them. And, Mitchell, once you've tied the ribbons to the steer, let him go."

Major Ella got up, went to a golden oak highboy,

opened a drawer, and took out two wide ribbons. One was pink. One was white. "These were to have been hair bows for your birthday, Lorena, but they'll have to be put to emergency use now."

"That's just fine, ma'am," said Lorena. She whispered to Beeler, "Your steer will look right pretty with the pink one on him. I'll ask Mitchell to put it on his horn, not his tail. Pink up close to the face is mighty becoming."

"Holy gatlins," muttered Leo, who'd heard Lorena. "It's enough to make a coyote hoot like an owl."

Mr. Howard Hays, a round-faced man with black curling hair and a black-and-white checkered frock coat, was the newspaper editor. He was mighty pleasant to Nate and the Quineys and even wrote down notes on the back of an envelope in his pocket about their travels. Beeler thought he seemed very interested. He said he'd spotted Travis moseying around town and been struck by the ribbons fluttering on him. He was even more struck to hear that Beeler could whistle him in whenever she had a mind to. Beeler liked Mr. Hays.

So did Major Ella for a fact. She let him talk at the table with them—whether it was because she favored him or because he was a "paying guest," Beeler didn't know.

"What will you call the article, Mr. Hays?" asked the woman, as she set a dish of "spotted pup," rice and raisins, in front of the editor.

"Texas Longhorn and His Young Owners Surrender to the Hospitality of Hard Rock."

"We ain't surrenderin' to anybody," came from Leo.

"It's only a manner of speaking, Leo. It will attract readers and that's what we want, isn't it?"

"Yes sir, it is!" said Nate, as he dug into his spotted pup too.

Mr. Hays did fine by them. There was even a drawing of Travis running around town. The article was on the front page, and it took care just dandy of people who might have in mind to shoot Travis for beef. Mr. Hays said in it that the steer was "under the protection of the town," that he was a "child's pet" and that anyone who harmed him in any way would surely be "prosecuted to the fullest extent of the law." Beeler hoped that the folks who could read would read it to them that couldn't—the way she did to Leo.

They waited for four days while Travis roamed loose, coming back now and then to rest on Major Ella's front porch and to get a handout from Mitchell. And then on the morning of the fifth day, the man and woman showed up. The woman was a bitty thing and the man big, but you could tell right off who wore the bell. She had crackling black eyes under her sun-bonnet, and he wore a mournful look. She shoved the *Nugget* article into Major Ella's hand. "We're the Turners, Alfred and me. Alfred thinks he might know something about this place, Sundown. Tell the Major what you know, Alfred."

Alfred had a sheep's face. "Well, I ain't really sure, lovey."

"Of course, you ain't, you son of barley corn," said Mrs. Turner. She added to Major Ella, "Alfred's chief interest in life up to a couple months ago was Forty Rod."

Major Ella's lips tightened. "Kansas sheep dip! It's certainly no product of Scotland, that stuff. Forty Rod whiskey is made in Hard Rock and that explains much. It rots a man's innards."

Before the ladies could talk about Forty Rod some more, Nate put in, "Where is Sundown, Mr. Turner?"

Alfred let out a long mumble. "There's a Sundown saloon on the California side of the Colorado at Gila-ville."

"California or Colorado?" asked Nate. He looked puzzled.

Major Gordon explained. "The Colorado River is the boundary between Arizona Territory and Cali-fornia. Gilaville is a town in Arizona Territory."

"Sort of on both sides," put in Mr. Turner. "The Sundown saloon's next door to the Last Chance."

"The last chance to what?" asked Beeler.

"To wet your whistle before you get to San Diego out on the Pacific Ocean. San Diego's near three hundred miles across the desert. Them two saloons, the Sundown one and the Last Chance, are just about all there is on that side of the river. I know the area, because I've drove freight trains all over it. I been here since 1877."

Nate shook his head. "A saloon is the only place you know by that name, Mr. Turner?"

"It's all anybody knows."

"Alfred knows saloons!" said Mrs. Turner. She nodded to Major Ella, took her husband's arm, and left, leaving Nate looking more down at the mouth than Beeler had ever seen him. The idea that Sundown was a den of devilment wasn't appealing to him one bit.

"Now, Jonathan," said the Major, "saloon or no, you'll have to go there to satisfy your curiosity."

"Oh, I know that, but I don't want to."

"Nonsense. There is nothing so wretched to a body's peace of mind as unsatisfied curiosity."

Beeler felt her heart going out to Nate. His old whiskey soak of a pa in a saloon, not even a town. Poor cuss!

"I just don't want to get on that horse again," said

Nate. "They told me at the general store that it's all rattlesnakes and cactus west of here for hundreds of miles."

Major Ella snorted. "Who said anything about riding over that dreadful desert—which truly is nothing but lizards and scorpions and heat. You'll go by *train*! The horses and the longhorn will stay here and rest. Mitchell will hitch up my rig and drive you to Bartlett in the morning. There's a westbound passenger train going through there at noon."

Beeler watched Nate brighten up. She guessed he'd never set foot on a train either. "Are Leo and me goin' with you on a train too?" she asked Nate. Being a waiter-girl wasn't to her liking.

"In for a penny, in for a pound," he told her, sounding sad.

Leo wanted to know, "What does that mean?"

"Oh, you two will go all the way with me."

Beeler was glad she didn't have to convince Graber. She wanted to grab him and hug him but didn't in public. Instead she got him by the hand and hauled him out onto the front porch where Travis was standing blocking everybody's way, his ribbons blowing in the hot wind off the desert. Beeler wanted to call out to all of Hard Rock that they'd located a Sundown! But that would embarrass Nate. She hugged Travis around the neck and told him, "We found it."

Nate smiled weakly and put out a hand to pat the

steer on the flank. Travis looked mildly at him and for the first time showed some affection for him by shifting his weight and leaning toward him.

The trouble was that Nate didn't move his feet fast enough, the way Beeler had learned to. Travis's right hind foot came down on top of Nate's left foot. It only rested there for a second, but it was enough. Graber let out a howl that drove Travis down the street, taking out a porch post as he went. Nate grabbed his injured foot in both hands, hopping up and down on his good one, yelling all the time.

10 UNDER THE BRIDGE

Major Ella was on top of the trouble right away. She sent Mitchell for the doctor while Nate limped upstairs to his room. Beeler and Leo stood outside the door, waiting while the doctor looked at Nate's foot.

"It wasn't my critter's fault," Beeler told her brother for the third time.

The doctor wouldn't speak to the Quineys, though they tugged at his coat sleeves. But he talked with Major Ella, and when he did, the Texans heard him. "There are a couple of bones broken in that lad's foot. I've bandaged it."

"He's supposed to take the westbound train to Gilaville tomorrow," said the Major.

"That boy isn't going anywhere. He won't be able to get a boot on for some time. One thing you can say about being stepped on by a cow, it usually creates some damage!"

Beeler and Leo looked at one another. Graber *not* able to go now that they'd finally found a place called Sundown!

"I guess this is the end of our string, Beeler," said Leo. He turned his back on her, put his hands in his pockets, hunched up his shoulders, and walked off down the hallway.

Beeler didn't follow him. She opened Nate's door without knocking and went inside. Nate was flopped on the bed, his feet on a pillow. He looked at her. Then, not letting her get out one word about how sorry she was Travis had stepped on him, he yelled, "You and that damned animal of yours! Leave me alone! I don't ever want to see either of you again!"

"He's only a critter. He didn't mean to walk on you."

Graber reached under his head, grabbed the pillow, and threw it at her. "You're a critter, too. All of you Quineys are. You're mean enough to have a reserved seat in hell and as conceited as a barber's cat."

Beeler felt her feelings growing fiery. "There ain't no call to talk like that about Leo and me. We done plenty for you."

"I wish you hadn't. I must have been crazy to come to the ranch hunting for Quineys. You have to be the most stubborn and ornery people in all of Texas."

"No, we ain't. Don't forget, you're from Texas too. There are others I could lay tongue to. You wasn't so mad at us before you had this accident. You got a mean disposition." She put her hand on the doorknob. "And I was startin' to have tender feelings toward you."

"*Tender!*" Nate was screeching like an owl now. "You mash up my foot so I can't go to Sundown and you call that 'tender.' Do you think I could feel tender about you? You scare me half to death when you're not making me mad enough to explode. You don't even know enough not to ask a stranger his name." His face grew calmer, and he smiled in a mean way. "Besides, there's somebody else I feel tender towards."

Beeler froze. This was something different. Nate had been mad at Travis and was taking it out on her and Leo. She could understand his doing that. It was natural, and it'd pass. But another girl! "Who'd she be? Are you tellin' me Cupid's already throwed his rope on you?"

"He surely has. Her name is Bonnie Annie Laurie. She lives up on that wheat farm where I do. She reads books, plays the harp, and is as pretty as can be."

"Has she got blue eyes and yeller hair?"

"Yes. Bee trees are gall beside her."

Beeler opened the door and slammed it behind her. "No-good son of a goat," she said to herself, as she leaned against the door. She wondered how many sweethearts old Graber had staked out over Texas. Mad as a rooster caught in a rainstorm, Beeler tromped downstairs. Right now what she needed was a few kind words—but where to get them? She had to talk woman to woman, and Lorena wasn't one yet. There was hope, though, with Major Ella.

Fuming at the meanness of Graber, Beeler went outside behind the big adobe. That's where the cook said the Major would be. She was taking down laundry.

Beeler came straight out with it. "Graber, he just now told me he hasn't got any use for me. He says there's a yeller-headed gal in north Texas he favors."

Major Ella nodded. Through a clothespin in her mouth she said, "That's his privilege. What do you have in mind to do? Ride back there and shoot her?"

"It did come to mind. He told me he knew somethin' about unrequited love once. I thought mebbe he meant me."

"He must have meant the blond girl, Beulah Land."

"It must of been her." Suddenly Beeler felt some hope rising up yeasty in her. She snapped her fingers. "He favors her, but it looks like she don't favor him. Y' know, ma'am, he never wrote her one letter all the time we been gone." Suddenly she asked, "Major, have you ever felt tender toward somebody?"

The woman dropped a pillow case into the laundry basket before she answered. "In love you mean, don't you? Yes, I loved a man once enough to marry him. But for a couple of reasons I never did. Now that I look back on it, it was a good thing, too." She reached up for a towel, pulling off the clothespin. "If I had married him and had a big family, I'd have ended up doing things only for them for years and years, wouldn't I? The way it turned out, I've had to work just as hard and spread my work out over a lot more people who needed me. As for Jonathan and that blond girl, don't you fret. There's much truth in old sayings or they wouldn't be old sayings. There's many a slip 'twixt the cup and the lip—not to mention lots of fish in the sea."

"I reckon so, ma'am."

Major Ella dumped the towel too. She put her hands on her hips. "Well, we've discussed love, haven't we? Now let's talk about duty. Duty comes along in a person's life more than love does, believe me! You may be angry with Jonathan but you and Leo could still go to this saloon for him, couldn't you?" She smiled. "Leo tells me all you Quineys are 'hogs for duty.' "

Beeler pondered, scowling, then said, "Yes, ma'am, I reckon that's so. First of all, I came along to look after my horse; then after that came Quiney duty. Any feeling I used to have for Graber came snailin' in last of all."

"Good! That puts duty first. Even if you don't like Jonathan, you've come many miles with him, and you ought to see this through. My heavens, girl, don't you have any curiosity at all?"

Beeler examined her boots for a spell, teetering on

their high heels, telling herself there was a lot in what the Major said. While the woman took down a sheet, she asked, "Ma'am, do you find it bothersome to be bogged down in carpets?"

"Not when the carpets belong to me! I've been all over the West in one mining town after another, and I expect to be in a lot more. I take up my carpets and go with them." She gave Beeler a severe look over the top of her spectacles. "But I'm the one who decides where my carpets and I go—not my husband or my father or brother."

Beeler brightened. "I guess that's one way to have your carpets and not get bogged down in 'em too."

"Well, that's the way this woman does it. I can't say that not having married made me miss out on being a woman. It seems to me that I do a woman's work as well as a man's. Single blessedness is a lot better than misery in double harness. Everybody isn't cut out for wedlock. Some people are cut up by it. I never had any children of my own, but I've raised fourteen orphans and turned them loose as good people to write me letters now and then."

Beeler exclaimed, "Holy gatlins, that's more kids than my ma and pa had!"

Major Ella nodded as she started struggling with another big white sheet. "And I'm still around to take in more, like the three I have right now. Tell me,

Beulah Land, are you going to this Sundown saloon tomorrow?"

"Yes'm."

"Why? Duty or curiosity?"

Beeler laughed. "Both of 'em, ma'am, though I think our luck'll run muddy."

"Maybe so, child. The pleasure duty brings is generally to the person who does the chore. Having done it is his chief reward. As for satisfying curiosity, that's the real big grab bag in life!"

Mitchell drove the Quineys in the rig to Bartlett the next morning and saw them aboard the train after they'd bought round-trip tickets. Major Ella had fixed them a basket of grub and given Beeler a note to give the proprietor of the Palace Hotel in Gilaville, where they'd stay overnight. She had kept both Leo's Winchester and Beeler's pistol locked up, claiming they wouldn't need them.

The train scared Beeler. The smoking engine was big and black and noisy. The passenger cars were dark red with gold scrollwork on their outsides and scarlet plush on their seats. It made a person nervous just to sit down. And how fast the train went—sometimes as fast as thirty miles an hour, according to the ticket taker.

It took some time to get to Gilaville because the

train wandered north a bit from one little town to another and sometimes stopped at depots for freight or to take on water. Beeler watched Arizona Territory passing from a window on the left side of the train while Leo watched across the aisle on the right. They agreed there wasn't much to see—gravelly pinkish ground, cactus, and sometimes the bright green of paloverde trees or mesquite.

Midmorning of the next day they reached Gilaville and got off at the depot, stiff from sitting up all night. Gilaville was mostly an adobe town too. The most interesting thing about it was the Colorado River. It was the biggest, widest bunch of water the Quineys had ever set eyes on. But looking at it didn't cool a person off one bit. Gilaville was hell-hinge hot.

A blue-belly soldier from the fort on the bluff over the river was mighty polite and helpful. He said that there was a Sundown saloon on the California side and told them about the ferry over the river.

As she crossed on it with Leo beside her, Beeler admitted to herself that she was plenty nervous. What would they say to Mr. Graber if they found him in a saloon? They hadn't let Nate know they were going on without him. They'd left the job of telling him to Major Ella, which was the way she wanted it. Beeler figured the Major planned to patch things up between her and Nate. If anybody could do it, she could.

The saloon they were looking for wasn't much to

see. It wasn't even a big one. Facing west under the
railroad bridge, it had the words *Cantina Sundown*
painted on its adobe front. Two men were sitting in
chairs in the shade of its front porch. One was in a
straight chair, the other in a rocker. One man was very
large and burly, the other one oversize tall and long-
shanked with Mexican rowel spurs on his boots. Both
men had dark brown beards.

Beeler poked Leo. "That's two of them galoots we
been huntin'. We come to the right place." Taking off
her hat, she walked up to them, feeling the sun's heat
on her back. She was nervous enough to be sweating
but wasn't one bit. Sweat dried on a person fast in
crackling-dry Arizona Territory in August.

"We're lookin' for a Mr. Graber," she told the
biggest man.

"Who'd you be?" he asked sharply.

Beeler took note that he didn't say he didn't *know*
any Graber. "Beulah Land Quiney from Santa Rosa
County, Texas. This is my brother Leo. We'd like to
see Mr. Graber, please."

"Did you come all the way from Texas lookin' for
him?" The grasshopper-legged man wanted to know.
"How come you'd do such a thing? Are you kin to
him?"

"We ain't, but his son is. We come with his son all
the way from Texas until yesterday when a steer upped
and stepped on his foot in Hard Rock."

"Graber didn't have no living boy," said the big man.

Leo put in, "Yep, he surely does—name of Jonathan, but we call him Nate."

"*Jonathan?*" The tallest man got up out of his rocking chair. He called inside, "Juanito, bring out some lemonade. Put some ice in it."

Ice! That was something to look forward to. Beeler and Leo went up onto the porch to sit on the top step. The tallest man stuck out his hand. "I'm Vincent Owensby, and this is my brother, Ralph. Tell us about this Jonathan."

Beeler noticed how closely the men listened to her while she drank cold lemonade the Mexican boy had brought. She told about Nate's ride down into Mexico after getting a letter from his pa and about him being confused when he found him gone and heard the name Puesta del Sol. And how they'd hunted Sunset and Sundown for weeks and weeks. She didn't ask, but from the way the Owensby brothers acted, they knew Mr. Graber and they were protecting him. He must be wanted. Maybe they all were. She was very careful not to rile them.

Mr. Vincent asked, "What's this here Nate of yours look like, little lady?"

Beeler answered, "Sort of lardy, curly-headed, and pale in the face."

"It has to be Graber's boy," said Mr. Ralph. "And he's alive after all!"

"It's him," said Beeler. Holy gatlins, they seemed to think Nate was dead. Just to identify the older Graber better she asked, "Is this here Graber bald all over his head and used to be curly-headed?"

"He was. Wilberforce Graber was," said Mr. Vincent.

"*Was?* Ain't he bald anymore? Does hair grow back?"

"It don't. Hair never does grow back on a man's head. Wilberforce is who I'm talking about. *He* ain't no more. He's dead. Died three weeks ago. He started to sweat some and then he died."

Beeler shivered to her toes. She put down her lemonade, because after news like that it didn't seem right to go on drinking. Nate was a real "leppie" now. She asked, "Mr. Graber didn't even know his kid was looking for him?"

"No, girlie, he never did," came from Mr. Ralph. "We got news at the mine down near Santa Inez that a yellow-haired gringo boy got shot and killed by bandits. We all figured it was Wilberforce's son on his way to see his old pa. We knew Wilberforce had writ him a letter sayin' where he was and to come down. Some Mexicans buried the yellow-headed boy before Wilberforce got to identify him. There wasn't nothing the boy had that would show anybody who he was."

"It wasn't Nate!" cried Leo.

"Wilberforce and us—we thought sure it was. Wilberforce didn't want no more of Mexico after that. And them bandits was so bad hangin' around after the mine payroll that we lit out the next day after we checked on the boy who got killed. There wasn't any real cause to hang around anymore anyhow. Foremen like us and bookkeepers like Wilberforce draw good pay down there. We had enough money to last each of us awhile, so we left while the going was good. It was safest travelin' together in a band."

Leo interrupted. "Did Mr. Graber leave any cash money for Nate?"

Mr. Vincent looked mournful. "No money at all. He lost all he had in New Mexico Territory. So did Ralph and me."

"Now you be fair to Wilberforce," came from Mr. Ralph. "You and me didn't lose our money the same way he did. We lost ours playin' faro and poker. Wilberforce put his in a hotel safe, and in the night robbers ran off with the safe. That was the end of our money and his. But we got some dandy times outa ours. Wilberforce didn't."

"How come you came here?" asked Beeler. "We had a real hard time findin' Sundown."

"Well, our old pa owns this saloon," came from Mr. Vincent. "Ralph and me, we know what we always do when we get some money in our pokes. Money burns

a hole right through them. We figure we'll lose what
we earn somewheres along the line, and we always do.
Our old pa, he grubstakes us to go out mining again
and make more money. Some places we traveled coming
here from Old Mexico we told folks we met that we
was on our way to Sundown, meaning this here saloon.
But to save Wilberforce from turnin' red in the face
the way he did about saloons, we didn't ever say it was
a Gilaville saloon. We let 'em think it was a real town."

Mr. Vincent paused for a moment and grinned at
them. Then he went on with his story. "We knew
we'd end up here sooner or later, Ralph and me, but
we never reckoned that Wilberforce would, too. It
wasn't what he had in mind before them bandits made
off with the hotel safe and his money. Wilberforce
didn't really have any place else to go, and he didn't
have the heart to start out fresh. He said he'd throw
in his luck with the two of us because none of us was
lucky. He stuck with us, even before we got to New
Mexico Territory, when we got in a bit of a ruckus
along the way. Staying with us after that showed how
Wilberforce had changed since he figured his kid was
dead."

"Ruckus?" Beeler saw how Leo had pricked up his
ears at the word. "Was *Nate's* pa mixed up in a
ruckus?"

"Naw, not Wilberforce. Ruckuses weren't in his

nature. The ruckus was nothin' much. One of us, not Ralph or me, had to shoot and wound a man who tried to steal his horse." Mr. Vincent nodded his head. "The man who got wounded was only winged, but he turned out to be the sheriff's brother, and the sheriff where we was in Texas didn't take it kindly. We got away after we stood off the sheriff and some of his men, but after that we always said we was on our way to Sundown—or most of the time didn't say where we was headed at all. We didn't choose to be trailed."

Beeler said, "It's too bad you only winged the sheriff's no-good brother. I get worked up easy when it comes to horse thieves. Where would them other galoots be?"

Mr. Ralph scratched his ear. "They hung onto their money. Slept on top of it wherever we went and never went near no faro tables. They went on to the Pacific coast. They been gone quite a while now. Someday when I find somebody willin' to do it I'll have a letter writ them tellin' 'em Wilberforce passed over the Great Divide and into the Great Unknown."

"How come he didn't go with them?" asked Beeler.

"He didn't seem to have the heart to budge from here. And he didn't have the stomach for it neither. Nothin' he ate agreed with him all the time we was on the trail. The trip here tuckered him out somethin' terrible. It's lotsa miles from Santa Inez down in Mexico to here."

"Where's he buried?" Leo wanted to know.

"In the nice graveyard over the river. We gave him a good funeral—a dandy send-off with the Gilaville String Band playin' tunes he used to favor."

"He was a Texan," said Beeler. "Once a Texan, always a Texan. He shoulda been laid to rest in Texas dirt."

"Now that woulda been hard to arrange, girlie," said Mr. Ralph.

"Mebbe so. It's a long way from here to Santa Rosa County." Beeler rested her elbows on her knees and put her chin into her hands. "Us Quineys woulda been honored to have Mr. Graber, a wisdom bringer, down by the creek in our family graveyard. It's my plan someday to have Nate restin' in it. Mebbe."

The Owensby brothers, Westerners too, looked at each other nodding their heads. They understood.

Suddenly Leo asked again, "Didn't old man Graber leave anythin' to Nate—not even his horse and saddle and hogleg?"

"There wasn't hardly anythin' to leave. You gotta remember, too, we thought his kid was dead. We sold the horse and saddle to buy Wilberforce a headstone. His pistol never did have a hammer on it. He just wore it for show."

"He's got a headstone?" Beeler wanted to know.

"Sure he has. A nice one, with *W. W. Graber 1834-1881* carved on it."

"Has it got an angel on top?" Leo asked.

"Nope, no angel. That cost too much money. It's white marble, though."

Beeler nodded. Nate would like that. She doubted if he would come to Gilaville to see the headstone for himself, though. She didn't think he'd have the heart for it.

For a while there was a mournful silence. Then Mr. Vincent answered Leo's question, sounding very sad. "All we got left of dear old Wilberforce is a Bible and a watch. They're still around here someplace. He was flat broke as a salted snail when we got here. Do you suppose his kid would want the book and the time-piece? The watch ain't even gold."

Beeler spoke up. "Yes, sir, we'd like to take him somethin' that was his pa's."

"You wait. I'll fetch 'em for ya. We didn't know what to do with 'em so we just kept 'em. We'd be honored if you'd take 'em." Mr. Ralph heaved himself up. He was back in a little while with a plain black-bound Bible and an ordinary-looking silver case watch.

Mr. Ralph stared at the two Quineys on the front steps for a long solemn moment, looking from face to face. He handed the Bible to Leo, then the watch to Beeler.

Beeler studied the tracings of ivy leaves on the face of the watchcase, then turned it over to see *WWG* on its back. She pressed the little spring along its side, and it flipped open, the way men's pocket watches did. Music came out—the pretty tune of "Evalina." With Leo watching over her shoulder, Beeler examined what else there was in the watchcase besides the time-piece itself. On one side of it there was a picture of a lady with a lock of light brown hair curled around it. She had a sweet smile and her hair was pulled back in a way that was out of style now when most ladies wore frizzled bangs. The picture looked to be old. Nate's ma, for sure! The lady had a smile a lot like his, come to think on it.

"Thank you kindly," said Beeler, putting the watch into her shirt pocket where it would be safe. She got up. "I guess Leo and me are satisfied now that we found the right Sundown," she told the Owensbys.

The brothers got up, too. Mr. Vincent said, "We wish to God we had better news for ya to take back to Graber's boy."

Beeler told him, "It ain't your fault his pa died."

"It surely ain't. We got a doctor from Gilaville for him when he took sick."

"Mebbe it was the doctor's fault he died!" Leo said. "Some doctors know horses better'n they know folks."

"This wasn't that kind of doc. One thing doctors can't mend is busted hearts. Wilberforce took it mighty hard when he heard he'd lost his kid. He was always a silent cuss. But after that he got silenter and politer. Them are bad signs in most folks. I surely hope his boy don't take the news that hard."

"Well, mebbe he'll try to," came from Beeler, "but Leo and me will talk him out of it, and if we can't, Major Gordon ought to be able to. She talks good cow sense."

Mr. Vincent started to laugh. "We know her. Who don't in these parts? There ain't nothin' like her. She can argue a second man to death while the first one's in the hospital slowly recoverin'."

Beeler poked Leo to get him up off the porch. She said, *"Adiós,* Mister and Mister. We'll leave now."

"Gracias for the lemon squeezin's," said Leo.

After they'd walked away a couple of steps, the girl turned around to call back, "Hey, was Mr. Graber a old whiskey soak?"

"He never touched a drop," said Mr. Ralph.

Beeler pondered some. They'd already said he didn't carry a pistol that worked, and he didn't gamble. She called out again, "Did he do anythin' that was bad?"

"Not that we ever saw!" came from Mr. Vincent. "You might say he was a saint. Mighty hard to live with!"

"Mighty hard!" agreed Mr. Ralph.

Beeler nodded. She'd be sure to tell Nate all those things about his pa. They'd pleasure him, but she doubted if they'd make him any easier to live with either. She'd have to think a bit before she tied up with a saint.

Speaking of saints made a body think about angels. Before they climbed back on that train, she and Leo would pay a visit to the Gilaville graveyard. They'd check Mr. Graber's headstone, not that she didn't believe the Owensby brothers had got one for him. White marble sounded mighty fine. Maybe she and Leo would make up a story to tickle Nate that there was an angel standing on top of the headstone, an angel with wings and a trumpet. But somehow she doubted if Leo would go along with the lie. He probably would say it wasn't the right thing to do to Nate. Besides, Nate might get the idea to come here on the train, too, to see an angel that wasn't there.

The two Quineys went side by side to the banks of the Colorado where they stood waiting for the ferry to come back to the California side. For a fact, they hadn't been long in California. But it was a new place they'd visited, and it would make a good story back home.

While they waited, Beeler opened Mr. Graber's watch to hear "Evalina" another time. She remembered that tune. That was the very one she and Nate had danced to in the mountain meadow the night the Apaches had come. She might never corner Nate and

reform him to Quiney ways. She might marry somebody else. Or she might never take on double-harness
hitching at all!

Whatever she did, though, she'd learned one thing
from all the traveling around she'd done. She wouldn't
be hasty about getting hitched. She was going to see
some of the world first. She recalled what poor lonesome Mr. McCarty had said about wanting to see
England. Well, she might just go there someday. She'd
learned a thing or two wandering around with Nate
Graber. And whenever she heard "Evalina," she knew
he'd come to mind. That was something nice to think
of a person by—a tune!

Beeler and Leo got onto the ferry and stood on the
deck, again spitting together down into the brown
water of the Colorado. Beeler looked at Leo out of the
corner of one eye. He wasn't so bad a brother after all.
He'd saved her from having to ask the Owensby
brothers to cough up what Nate's pa had left to him.
Leo had taken it on himself to be bad mannered,
which had been right noble of him. And he hadn't said
one word to her after they'd left the saloon steps about
how she'd been the one to make up the big story that
the five men were bandit desperadoes. She supposed
he'd tell Nate, though, that she'd been wrong. Well,
she'd just have to grin and bear what Nate would say
to her.

She gazed at the Colorado, rushing south toward Old Mexico. It was sure in a hurry for a river. Well, that didn't mean she had to be in a rush to settle her life. But she guessed now might be a good time to settle something with Leo.

She said, "Leo, I think in time I could forgive ya for lockin' me up in that root cellar and for stealin' Jingle-bob. In a way you mebbe done me a favor. If you hadn't run off with him, I'd never have got to see so much of the world. I'd still be down in Santa Rosa County with the weaner gals and Nerissa tryin' to keep Travis from bustin' down the front porch. Even if you're a two-time horse stealer, I think I'll be able to forgive ya."

AUTHOR'S NOTE

After librarians and teachers had asked me for a number of years to write a book for boys, I complied with *A Long Way to Whiskey Creek*. But though I took Parker Quiney and Jonathan Graber all over Texas in 1879, I didn't forget the "womenfolks stuck to home." Those nineteenth-century Texas women were every bit as strong as their men.

I like to think of this book as a companion piece to the earlier one about the Quineys. Beulah Land Quiney does not appear in that one. Leo is mentioned only briefly in its first chapter along with Nerissa. Jonathan Graber and J.E.B. Stuart are the only characters common to both novels.

Readers tell me they like to know what is fact and what is fiction in historical novels. Many things in this story are fact.

To begin with, Texas readers might rise up in wrath

at the thought that I overlooked the existence of a Sundown in northwest Texas, the very territory my characters search in. Sundown, Texas, did not exist— at least by that name—in 1881. It was laid out in 1928 and had its first store in 1929. For this information I an indebted to Sara E. Niles of the Reference Staff of the Lubbock Public Library.

The towns mentioned in the novel have fictional names, although they are based on real places and real descriptions. My young Texans crossed real rivers.

It would not have been at all impossible for Beeler, Leo, and Nate to have met Billy the Kid under one of his aliases, Henry McCarty. He was in this particular part of New Mexico Territory in late June/early July, 1881. He is described as eyewitnesses knew him—lithe and small, ambidextrous, and supposedly able to do remarkable things with a pistol. Wanted as a horse thief and a murderer, he had escaped from jail in Lincoln, New Mexico Territory, that same spring. It is a fact that he liked an Englishman, John H. Tunstall, who had been his employer in 1878. Tunstall's murder drove Billy to outlawry. Although pursued by John Poe, Billy the Kid was shot to death on July 14, 1881, by a man named Pat Garrett. Until Garrett published a book about Billy in 1882, the Kid was known chiefly in New Mexico Territory. His is an example of a literary reputation.

Circuses were not at all unknown in the Old West, odd as it may seem. A woman named Annie Sylvester was a noted bicyclienne in the 1880's. Marvelous Melinda is based on her. Miss Sylvester was the first woman to ride a unicycle and for this feat received a diamond-studded gold medal from the San Francisco and Oakland Bicycle Club as the World's Champion Trick and Fancy Bicyclienne. Annie Sylvester trouped with fifteen different circuses. She did indeed drive a chariot and participated in chariot races. She worked with lions, as many as six at a time. Miss Sylvester, who reputedly guarded herself from bandits by carrying a Colt .45 in her muff, lived in Southern California during her later years and died in 1938. An account of her life can be found in *True West* magazine, August, 1972.

Camels would have been familiar animals to people in the Southwest in the 1880's. The Federal government imported them in the 1850's, thinking that they would adapt to the Sonora and Mojave deserts. During the Civil War a camel driver from Syria carried military dispatches on camelback from Fort Yuma, Arizona Territory, to the pueblo of Los Angeles, California. The camel experiment was no great success—chiefly because horses and mules cannot abide the company of camels. Some were released to forage for themselves in the desert. Others were sold to circuses or down into Old Mexico. Wild camels roamed the West for many years.

New Mexico Territory was a haven for wanted men from Texas. This added to the general dislike of Texans, as well as the fact that the New Mexicans felt for many years that Texas was about to annex their territory.

The saloon sign Nate commits to memory existed, though I have no idea what sort of burial insurance plan the management had.

Skunks were far more feared in the Old West than people would ever believe. They were sometimes rabid and, seeking warmth, would get into a man's bed with him during cattle drives, when cowboys slept on the ground. The Pasteur treatment for rabies was not developed until 1885. Before that, contracting hydrophobia was indeed a death sentence. Skunks have many characteristics of the cat, and one particular pet skunk delighted in eating the "holes" in doughnuts, punched out of the raw dough before the doughnuts are deep-fried. (Doughnuts were much indulged in in old Texas. The hole was needed to make them truly "finger food." They were a cowboy's delight.)

"High-grading" was a name for stealing very rich ore from a mine. There is a true story of a man who claimed to be bringing a letter and instead stayed to rob his host.

220 HOW MANY MILES TO SUNDOWN

Major Ella Gordon is fictional in this story. The woman on whom she is based was real—Miss Nellie Cashman, commonly referred to as Colonel Nellie. She was one of the most remarkable women of the Old West. Born in Ireland, she ran boardinghouses all over the West—in Canada, Idaho Territory, Nevada, Arizona Territory, and Alaska. Colonel Nellie never married. In her own words, she considered men to be "nuisances." Renowned for her good deeds, the rearing of orphans, founding of hospitals, and welfare work with the destitute and prisoners, she died in 1925. *The West* magazine of July, 1972, carries a very interesting article about her.

Travis's behavior is pretty much that of a typical hand-raised longhorn. Readers might be entertained and educated by *The Longhorns* by J. Frank Dobie. There is also an interesting article, "Those Amazing Texas Longhorns," by Charles J. Haluska, in a 1970 issue of *Southland,* a pictorial supplement to the Long Beach (Calif.) *Independent.* It features the herd of 106 longhorns living today in California. A rancher, whose real business is raising grapevines, maintains the herd as a hobby and considers the cattle "interesting characters." They hate dogs and umbrellas and seem to favor music.

The medical remedies mentioned in this novel were actually employed. Sulphur, molasses, and cream of tartar as a blood purifier was a very common remedy. Sassafras tea thinned blood, while rusty nail water supplied iron for it. Morley's Vitalizer could be bought in general stores. Goose grease gizzard oil was for chest colds, turpentine and lard for coughs.

The Quineys could have traveled on the Southern Pacific Railroad across Arizona Territory in 1881. They could have crossed the Colorado River by railroad bridge at Yuma and gone into California. They would have found the Colorado River a far broader and more unruly stream than it now is. Today it is dammed.

In researching *How Many Miles to Sundown*, I've used a number of books. I will list only those that deal with the humor, wit, and language of the period. Ramon Adams is the author of several of them: *The Oldtime Cowhand, The Best of the American Cowboy, The Cowboy and His Humor*, and *Burs Under the Saddle*. I also drew on *The Log of a Cowboy* by Andy Adams, *The Cowboy Reader* edited by Lon Tinkle and A. Maxwell, and *From the Pecos to the Powder* by Bob Kennon and Ramon Adams.

As usual, the Beatty-bedeviled reference staffs of the Riverside Public Library and University of California (Riverside) Library were queried on various topics. I thank a number of librarians for their searchings—whether fruitful or no. I must also say thank you to Ella Jahnke and Howard Hays, Jr. (a real-life newspaper editor) for saying they would like to "be" in my book.

Dr. Myra Ellen Jenkins, archivist of the State of New Mexico, also deserves my gratitude for research.

Lastly, I should acknowledge my debt to my husband, Dr. John Beatty, and teen-age daughter, Alexandra, for listening to *How Many Miles to Sundown* being read aloud, chapter by chapter, as the book progresssed. They criticized every other word!

Someday I shall thank them.

Patricia Beatty
January 1973

ABOUT THE AUTHOR

Now a resident of Southern California, Patricia Beatty was born in Portland, Oregon. She was graduated from Reed College there, and then taught high-school English and history for four years. Later she held various positions as science and technical librarian. Recently she taught Writing Fiction for Children in the Extension Department of the University of California, Los Angeles. She has had a number of historical novels published by Morrow, several of them dealing with the American West in the 1860 to 1895 period.

Mrs. Beatty has lived in Coeur d'Alene, Idaho; London, England; and Wilmington, Delaware, as well as on the West Coast. Her husband, Dr. John Beatty, her co-author for a number of books, teaches the history of England at a major California university. One of their books, *The Royal Dirk*, was chosen as an Award book by the Southern California Council on Children's and Young People's Literature. The Beattys have a teen-age daughter, Alexandra.